AIRCRAFT MATERIALS
AND
PROCESSES

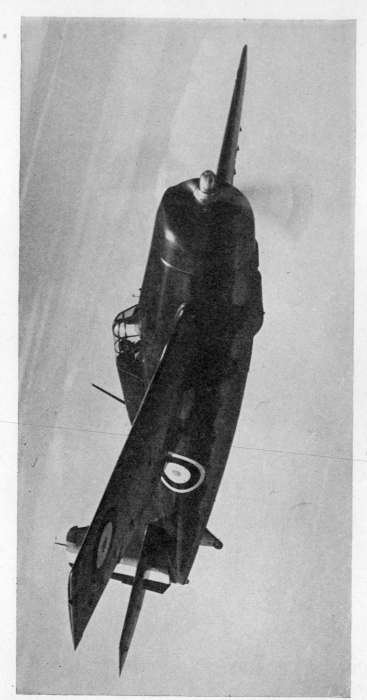

GRUMMAN MARTLET—BRITISH FIGHTER

AIRCRAFT MATERIALS
and
PROCESSES

69994

by

GEORGE F. TITTERTON, B.S. in M.E., A.F.

ASSISTANT CHIEF ENGINEER
GRUMMAN AIRCRAFT ENGINEERING CORPORATION

FORMERLY ASSOCIATE AERONAUTICAL ENGINEER
UNITED STATES NAVAL INSPECTION SERVICE

FACULTY LECTURER
GRADUATE DIVISION
COLLEGE OF ENGINEERING, NEW YORK UNIVERSITY

PITMAN PUBLISHING CORPORATION
NEW YORK   CHICAGO

Revised Edition, 1941

ASSOCIATED COMPANIES
SIR ISAAC PITMAN & SONS, LTD.
Bath • London • Melbourne • Johannesburg • Singapore
SIR ISAAC PITMAN & SONS (CANADA), LTD
381–383 Church Street, Toronto

Advisory Editor
PROFESSOR ALEXANDER KLEMIN
DANIEL GUGGENHEIM SCHOOL OF AERONAUTICS
COLLEGE OF ENGINEERING, NEW YORK UNIVERSITY

PRINTED IN THE UNITED STATES OF AMERICA

PREFACE

The author's purpose in writing this book was to present in one coördinated volume the essential information on materials and processes used in the construction of aircraft. Unimportant details have been purposely omitted in the interest of brevity and readability. Within the aircraft field this volume is rather general in scope and should meet the needs of students, engineers, and designers, as well as practical shop men.

This book is based largely upon a series of lectures given by the author at New York University. Similar lectures were also given to a miscellaneous group composed of engineers, shop men, and purchasing department employees of a large aircraft manufacturing corporation. Both in these lectures and the book itself, the author has drawn freely on a fund of information obtained while employed as an engineer in the Naval Inspection Service. As a result, the latest materials and processes used in aircraft construction have been described from a utilitarian point of view. Numerous suggestions have been included on the choice of material for a particular job and on the best way of working, heat treating, and finishing materials for specific applications.

The technical data for a book of this type must, of necessity, be collected from many sources. Government publications have been used to a large extent. These include Army, Navy, and Federal specifications as well as reports of the Forest Products Laboratory. The Handbook of the Society of Automotive Engineers has also been invaluable for reference purposes. The author is also indebted to many persons and companies for their coöperation in supplying data, and for proofreading portions of the text. The following named deserve special mention for their efforts along these lines:

Mr. Frederick C. Pyne of the Aluminum Company of America
Mr. Frank G. Flocke of the International Nickel Company
Mr. Harry A. Goslar of the Naval Inspection Service
The Dow Chemical Company

vii

The author also wishes to thank those who so generously provided illustrations for the text. Insofar as possible these contributions have been acknowledged in the title of the illustration.

It is, of course, improbable that a book such as this is wholly free of errors. The author will appreciate having errors brought to his attention to insure their correction in future revisions of this volume.

GEORGE F. TITTERTON

PREFACE TO SECOND EDITION

The reception this book received during the last four years has indicated its value to students, engineers, designers and shop men. At this time of national emergency, the book has been carefully revised to include the latest materials and processes. It is the author's hope that the revised edition will prove useful in training the new personnel now entering the rapidly expanding aircraft industry.

GEORGE F. TITTERTON

CONTENTS

ix

CONTENTS

ILLUSTRATIONS

TABLES AND APPENDIXES

Tables

Appendixes

Chapter I

DEFINITIONS

Physical Terms

There are many terms used in describing the properties of materials which should be clearly understood by the reader. Many of these terms have acquired popular meanings which are not necessarily correct, while others are very hazy in the minds of a majority of people. It is the author's intention to define these terms in the following pages so that a firm foundation may be established before proceeding further.

Hardness. Hardness is the property of resisting penetration or permanent distortion. The hardness of a piece of metal can usually be increased by hammering, rolling, or otherwise working on it. In the case of steel, some aluminum alloys and a few other metals hardness can also be increased by a heat treatment. A modified heat treatment known as annealing will soften metals.

Increased hardness and strength go hand in hand. Testing apparatus has been developed for testing hardness rapidly without destroying or harming the tested metal or part. The principle usually employed in this type of apparatus is to sink a hardened steel ball under a definite load into the material being tested. The impression made by the ball is then measured and recorded; the smaller the impression, the harder the material. For each type of material there is a fairly definite relationship between the depth of penetration (which is represented by a Hardness Number for convenience) and the ultimate strength of the material. Tables have been worked up for different materials based on this relationship. By means of a simple hardness test and the use of such a table the approximate tensile strength of a piece of material or finished part can be obtained without cutting out tensile test specimens or mutilating the part.

1

Brittleness. Brittleness is the property of resisting a change in the relative position of molecules, or the tendency to fracture without change of shape. Brittleness and hardness are very closely associated. Hard material is invariably more brittle than soft material. In aircraft construction the use of too brittle material must be avoided or failure will be caused by the shock loads to which it will be subjected.

Malleability. Malleability is the property of metals which allows them to be bent or permanently distorted without rupture. It is this property that permits the manufacture of sheets, bar stock, forgings, and fabrication by bending and hammering. It is obviously the direct opposite of brittleness.

Ductility. Ductility is the property of metals which allows them to be drawn out without breaking. This property is essential in the manufacture of wire and tubing by drawing. It is very similar to malleability and, in fact, is generally used in place of that term to describe any material that can be easily deformed without breaking. Thus in aircraft work a material is usually referred to as soft or hard, or else as ductile or brittle. Ductile material is greatly preferred because of its ease of forming and its resistance to failure under shock loads. In order to obtain the required strength it is often necessary, however, to use a hard material.

Elasticity. Elasticity is the power to return to the original shape when the force causing the change of shape is removed. All aircraft structural design is based on this property since it would not be desirable to have any member remain permanently distorted after it had been subjected to a load. Each material has a point known as the elastic limit beyond which it cannot be loaded without causing permanent distortion. In aircraft construction members and parts are so designed that the maximum applied loads to which the airplane may be subjected will never stress them above their elastic limit.

Density. Density is the weight of a unit volume of the material. In aircraft work the actual weight of a material per cubic inch is preferred since this figure can be used in calculating the weight of a part before actual manufacture. The density of a material is an important considerating in deciding which material to use in the design of a part.

Fusibility. Fusibility is the property of being liquefied by heat. Metals are fused in welding. Steels fuse around 2500° F., aluminum alloys around 1100° F.

Conductivity. Conductivity is the power of transmitting heat or electricity. The conductivity of metals is of interest to the welder as it affects the amount of heat he must use and, to a certain extent, the design of his welding jig. Electrical conductivity is also important in connection with the bonding of airplanes to eliminate radio interference.

Contraction and Expansion. Contraction and expansion are caused by the cooling or heating of metals. These properties affect the design of welding jigs, castings, and the tolerances necessary for hot rolled material.

HEAT TREATMENT TERMS

Critical Range. Critical range is a term applied to steel, which refers to a range of temperature between 1300° F. and 1600° F. When steel passes through this temperature range, its internal structure is altered. Rapid cooling of the metal through this range of temperature will prevent the normal change of the structure, and unusual properties will be possessed by the material so treated. The heat treatment of steel is based on this phenomenon.

Annealing. Annealing is the process of heating steel above the critical range, holding it at that temperature until it is uniformly heated and the grain is refined, and then cooling it very slowly. Other materials do not possess critical ranges, but all are annealed by a similar heating process which permits rearrangement of the internal structure and then cooling (either slowly or quickly), depending on the material. The annealing process invariably softens the metal and relieves internal strains.

Normalizing. Normalizing is similar to annealing, but the steel is allowed to cool in still air—a method that is somewhat faster than annealing cooling. Normalizing applies only to steel. It relieves internal strains, softens the metal somewhat less than annealing, and at the same time increases the strength of the steel about 20% above that of annealed material.

Heat Treatment. Heat treatment consists of a series of operations which have as their aim the improvement of the physical properties of a material. In the case of steel these operations are hardening (which is composed of heating and quenching) and tempering.

Hardening. Hardening of steel is done by heating the metal to a temperature above the critical range and then quenching it. Aluminum alloys are hardened by heating to a temperature above 900° F. and quenching.

Quenching. Quenching is the immersion of the heated metal in a liquid, usually either oil or water, to accelerate its cooling.

Tempering. Tempering is the reheating of hardened steel to a temperature below the critical range, followed by cooling as desired. Tempering is sometimes referred to as "drawing."

Carburizing. Carburizing is the addition of carbon to steel by heating it at a high temperature while in contact with a carbonaceous material in either solid, liquid, or gaseous form. Carburizing is best performed on steels containing less than .25% carbon content.

Casehardening. Casehardening consists of carburizing, followed by suitable heat treatment to harden the metal.

Physical Test Terms

Strain. Strain is the deformation of material caused by an applied load.

Stress. Stress is the load acting on a material. Internal stresses are the loads present in a material that has been strained by cold working.

Tensile Strength. This is often referred to as the ultimate tensile strength (U.T.S.). It is the maximum tensile load per square inch which a material can withstand. It is computed by dividing the maximum load obtained in a tensile test by the original cross-sectional area of the test specimen. In this country it is usually recorded as pounds per square inch.

Elastic Limit. The elastic limit is the greatest load per square inch of original cross-sectional area which a material can withstand without a permanent deformation remaining upon complete release of the load. As stated under "elasticity," the aim in aircraft design is to keep the stress below this point.

Proportional Limit. The proportional limit is the load per square inch beyond which the increases in strain cease to be directly proportional to the increases in stress. The law of proportionality between stress and strain is known as Hooke's Law. The determination of the proportional limit can be more readily accomplished than that of the elastic limit, and since they are very nearly equivalent, the proportional limit is usually accepted in place of the elastic limit in test work.

Proof Stress. The proof stress is the load per square inch a material can withstand without resulting in a permanent elongation of more than 0.0001 inch per inch of gage length after complete release of stress. With the standard 2-inch gage length the total permissible elongation would be 0.0002 inch.

Yield Strength. Yield strength is the load per square inch at which a material exhibits a specified limiting permanent set or a specified elongation under load. This load is fairly easily determined and is commonly used.

Yield Point. The yield point is the load per square inch at which there occurs a marked increase in deformation without an increase in load. Only a few materials have a definite yield point. Steel is one of these materials.

Elongation (Percentage). The percentage elongation is the difference in gage length before being subjected to any stress and after rupture, expressed in percentage of the original gage length.

The length after rupture is obtained by removing the two pieces from the machine and piecing them together on a flat surface. The distance between the gage marks is then accurately measured.

Reduction of Area (Percentage). The percentage reduction of area is the difference between the original cross-sectional area and the least cross-sectional area after rupture, expressed as a percentage of the original cross-sectional area. This information is seldom used other than as an indication of ductility.

Modulus of Elasticity. The modulus of elasticity of a material is the ratio of stress to strain within the elastic limit. Thus $E = $ unit stress/unit strain.

Chapter II

TESTING AIRCRAFT MATERIALS

In aircraft construction it is essential that materials with a high strength/weight ratio be used. For this reason the designer tries to get the last ounce of strength out of each part. This procedure would be very dangerous if the exact strength of the basic material were not known. As a result, the materials entering into the construction of aircraft are probably more thoroughly tested than those employed in any other industry. In this chapter the test methods commonly used will be summarized for ready reference. Many of the tests are standard but are included for completeness.

TENSION TESTING

A tension test is probably the most valuable test that can be made to obtain the basic properties of a material. Besides the ultimate tensile strength it is possible to obtain the yield strength, the elongation, and the reduction of area. The yield strength is a definite indication of the maximum applied load that the material can withstand, and the elongation and reduction of area are a measure of its ductility and ease of working.

All tests should be made with a standard type of machine in good condition. All knife edges should be sharp and free from oil or dirt. The testing machine should be sensitive to a variation of 1/250 of any registered load. It should also be accurate to within ± 1½% throughout its range. These requirements are the minimum acceptable for material to be tested for government inspectors.

During the test the specimen must be held in true axial alignment by the grips. This is particularly important with the relatively thin material used in aircraft construction. The speed of the testing machine crosshead should not exceed ⅟₁₆ inch per inch of gage length per minute up to the yield point, and it should not exceed ½ inch per inch of gage length per minute beyond the yield point up to rupture. For a 2-inch gage length these speeds would be ⅛ inch and 1 inch per minute, respectively. When using an extensometer to determine the elastic limit or the yield strength, the crosshead speed should not exceed 0.025 inch per inch of gage length per minute. The extensometer must be calibrated to read 0.0002 inch or less. It must be attached to the specimen only, at the gage marks, and not to the shoulders of the specimen or any part of the testing machine.

Figures 1, 2, 3, 4, and 5 show the standard tension test specimens. All specimens must be strictly straight and must be free from scratches. Test specimens should be subjected to the same treatment and processes as the material they represent in order to obtain a true indication of strength. When elastic properties are to be determined, the test specimen must not be bent, ham-

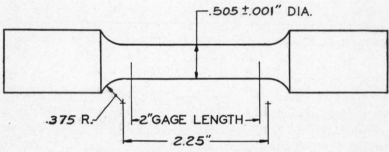

.505 ±.001″ DIA.

.375 R.   2″ GAGE LENGTH

2.25″

FIGURE 1. ROUND TENSILE TEST SPECIMEN

mered, or straightened by any method involving cold working of the part. In preparing a test specimen for bar or forging stock of uniform cross section and less than 1½ inches thick, it should be machined concentrically from the stock. When the stock is over 1½ inches thick, the specimen should be taken from a point midway between the outer surface and the center. By this method the average strength of the material will be obtained. This will be less than the hard surface and more than the soft center strength.

Figure 1 shows a tension test specimen which is circular in cross section and has a 2-inch gage length. The dimensions of the ends may be varied to suit the testing machine grips to insure axial loading. It is permissible to taper the specimen inside the gage length toward the center to an amount not to exceed 0.003 inch. This taper will insure breaking between the gage marks.

The diameter of the center must be 0.505 ± .001 as noted in Figure 1.

Figure 2 shows the dimensions of a tension test specimen used for material over ⅜ inch thick. It is rectangular in cross section and may be used with either a 2- or 8-inch gage length.

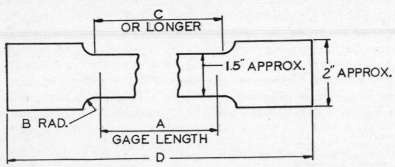

FIGURE 2. FLAT TENSILE TEST SPECIMEN FOR MATERIAL OVER ⅜ INCH THICK

When A = 2, B = 0.25, C = 2.25, D = 9
When A = 8, B = 1 to 3, C = 9, D = 18

Figure 3 shows a specimen used for testing material over ⅜ inch thick when it is impractical to use a specimen of the type shown in Figure 2. The specimen of Figure 3 is not so wide as that shown in Figure 2.

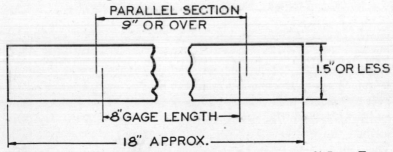

FIGURE 3. FLAT TENSILE TEST SPECIMEN FOR MATERIAL OVER ⅜ INCH THICK AND UNDER 1½ INCHES WIDE

Figure 4 shows a subsize specimen that may be substituted for the specimen of Figure 1. Like Figure 1 it is circular in cross section, but its diameter and gage length are much smaller. It may also be tapered 0.003 inch toward the center to insure proper breaking.

Figure 5 shows the type of specimen used for material not over ⅜ inch thick. It is rectangular in cross section and requires a gage length of either 2 or 4 inches. The specimen may be reduced to the required width at the center of the gage length

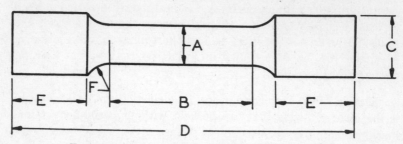

FIGURE 4. SUBSIZE ROUND TENSILE TEST SPECIMEN

NOMINAL DIAMETER	A ±0.001	B GAGE LENGTH	C ±1⁄64	D APPROX.	E APPROX.	F RADIUS
0.357″	0.357″	1.4″	0.5″	3.5″	0.75″	0.375′
.250	.252	1.0	.375	3.0	.625	.125
.125	.126	.5	.25	1.875	.375	.375

by draw filing not more than 0.004 inch for a ½ inch width, or 0.006 inch for a ¾ inch width. This type of specimen with a 2-inch gage length is the one most commonly used in aircraft materials testing.

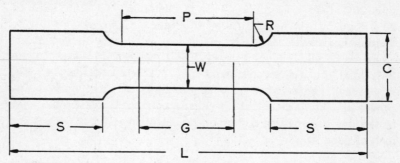

FIGURE 5. FLAT TENSILE TEST SPECIMEN FOR MATERIAL ⅜ INCH THICK AND UNDER

DIMENSION		UP TO ¼ INCH SHEET	¼ to ⅜ INCH SHEET
C	(max.)	1.13 W	1.15 W
G	(gage length)	2 or 4	2 or 4
L	(approx.)	9 or 11	9 or 11
P	(min.)	1⅛ G	1⅛ G
R	(min.)	W	W
S	(approx.)	3	3
W		½ ± 0.010	¾ ± 0.015

Rods, bars, and shapes should be pulled in full size when practicable. This method eliminates a number of possible variables and gives the actual strength directly.

Tubing is tested by putting solid plugs in each end, which permit gripping without crushing. It is standard practice to keep at least 6 inches of hollow tubing between the near ends of the plugs. If it is not practical to test the tubing in full section, a specimen (of the type shown in Figure 5) may be cut parallel to the axis of the tubing.

Elastic Limit Determination. The elastic limit of a material is the greatest stress that can be held without permanent deformation remaining upon complete release of the stress. In practical testing the elastic limit is considered to have been reached when a permanent set of 0.00003 inch per inch of gage length has been obtained. An accurate reading extensometer must be used to read the permanent set. The method of testing is as follows: a load is applied until the stress is 20% of the expected elastic limit and the extensometer reading is recorded. The load is then increased to about 75% of the elastic limit, after which it is dropped to below 20% and then brought up to 20%, and then the extensometer read. If no permanent set has been obtained the extensometer should read identically the same as when the first 20% load was imposed. It is customary to refer back to 20% load rather than zero load to eliminate inaccuracies due to friction in the extensometer. After the 75% load, additional increments of load should be added and released as before to the 20% load, and the extensometer read. These increments should not exceed about 3% of the elastic limit as this point is approached. The elastic limit is calculated from the last load prior to the one that caused a permanent set of over 0.00003 inch per inch of gage length.

Proof Stress Determination. The proof stress of a material is the greatest stress it can withstand without resulting in a permanent set of over 0.0001 inch per inch of gage length after complete release of stress. For the standard 2-inch gage length this amounts to a permanent set of 0.0002 inch. The proof stress can be determined in the same manner as the elastic limit, or the load can be released to zero after each increment. The proof stress of a material is also referred to as its Proportional Limit.

Yield Strength Determination. The yield strength is the stress at which a material exhibits a specified limiting permanent set or a specified elongation under load. There are two commonly used methods for determining this stress which are known as (1) *Set Method* and (2) *Extension under Load Method*. Either of these methods is easily applied and will give consistent results if an accurate testing machine and extensometer are employed.

1. Set Method. In this method the loads are applied and the extensometer readings taken for a number of loads. The loads usually selected are 20%, 75%, 90%, and several other loads just under and over the expected yield strength. A curve is then plotted, as shown in Figure 6, in which the applied loads are ordinates and the extensometer readings are abscissas. This curve will be similar to the curve OD of Figure 6. It will be noted that the lower part of this curve is a straight line. The line CD is constructed parallel to the straight portion of line OD and at a distance to the right equal to the specified set. The point of intersection D, read as an ordinate, gives the applied load for the yield strength. The applied load divided by the original cross-sectional area is the yield strength.

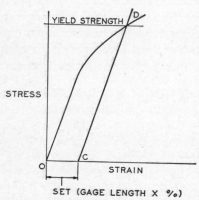

FIGURE 6. SET METHOD OF YIELD STRENGTH DETERMINATION

This method of determination is used when the yield strength is specified as Yield Strength (Set = per cent) pounds per square inch. For metals a set = 0.2% is usually specified. For the standard 2-inch gage length this set would be 0.004 inch. In this case the point C in Figure 6 would be at an abscissa of 0.004 inch. The principle of this method is based on the fact that if the load was released at D, the curve for the decreasing load would follow the line DC. OC would then represent the permanent set. The yield strength value obtained by the Set Method is arbitrary, but it is a measurable value of plastic yielding of the material below which the damaging effects are considered to be negligible.

The Set Method is frequently specified for determining the yield strength of aircraft materials. Steel, aluminum alloys, magnesium, and structural corrosion-resisting steel are metals whose yield strength is often determined as the point where a permanent set of 0.002 inch per inch of gage length is obtained. Very often there is a choice between the use of the Set Method and the Extension under Load Method.

2. Extension under Load Method. This method is easier of application than the Set Method since no curve need be plotted, and it is frequently used. It is based on the same principle as the Set Method. The specified extension is made up of two parts: (a) the normal elongation based on the modulus of elasticity of the material and the expected yield strength, plus (b) a definite additional elongation which is usually 0.002 inch per inch of gage length, the same as specified for the permanent set in the Set Method. The normal elongation must be computed for each material for the expected yield strength by the following formula:

$$\text{Normal Elongation} = \frac{\text{Expected Yield Strength}}{\text{Modulus of Elasticity}}$$

In the case of heat treated steel with a 100,000 pound per square inch yield strength and a modulus of elasticity taken as 30,000,-000, the normal elongation would be 100,000/30,000,000 = 0.0033 inch per inch of gage length. Adding 0.002 inch to this makes the specified elongation 0.0053 inch per inch or 0.0106 inch for a 2-inch gage length. If, in testing, the yield strength obtained at this elongation is higher than 100,000, the material is better than anticipated.

This method is used generally for establishing the yield strength of aircraft materials. The modulus of elasticity used for the calculation of the normal elongation is as follows for the various metals:

Steel = 30,000,000 pounds per square inch
Aluminum alloys = 10,000,000 pounds per square inch
Magnesium = 6,500,000 pounds per square inch
Corrosion-resisting steel = 25,000,000 pounds per square inch

Yield Point Determination. The yield point of a material is the point at which there is a marked increase in elongation without increase in load. This phenomenon is only found in some materials, such as wrought iron and mild carbon steel. For these materials the stress strain curve has a sharp break at the yield. When the stress strain curve of a material is smooth in this region, the material does not have a yield point. The yield point of a material can be determined by either of two methods: (1) *Divider Method* or (2) *Drop of Beam Method*.

1. Divider Method. In this method a pair of dividers is set to the exact distance between two gage marks. The load is then applied to the specimen with one arm of the dividers centered in one gage mark and the other arm held free above the other gage mark. At the instant visible stretch is noted between this latter gage mark and the dividers, the load should be noted. The yield point stress is computed from this load.

2. Drop of Beam Method. In this method the load is applied uniformly and the recording beam kept balanced by the operator. At the yield point load the beam will drop suddenly as the elongation increases rapidly at this point without increase in load. If the testing machine is equipped with a self-indicating load measuring device, the pointer will halt momentarily at the yield point load. The yield point stress is computed from this load.

HARDNESS TESTING

There is no positive assurance that a manufactured article has the same strength as developed by a tested specimen. The test specimen has different dimensions and may have responded to heat treatment better, or it may have been taken from a different location, or it may not have been subjected to the same fabricating stresses as the manufactured article. It is apparent that some means is needed to check the comparative strength of manufactured articles without destroying or harming them in any way. The development of a hardness test has solved this problem.

It has been found that hardness and tensile strength will correspond very closely for any particular material. By coördinating a large number of tensile and hardness tests made on the same specimens, it has been possible to construct a table from which the tensile strength can be obtained if the hardness is known. Manufactured articles need only be subjected to a simple hardness test to determine their approximate tensile strength.

This does not apply to relatively soft materials such as aluminum alloys. Hardness testing devices are not sufficiently sensitive, particularly on thin sheet aluminum alloy, to warrant even a reasonably accurate correlation between hardness and tensile properties. Hardness testing is accurate enough, however, to distinguish between annealed and heat-treated material of the same aluminum alloy. Table 1 gives the equivalent tensile strength of S.A.E. steels for hardness numbers obtained by any one of four commonly used methods. The strengths listed in this table correspond only approximately with the hardness numbers, due to the fact that no two hardness testing machines, even of the same type, will read exactly alike. It is necessary occasionally to calibrate each machine against standard specimens.

There are four methods in general use for determining the hardness of metals: Brinell, Rockwell, Vickers, and Shore Scleroscope. These methods depend upon the impression made in the tested metal by a diamond cone or hardened steel ball, or the rebound of a small diamond pointed hammer dropped from a fixed height. Each of these methods has its limitations and special uses which are described below under the specific method. It is important in all cases, however, that the tested surface should be smooth and free from scratches, ridges, scales, or other unevennesses. The specimen must also be sufficiently thick so that the impression made by the testing apparatus does not bulge the opposite side and thereby give a false reading. Care must also be taken to see that there is sufficient edge-distance to avoid any deflection due to the depression.

Brinell Hardness. The Brinell test consists in pressing a hardened steel ball, under a known pressure, into a flat surface of the specimen to be tested. For testing steel a ball 10 mm. in diameter under a pressure of 3000 (6600 lb.) kilograms is used. For softer metals, such as aluminum alloys and bronze, a 500-kilogram load is used. The load should be applied for at least 30 seconds before release.

The area of the impression made by the ball is measured by a calibrated microscope that reads accurately to 0.05 mm. The Brinell number is the load in kilograms divided by the area of the spherical surface of the impression in square millimeters. It

TABLE 1

HARDNESS *vs.* TENSILE STRENGTH—S.A.E. STEELS

Tensile Strength Lbs./sq. in.	Shore	Rockwell B (100 Kg— 1/16 Ball)	Rockwell C (150 Kg— 120° Cone)	Vickers	Brinell (3000 Kg— 10 mm. Ball)
55,000	......	64	......	107	107
56,000	......	65	......	109	109
58,000	......	66	......	112	112
59,000	......	67	......	114	114
60,000	......	68	......	116	116
61,000	......	69	......	118	118
62,000	......	70	......	121	121
63,000	......	71	......	124	124
64,000	......	72	......	126	126
65,000	20	73	......	128	128
66,000	20	74	......	131	131
68,000	21	76	......	134	134
70,000	21	77	......	137	137
71,000	21	78	......	140	140
72,000	22	79	......	143	143
74,000	22	80	......	146	146
75,000	23	81	......	149	149
76,000	23	82	......	153	153
78,000	24	83	......	156	156
80,000	24	84	......	159	159
82,000	25	85	......	163	163
83,000	25	86	......	166	166
85,000	26	87	......	170	170
87,000	26	88	......	174	174
89,000	27	89	......	179	179
91,000	27	90	......	183	183
93,000	28	91	......	187	187
95,000	28	92	......	192	192
97,000	29	93	......	197	197
99,000	30	94	......	202	202
101,000	30	95	......	207	207
104,000	31	96	......	212	212
107,000	31	96	......	217	217
110,000	32	97	20	223	223
113,000	33	98	21	229	229
116,000	34	99	22	235	235
119,000	35	100	23	241	241
122,000	36	......	24	248	248
125,000	37	......	25	256	255
128,000	37	......	26	263	262
131,000	38	......	28	270	269
134,000	39	......	29	279	277
138,000	40	......	30	287	285
142,000	42	......	31	296	293
146,000	43	......	32	305	302
150,000	44	......	33	316	311
155,000	45	......	34	327	321
160,000	46	......	35	339	331
165,000	48	......	36	350	341
170,000	49	......	37	363	352
176,000	51	......	38	375	363
182,000	52	......	40	389	375
189,000	54	......	41	404	388
196,000	55	......	42	420	401
204,000	57	......	44	437	415
212,000	59	......	45	454	429
220,000	61	......	46	472	444

is obvious that hard materials will have small impressions and consequently large Brinell numbers. A rough check of Table 1 will show that for steel the Brinell number is almost exactly twice the equivalent tensile strength throughout the whole scale. This is a useful relationship to keep in mind for occasions when a hardness table is not available.

For Brinell testing the surface should be free from scratches, and prepared by filing, grinding, machining, or polishing with emery paper. A smooth surface is essential to permit reading the small impression accurately.

Rockwell Hardness. Rockwell hardness is determined by measuring the penetration of a diamond cone or hardened steel ball under definite loads. The machine first applies a minor load of 10 kilograms, the direct reading dial is set to zero, and the major load is applied. This forces the penetrator into the metal, and after removal of the load, the Rockwell hardness can be read from the dial. There are two scales on the dial called the C and B scales. Each of these scales applies when definite penetrators and loads are used. To distinguish the test conditions a letter such as C, B, E, or S must be placed before the Rockwell number. These letters have the following significance:

LETTER	PENETRATOR	LOAD (Kilograms)	SCALE
C	Diamond cone	150	C
B	1/16-inch ball	100	B
E	1/8-inch ball	100	B
S	1/8-inch ball	60	B

The accuracy of Rockwell hardness numbers depends, to a great extent, upon the surface condition of the specimen. Both sides of test surfaces should be free from scale and surface ridges caused by rough grinding or machining. The surface roughness must be much less than the depth of the impression.

A thickness of 0.027 inch or over is all that is necessary with hard steel to obtain a true hardness reading. For softer materials it is necessary to reduce the applied load and increase the penetrator diameter to obtain satisfactory readings if the material is thin. Penetrators as large as ½ inch in diameter, with a load of only 60 kilograms, are used on very thin aluminum. The results obtained by these means are purely relative and do not correspond to a set of tensile strengths.

The true hardness of curved surfaces with a 3/16 inch or greater radius can be obtained by the Rockwell tester. Smaller round surfaces must have a small flat spot filed on them if true readings are desired. The Rockwell apparatus is used very generally by aircraft manufacturing concerns because of its direct reading qualities, ease of operation, and reliability.

Vickers Hardness. The Vickers hardness test is made with a diamond penetrator in the form of a square base pyramid having an included angle of 136°. A normal loading of 30 kilograms is used for homogeneous material, and a 5-kilogram load for soft, thin, or surface hardened material. It should be noted from the table that the Vickers hardness numbers are identical with the Brinell numbers for all but very hard material.

Shore Scleroscope Hardness. Shore scleroscope hardness testing consists of dropping a small diamond pointed hammer from a fixed height and measuring and comparing the height of rebound with that from a standard test piece. It is an excellent means of obtaining comparative hardness of a large number of production parts. If absolute hardness is desired, it is essential that the instrument be set level and rigidly fixed in position to prevent movement in any direction. If the slightest movement occurs, the rebound will be inaccurate. The rebound is measured directly on a vertical scale in one instrument, and in another it is registered on a recording dial.

The test specimen should be smooth and free from scratches. The average of five separate determinations are usually taken as the hardness of a part. By this means errors due to rebound or a hard spot in the material are eliminated. The scleroscope hardness scale ranging from 0 to 120 is purely arbitrary.

BENDING TESTS

Most specifications for aircraft metals require them to pass a bending test. The usual test requires cold bending through an angle of 180°, over a pin equal to the diameter or thickness of the test specimen, without cracking. This type of test will give definite assurance that a metal is ductile and not inclined to brittleness. Although it is difficult to obtain the exact radius of bend specified even under laboratory conditions, this test can be readily applied in the shop to check doubtful material.

Bend test specimens for sheet or strip stock are usually 1 inch wide by 6 inches long and the full thickness of the material. The edges of the specimen should be rounded with a file making sure there are no rough spots or ragged edges where cracks can start. For heavy plate or shapes a specimen rectangular in cross section is required. The corners of the cross section may be just broken with a smooth file. The full thickness of the material and a width from 1 to 2½ inches with a suitable length should be used. Rods and bars are submitted to bend tests in their full section. Specimens of forging stock are machined to a section 1 by ½ inch in cross section and at least 6 inches long. The edges of these specimens are rounded to a ¹⁄₁₆ inch radius. For heavy material 1½ inches or over these specimens must be taken from a point midway between the center and outer surface of the stock.

The actual bending may be accomplished either by a constant pressure or by blows from a hammer. The latter is somewhat more severe but represents an actual condition that exists in most shops in forming aircraft parts. Specifications usually require that bend test specimens be taken both parallel to and across the grain. The high quality of aircraft material now available will permit bending in any direction relative to grain and still meet the rigid requirements of the specifications. For shop bending it is preferable, however, to make all bends across the grain. If this is done there is less likelihood of cracking in forming or in subsequent service due to fatigue stresses.

The severity of the bend test will be realized if the elongation necessary on the outer circumference of the bend is computed. This figure greatly exceeds the elongation value obtained from straight tension tests.

Reverse Bend Test. Round steel wire is usually subjected to a reverse bend test. In this test a specimen of wire at least ten inches long is held in a vise or bend testing machine and bent back and forth 90° each way through a total angle of 180°. The jaws of the vise are rounded to the required radius—³⁄₁₆ inch for wire up to ³⁄₁₆ inch in diameter and 3 times the diameter or thickness of the wire for heavier wire. Bending is done at a rate not exceeding 50 bends per minute, and slow enough not to cause undue heating of the wire. In this test each 90° bend counts as one bend. Specification requirements vary from 50 bends for small wire to 7 bends for heavy wire.

Flattening Test. This is a form of bending test applicable to tubing. A length of tubing equal to twice its diameter is flattened sideways and examined for cracks or other defects. In the test applied to bronze tubing, the flattened tube must not exceed three times the wall thickness.

Impact Tests

These tests consist of notching a piece of material on one side and then fixing it in a machine so that it can be broken by means of a falling weight or a heavy swinging pendulum. The

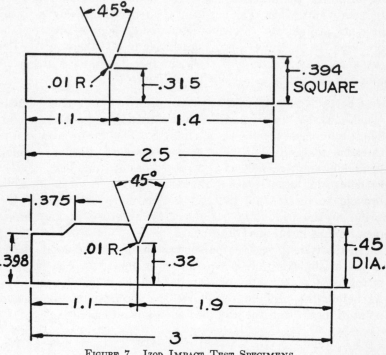

FIGURE 7. IZOD IMPACT TEST SPECIMENS

test has practically no absolute value, but can be used to compare two pieces of material of identical composition and tensile strength. Even two pieces of the same steel which have been subjected to different tempering treatments to obtain different tensile strengths will not give comparable impact values. The chief use of this test is to determine whether a batch of material has been subjected to the correct heat treatment. It does not indicate the shock resistance of a material, but it will show whether material is excessively brittle. Extremely ductile material cannot be impact tested satisfactorily because it bends while breaking. There are two standard impact tests: namely, the *Izod* and the *Charpy* tests.

Izod Test. In this test a notched specimen is clamped in heavy jaws, with the notch level with the top of the jaws and facing a heavy pendulum. When the pendulum is released from a fixed height, it swings down and hits the specimen at the lowest point of its path. Breaking the specimen retards the pendulum and reduces its upswing. The height of the reduced upswing is measured on a quadrant calibrated in the foot-pounds absorbed in breaking the specimen. For comparable results the notch in the specimen must be held to close limits. Standard square and round Izod specimens are shown in Figure 7.

Charpy Test. In this test there are two types of specimens which may be broken under either a tensile or transverse load. These specimens are shown in Figure 8. The tensile specimen is threaded at both ends. One end is threaded into a swinging pendulum and a stop block is threaded on the other end. As the swinging pendulum reaches its lowest point, the stop block is brought to rest. This ruptures the specimen and reduces the swing of the pendulum. The energy absorbed in rupture is measured as in the Izod test.

In the transverse test the square Charpy specimen is placed in the machine so that it straddles two supports. The notch is at the exact center and facing away from the swinging pendulum. As before the pendulum ruptures the specimen at the lowest point of its arc and the absorbed energy is measured.

CRUSHING TESTS

Aircraft tubing is nearly always subjected to a crushing test. For this test a piece of tubing $1\frac{1}{2}$ diameters long, with its ends machined normal to its axis, is used. This tube is compressed endwise under a gradually applied load until its outside diameter is increased on one zone by 25%, or until one complete fold is formed, or the specimen is reduced to two-thirds its original length. The tubing must stand this test without cracking. Tub-

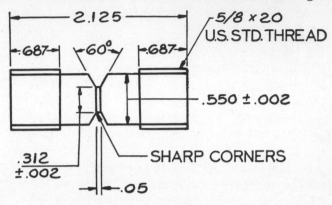

TENSILE CHARPY

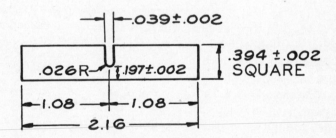

SQUARE CHARPY

FIGURE 8.   CHARPY IMPACT SPECIMENS

ing must be in the annealed condition when subjected to this test. It should not be in the normalized or heat treated condition.

HYDROSTATIC TEST

Seamless tubing that is to carry pressure in service or welded tubing, such as the corrosion-resisting steel tubing used for exhaust collectors, is subjected to a hydrostatic pressure test. Welded exhaust tubing is subjected to an internal pressure sufficient to put the welded seam under a tensile stress of 10,000 pounds per square inch.

For any size tubing or wall thickness the tensile stress along any seam can be computed from the following formula:

$$\text{Tensile Stress} = \frac{\text{Internal Hydrostatic Pressure} \times \text{Diameter}}{2 \times \text{Wall Thickness}}$$

It should be noted that extremely high internal pressures can be carried in small diameter tubes without overstressing the material. It is common practice to carry oxygen under an 1800 pound per square inch pressure through a $\frac{3}{16}$ copper tube when conveying it from the storage tank to the regulator in aircraft oxygen apparatus.

Torsion Test

Wire is always subjected to a torsion test. For wire over 0.033 inch in diameter the test specimen must be at least 10 inches long. It is held by two clamps 8 inches apart. One of these clamps is fixed and the other is rotatable. The movable clamp is rotated at a uniform speed not exceeding 60 revolutions per minute or slower, if necessary, to prevent undue heating of the wire. The wire is under sufficient tension to prevent it from kinking during the test.

When wire 0.033 inch or less is to be tested a specimen 30 inches long must be used. The center of this length of wire is passed around a hook held in the movable clamp, and the loose ends are clamped together in the fixed clamp. The movable head is then rotated as for the heavier wire, and the number of revolutions are counted before the wire splits.

Fatigue Testing

Materials subject to vibrational stresses have frequently failed at much smaller loads than anticipated. Investigation disclosed that each material has a fatigue stress beyond which it is not safe to load it repeatedly. The fatigue stress is defined as that stress which the material will endure without failure no matter how many times the stress be repeated. Testing for fatigue strength is so laborious that many materials have not yet been tested. For hard steels a 2,000,000 cycle test is necessary to definitely establish fatigue stress; for soft steels 10,000,000 cycles are necessary; for aluminum and magnesium alloys 500,000,000 cycles of completely reversed stress are required.

Many types of fatigue testing apparatus have been developed. The most common are rotating beam or rotating cantilever tests. These rotating tests give a completely reversed stress in which the maximum unit tensile and compressive stress in the surface of the specimen is equal. The speed of rotation varies in different machines but is usually of the order of 2000 r.p.m. or in high speed work 12,000 r.p.m. Axial loading tests in which the specimen can be subjected to reversed stresses or from zero load up to a definite tensile load are also used.

Fatigue test specimens are usually rolled or forged bar stock 1 inch in diameter. It must be remembered that these smooth, cylindrical test rods are free from holes, notches, or abrupt changes of cross section and give maximum test results. The slightest corrosion or flaw will greatly reduce the fatigue limit of a part in service.

The fatigue limit of a material is one half its fatigue range. In other words, it has the same limit for a plus or minus load. For steel the fatigue limit is about .5 of the ultimate tensile strength; for nonferrous metals it is about .3 to .4 of the tensile strength. An initial static stress in a part decreases the permissible dynamic stress. Heat treated materials have higher tensile strengths and fatigue limits than annealed material.

INSPECTION METHODS

It is essential that all parts of the airplane structure be free of cracks which in service might cause severe failures. Two methods are commonly used to detect minute surface or internal cracks in welded, forged, cast, or machined parts. These methods of inspection are known as Radiography and Magnaflux inspection.

Radiography. Radiography is a non-destructive method of locating cracks by means of X-rays or gamma-rays. A radiograph, or shadow picture, is obtained by passing X-rays or gamma-rays through the object being inspected. Cracks show up in the shadow picture as light spots. By taking pictures in two different places it is possible to locate the crack accurately and to determine its magnitude.

Exographs are radiographs, or shadow pictures, produced by passing X-rays through an object. X-rays are light rays having wave lengths of the order of 10^{-6} to 10^{-9} centimeters. These X-rays emanate from a vacuum-tube operated electrically. The shadow picture is recorded on a special X-ray film coated on both sides to increase the intensity of the reaction. X-rays are used efficiently for the inspection of steel parts up to 3 inches in thickness. It is possible to obtain exographs of less dense materials, such as aluminum, in much greater thicknesses. Exographs are frequently used in the inspection of castings of a new design.

Gammagraphs are radiographs, or shadow pictures, produced by passing gamma-rays through an object. Gamma-rays are light rays having wave lengths of about 10^{-11} centimeters. Gamma-rays are obtained from radium usually in the form of radium sulphate, which is sealed in a small silver capsule. It is interesting to note that radium decays to one half its original strength in 1580 years. Gamma-rays are more powerful than X-rays and it is possible to obtain a gammagraph of steel parts up to 8 inches thick.

Magnaflux. Magnaflux is an inspection process for magnetic materials and parts which indicates cracks, seams, laps, and non-metallic inclusions. The process consists of magnetizing the part and then sprinkling it with magnetized powder. If a crack is present the distribution of the magnetic lines of force will be disturbed and opposite poles will exist either side of the crack. The magnetized powder forms a pattern in the magnetic field between the opposite poles and thus indicates the location and shape of defects which are frequently invisible to the eye. With proper equipment internal defects can be located.

To locate a defect it is essential that the magnetic lines of force pass approximately perpendicular to the defect. It is necessary therefore to induce magnetic flux in several directions. Circular magnetization is the inducing of a magnetic field consisting of concentric circles of force about and within a part by passing a high-amperage current through the part. This type of magnetization will locate defects running approximately parallel to the axis of the part. Bi-polar (longitudinal) magnetization is the inducing of a magnetic field within a part whose lines of force are parallel to the axis of the part. A high-amperage current passed through a coil wrapped around the part, or placing the part between the poles of electro-magnets will induce bi-polar magnetization which will indicate defects perpendicular to the axis of the part. Equipment now available will induce circular and longitudinal magnetization simultaneously and can be continuously in operation while the magnetic powder is applied. This so-called "continuous method" of testing in which the current is kept on throughout the inspection operation induces an intensified magnetic field and gives better results. Alternating or direct current can be used to magnetize parts.

Magnetic powder can be sprinkled on the work dry or applied wet. In the wet method the powder is suspended in a liquid such as kerosene. The wet method has better sensitivity than the dry powder method and is more generally used.

After inspection the part must be demagnetized before installation in the airplane. Demagnetization is accomplished by passing the part through a coil carrying alternating current. The part must be withdrawn about 18 inches from the coil so as to obtain the effect of a progressively weaker current. Another method of demagnetization is to leave the part in the coil and gradually reduce the current to zero. It is extremely important that all parts be demagnetized to as great an extent as possible to prevent interference with the airplane's compass.

CHAPTER III

STEEL AND ITS ALLOYS

The basis of all steel is iron which, when combined with carbon and other elements in varying amounts, gives a wide range of physical properties. Exact control of the alloying elements is essential to obtain a high grade steel for aircraft use. Each element contributes definite characteristics which depend upon the amount of the element present in any particular steel. Due to the large number of elements that will combine with iron, an infinite number of steels is obtainable. In order to classify the better grade steels used in automotive and aircraft work, the Society of Automotive Engineers has formulated a numerical index system which is generally used. This system has the great advantage of partially describing the steel insofar as the approximate percentage of the two most important elements is concerned.

The Navy Department and the Army Air Service each issue their own specifications covering all types and forms of material used in the construction of military aircraft. These two types of specifications are gradually being coördinated with Federal specifications covering the same materials. These Federal specifications will be binding on all government departments in the purchase of material covered by them. Copies of such specifications can be obtained from the Government Printing Office, Washington, D.C., for a nominal charge. To insure receiving the exact grade and quality of steel and other materials ordered, it is advisable to require conformance with one of these specifications.

PLAIN CARBON STEELS

By far the most important element in steel is carbon. In fact the classification of iron and steel is based on the percentage of carbon present. The generally accepted classification is as follows:

Wrought iron	Trace to .08%
Low carbon steel	.10% to .30%
Medium carbon steel	.30% to .70%
High carbon steel	.70% to 2.2%
Cast iron	2.2% to 4.5%

An interesting fact in connection with the above percentages is that all carbon above 2.2% is uncombined with the iron and is present in the form of graphite. This graphite forms planes of easy cleavage, which account for the easy breakage of cast iron.

Besides iron and carbon the plain carbon steels normally contain small amounts of silicon, sulphur, phosphorus, and manganese. Silicon and manganese are beneficial elements; sulphur and phosphorus are harmful impurities which cannot be wholly eliminated but are kept as low as possible.

ALLOY STEELS

The addition of a metallic alloying element to plain carbon steels results in the formation of a new alloy steel with wholly different properties. The carbon content of alloy steels is still of prime importance but varying properties can be obtained by adding an alloy. The metals commonly used as alloys in steel are nickel, chromium, molybdenum, vanadium, and tungsten. Small amounts of titanium and columbium are also used, particularly in the corrosion-resisting steels. In some alloy steels two alloying elements are present, such as chromium-nickel and chromium-molybdenum. One alloy steel which is commonly used for propeller hubs contains chromium-nickel-molybdenum.

Silicon and manganese are also used as alloying elements but in much larger amounts than is usually present in the plain carbon steels.

EFFECT OF INDIVIDUAL ELEMENTS

The development of alloy steels in the past has been largely a result of trial and error. It is practically impossible to predict, with any degree of certainty, the exact properties that can be obtained by a given combination of elements. In a general way, the effect of adding a specific alloying element is known. This information is useful to the designer in deciding which material possesses just the right properties for the proposed design. The constituents of plain and alloy steels are discussed in detail in the following paragraphs, emphasis being placed on those properties which have a bearing on aircraft use.

Carbon. Carbon is by far the most important constituent of steel. It combines readily with iron to form iron carbide (Fe_3C)

which is a compound known as cementite. It is largely due to the quantity and behavior of this compound that steels can be heat treated to various degrees of strength and toughness. This fact is equally true of both plain carbon and alloy steels. The higher the carbon content of steel is, the greater will be the ultimate strength, the hardness, and the range through which it can be heat treated. At the same time, the ductility, malleability, toughness, impact resistance, and the weldability will be reduced as the carbon increases. In selecting a steel for a given design, the carbon content must be considered: a low carbon steel is necessary if deep drawing or excessive mechanical working are required without excessive strength, and a high carbon steel is necessary where great hardness is required and ductility is not important. In general, low carbon steels are used for formed fittings and welded parts, and high carbon steels for springs. The medium carbon steels are used for forged fittings and tierods where good strength, combined with ductility, is required.

Manganese. Next to carbon, manganese is the most important ingredient in steel. Its primary purpose is to deoxidize and desulphurize the steel to produce a clean, tough metal. It deoxidizes by eliminating ferrous oxide which is a harmful impurity; and it combines with sulphur to form manganese sulphide which is harmless in small amounts. Sufficient manganese is added to the steel to leave an excess of not more than 1% in the metal. This excess manganese exists as manganese carbide (Mn_3C) which has similar characteristics in hardening and toughening the steel as cementite (Fe_3C), although not to as great an extent. Manganese does possess the property known as "penetration hardness" which means that in heat treatment of large sections, the hardness is not merely on the surface but penetrates to the core as well. In addition to the above properties the presence of manganese will greatly improve the forging qualities of the steel by reducing brittleness at forging and rolling temperatures.

An excess of more than 1% of manganese will increase the brittleness of the metal. There is, however, a manganese steel containing approximately 13% manganese that is exceptionally hard and ductile; but it is too hard to cut and must be forged, rolled, or cast to practically the finished shape. Some finishing may be done by grinding. This material was used at one time for tail skid shoes on airplanes, which were cast to size. Commercially it is used for rock crusher jaws and railroad curves. It has the interesting property of being nonmagnetic.

Silicon. Only a very small amount, not exceeding .3% of silicon, is present in steel. It is an excellent deoxidizer, but it also has the property of combining with iron more readily than carbon. Therefore it must be limited. A small amount of silicon improves the ductility of the metal. Its main purpose, however, is to produce a sound metal.

Silicon and manganese in large amounts are used as alloying elements in the formation of silico-manganese steels. These steels have good impact resistance.

Sulphur. Sulphur is a very undesirable impurity which must be limited in amount to not more than .06%. The maximum permissible sulphur content is always specified in the chemical specification for any particular steel. The presence of sulphur renders steel brittle at rolling or forging temperatures. In this condition the steel is said to be "hot short." As stated previously, manganese combines with the sulphur to form manganese sulphide which is harmless in small amounts. When too much sulphur is present, an iron sulphide is formed which because of its lower melting point is in liquid form at the forging temperature of the steel. This liquid ingredient breaks up the cohesion of the crystals of the metal, which results in cracking and breaking. With a minimum of .30% manganese present (as usually specified) and not more than .06% sulphur, all the sulphur will be in the form of manganese sulphide, which is harmless in such small quantities.

Phosphorus. Phosphorus, like sulphur, is an undesirable impurity limited in amount to not more than .05%. The maximum permissible content is always specified. Phosphorus is believed responsible for "cold shortness" or brittleness when the metal is cold. Below the .05% specified there is little, if any, brittleness in the steel. There is some evidence that very small amounts of phosphorus increase the strength slightly.

Nickel. Nickel is a white metal almost as bright as silver. In the pure state it is malleable, ductile, and weldable. It does not corrode quickly as attested by its use in nickel plating. Nickel dissolves in all proportions in molten steel. The commonly used nickel steels contain from 3% to 5% nickel. The addition of nickel to steels increases the strength, yield point, and hardness without materially affecting the ductility. In heat treatment the presence of nickel in the steel slows down the critical rate of hardening which, in turn, increases the depth of hardening and produces a finer grain structure. There is also less warpage and scaling of heat-treated nickel steel parts. Nickel increases the corrosion-resistance of the steel. It is one of the principal constituents of the so-called "stainless" or corrosion-resisting steels.

Chromium. Chromium is a hard gray metal with a high melting point. Chromium imparts hardness, strength, wear resistance, and corrosion-resistance to steel. It also improves the magnetic qualities to such an extent that chromium steel is used for magnets. Chromium possesses excellent "penetration hardness" characteristics and its alloys heat treat well. The main use of chromium in alloys is in conjunction with nickel, molybdenum, and vanadium. About 1% of chromium is present in these alloys which are strong, hard, and have fair ductility. These alloys are also resistant to shock loads. It is possible to heat treat nickel-chromium alloys to an ultimate tensile strength as high as 250,000 lbs. per sq. in. and still retain ductility.

Corrosion-resisting steels contain large amounts of chromium. The most common of these steels is 18–8 steel—approximately 18% chromium and 8% nickel. Naturally this metal is very corrosion-resistant. At the same time, it is practically non-magnetic although some chromium steels are used for magnets and nickel in its pure state is magnetic. This material furnishes an excellent example of the fact that the alloy does not necessarily retain the properties of the constituents.

Some chromium alloys are used where great wear resistance is required. Thus a chrome-vanadium alloy is used for ball bearings, and a tungsten-chromium alloy for high speed cutting tools.

Molybdenum. Molybdenum is a very effective alloying element. A small percentage has as much effect as much larger amounts of other alloying elements. It improves the homogeneity of the metal and reduces the grain size. It also increases the elastic limit, the impact value, wear resistance, and fatigue strength. An exceptionally important property from the aircraft viewpoint is the improvement in the air-hardening properties of steel containing molybdenum. This is particularly useful where the steel has been subjected to a welding process as is very common with chrome-molybdenum steel in airplane construction. In general it may be said that while molybdenum is one of the most recently used alloying elements, it shows great promise and without doubt will find many new applications in the near future. The molybdenum steels are readily heat treated, forged, and machined.

Vanadium. Vanadium is the most expensive of the alloying elements. It is seldom used in amounts over .20%, but it is an intensive deoxidizing agent and improves the grain structure and fatigue strength. Vanadium also increases the ultimate strength, yield point, toughness, and resistance to impact, vibration, and stress reversal. These latter qualities are identical with fatigue strength and are the basis for using vanadium alloys for propeller hubs and engine bolts. The vanadium alloys, as used generally, contain about 1% chromium and are called chrome-vanadium steel. These steels have good ductility, along with high strength.

Tungsten. Tungsten steels have no direct application in aircraft construction, but they possess an interesting property known as "red hardness." "High speed steel" is a tungsten chromium steel used for tools which will retain their cutting edge even when heated to dull redness by working. This tool steel contains from 14% to 18% tungsten, and 2% to 4% chromium.

Titanium. Titanium is often added in small quantities to 18–8 corrosion-resisting steel to reduce the embrittlement at the operating temperatures of exhaust stacks and collectors.

S.A.E. STEEL NUMBERING SYSTEM

In the United States the S.A.E. Numbering System is commonly used to designate the steels used in aircraft and automotive construction. By means of a simple numerical system the

TABLE 2

S.A.E. STEEL NUMBERING SYSTEM

TYPE OF STEEL	NUMERALS (and Digits)
Carbon Steels	1xxx
Plain carbon	10xx
Free cutting (screw stock)	11xx
Free cutting, manganese	X13xx
High Manganese	T13xx
Nickel Steels	2xxx
0.50 per cent nickel	20xx
1.50 " "	21xx
3.50 " "	23xx
5.00 " "	25xx
Nickel Chromium Steels	3xxx
1.25 per cent nickel, 0.60 per cent chromium	31xx
1.75 " " 1.00 " "	32xx
3.50 " " 1.50 " "	33xx
3.00 " " 0.80 " "	34xx
Corrosion and heat-resisting steels	30xxx
Molybdenum Steels	4xxx
Chromium	41xx
Chromium nickel	43xx
Nickel	46xx & 48xx
Chromium Steels	5xxx
Low chromium	51xx
Medium chromium	52xxx
Corrosion and heat-resisting	51xxx
Chromium Vanadium Steels	6xxx
Tungsten Steels	7xxx & 7xxxx
Silicon Manganese Steels	9xxx

NOTE: The prefix " X " is used in several instances to denote variations in the range of manganese, sulphur, or chromium. The prefix " T " is used with the Manganese Steels (1300 Series) to avoid confusion with steels of somewhat different manganese range that have been identified by the same numerals but without the prefix.

composition of the steel is partially identified. Unfortunately, only the major alloying element is so identified, but no additional information could be included without destroying the simplicity of the scheme now in use. As explained by the S.A.E., the system is as follows:

A numeral index system is used to identify the compositions of the S.A.E. steels, which makes it possible to use numerals on shop drawings and blueprints that are partially descriptive of the composition of material covered by such numbers. The first digit indicates the type to which the steel belongs; thus "1-" indicates a carbon steel; "2-" a nickel steel; and "3-" a nickel-chromium steel. In the case of the simple alloy steels the second digit generally indicates the approximate percentage of the predominant alloying element. Usually the last two or three digits indicate the average carbon content in "points" or hundredths of 1 per cent. Thus "2340" indicates a nickel steel of approximately 3 per cent nickel (3.25 to 3.75) and 0.40 per cent carbon (0.35 to 0.45); and "71360" indicates a tungsten steel of about 13 per cent tungsten (12 to 15) and 0.60 per cent carbon (0.50 to 0.70).

In some instances, in order to avoid confusion, it has been found necessary to depart from this system of identifying the approximate alloy composition of a steel by varying the second and third digits of the number. An instance of such departure is the steel numbers selected for several of the corrosion and heat-resisting alloys.

Army-Navy Aeronautical Specifications

AN Aeronautical Specifications are prepared by the Permanent Working Committee of the Aeronautical Board. These specifications supersede the individual Army and Navy specifications. AN aero specifications have not yet been issued for all aircraft materials but have been listed in the following pages insofar as possible. The nomenclature of these specifications is the same as Federal specifications with AN prefixed. Thus we have:

AN–QQ–S–685—Steel; Chrome-Molybdenum (X4130), Sheet-and-Strip.

where AN—indicates "Army–Navy (Aeronautical) Standard."
     QQ—indicates the Federal Standard Stock Catalog group for procurement.
     S—indicates first letter of first word in specification title which in this case is "Steel."
     685—is a serial number determined by order of issue.

Chapter IV

AIRCRAFT STEELS—PROPERTIES AND USES

Up until a few years ago mild carbon steel was about the only steel used in aircraft construction. It was used for fittings, fuselages, brace struts for landing gears and wings, and wherever else a piece of metal was required. As airplane construction developed and became more complex, other steels with higher strengths and specialized properties were made available and utilized. There are now some twenty different kinds of steel regularly used in aircraft construction. In order to select the proper steel for a given purpose, the designer must know the capabilities of all available steels. This chapter will be devoted to describing the commonly used steels in as much detail as possible.

In selecting a type of steel for use, the designer must first assure himself that it possesses the requisite mechanical properties to withstand the loads and service conditions it will be subjected to. The steel chosen must also be capable of ready fabrication into the desired shape. Other important considerations are the availability and the cost of the material. These latter points can be quickly determined through the company's purchasing agent or the nearest supply house.

It is common practice in aircraft construction to heat treat, or caseharden steel to obtain desirable properties. Whenever there is a choice of two materials, it is advisable to select the one requiring the less severe treatment in order to avoid as much distortion or cracking as possible. A detailed description of the heat treating and surface hardening of steel is given in later chapters.

Table 3 summarizes the steels used in aircraft construction. This table lists the S.A.E. number, the Navy specification, and the Army specification by which the various steels are designated. It also gives the standard forms in which the material is available and the general use of each material.

35

TABLE 3
SUMMARY OF AIRCRAFT STEELS

S.A.E. Number	Shape	Specification			General Use
		AN Aero	Navy	Army	
1015	Wire	AN–QQ–W–435	22W10	48–19	Soft wire for wrapping, and locking
1020	Bar	AN–QQ–S–646		57–107–9	Casehardened parts
1025	Bar	AN–QQ–S–646	46 S 22	57–107–9	Machined parts; nuts
	Sheet	AN–QQ–S–651	47 S 17	57–136–3	Intricate secondary fittings
	Tubing	AN–WW–T–846	49 T 1	57–180–1	Structural tubing—moderate strength
1035	Bar			57–107–20	Light forgings; standard parts
1045	Wire			48–25	Tie rods
1095	Sheet	AN–QQ–S–666	47 S 15	57–136–6	Flat sheet springs
	Wire		22W11	48–26	Coil springs
2320	Bar			57–107–12	Casehardened parts
2330	Bar	AN–QQ–S–689	46 S 21	57–107–17	Machined parts; bolts
2515	Bar			57–107–18	Casehardened parts
3115	Bar			57–107–26	Casehardened parts
3140	Bar	AN–QQ–S–690		57–107–3	Machined parts
3250	Bar			57–107–6	High strength gears and splines
3312	Bar			57–107–22	Casehardened parts
X4130	Bar	AN–QQ–S–684	46 S 23	57–107–19	Structural fittings
	Sheet	AN–QQ–S–685	47 S 14	57–136–8	Structural sheet fittings
	Tubing—round	AN–WW–T–850	44 T 18	57–180–2	Structural tubing
	Tubing—straight line		44 T 17	57–183	Structural tubing
4140	Bar	AN–QQ–S–752	46 S 23	10083	High strength fittings and forgings
X4340	Bar	AN–QQ–S–756	46 S 28	11062	Forged parts; propeller hubs
4615	Bar			57–107–10	Casehardened parts
6115	Bar			57–107–2	Casehardened parts
6135	Bar	AN–QQ–S–687	46 S 25	57–107–5	Forged parts; propeller hubs
6150	Bar		46 S 24	48–7	Propeller cones and snap rings
	Wire		46 S 31	57–107–11	All important springs
6195	Bar	AN–QQ–S–688	46 S 31	57–107–24	Ball bearings
Silicon-Chromium	Rod		46 S 30		Important springs
Nitriding Steel	Forgings			11075	Nitrided parts
Steel Castings	Castings		49 S 6	57–64–1	Steel castings

For simplicity the steels will hereafter be designated only by their S.A.E. number. The description of each steel will include its specific uses, general characteristics as regards machining, forming and welding, and physical properties.

Table 4 gives the chemical composition of the steels as specified by the S.A.E. Individual metallurgists and government specifications often limit the phosphorus and sulphur content to less than that listed, but in other respects the specifications are about the same.

Carbon Steels

S.A.E. 1015. A galvanized (zinc-coated) steel wire is made from this material. It is used as a locking wire on nuts and turn-buckles. This wire has a maximum tensile strength of 75,000 lbs./sq. in. and a minimum elongation of 8–10%.

S.A.E. 1020. This steel is used for casehardened parts. In this form it is often used for bushings that must resist abrasion. It is also employed in the fabrication of stamping dies that require a hard, wear-resisting surface. When casehardened, this steel has a core strength of 60,000 lbs./sq. in. and good ductility. In its normal state it has an ultimate tensile strength of 55,000 lbs./sq. in., a yield strength of 36,000 lbs./sq. in., and an elongation of 22%.

This steel machines well. It can be brazed or welded.

S.A.E. 1025. This steel is commonly referred to as mild carbon steel or cold-rolled stock. For aircraft purposes the sheet is always purchased cold rolled to accurate dimensions. Bar stock is either cold rolled or cold drawn. For most purposes this steel has been superseded by chrome-molybdenum steel, S.A.E. X4130. It is still used for aircraft nuts and similar standard parts however, and also for nonstructural clamps requiring a lot of bending.

In all its forms this steel has an ultimate tensile strength of 55,000 lbs./sq in., a yield strength of 36,000 lbs./sq. in., and an elongation of 22%. When used for aircraft nuts, it is heat treated and develops a minimum strength of 70,000 lbs./sq. in.

In sheet form this material can be bent through 180° without cracking over a diameter equal to the thickness of the test sec-

TABLE 4

CHEMICAL COMPOSITION OF AIRCRAFT STEELS

S.A.E. Number	Carbon	Manganese	Phosphorus Max.	Sulphur Max.	Nickel	Chromium	Molybdenum	Vanadium	
1015	.10–.20	.30–.60	.045	.055					
1020	.15–.25	.30–.60	.045	.055					
1025	.20–.30	.30–.60	.045	.055					
1035	.30–.40	.60–.90	.045	.055					
1045	.40–.50	.60–.90	.045	.055					
1095	.90–1.05	.25–.50	.040	.055					
2320	.15–.25	.30–.60	.040	.050	3.25–3.75				
2330	.25–.35	.50–.80	.040	.050	3.25–3.75				
2515	.10–.20	.30–.60	.040	.050	4.75–5.25				
3115	.10–.20	.30–.60	.040	.050	1.00–1.50	.45–.75			
3140	.35–.45	.60–.90	.040	.050	1.00–1.50	.45–.75			
3250	.45–.55	.30–.60	.040	.050	1.50–2.00	.90–1.25			
3312	.17 max.	.30–.60	.040	.050	3.25–3.75	1.25–1.75			
X4130	.25–.35	.40–.60	.040	.050		.80–1.10	.15–.25		
4140	.35–.45	.60–.90	.040	.050		.80–1.10	.15–.25		
X4340	.35–.45	.50–.80	.040	.050	1.50–2.00	.60–.90	.20–.30		
4615	.10–.20	.40–.70	.040	.050	1.65–2.00		.20–.30		
6115	.10–.20	.30–.60	.040	.050		.80–1.10		.15–.20	
6135	.30–.40	.60–.90	.040	.050		.80–1.10		.15–.20	
6150	.45–.55	.60–.90	.040	.050		.80–1.10		.15–.20	
6195	.90–1.05	.20–.45	.030	.035		.80–1.10		.15–.20	
Silicon-Chromium	.45–.50	.70–.90	.040	.040		.25–.35		.18 min.	Silicon 3.00–3.50
Nitriding Steel	.30–.40	.40–.60	.045	.040	.50 max.	.90–1.50	.15–.25		Aluminum .90–1.50
Steel "	.20–.27	.40–.70	.045	.040	3.25–3.75	1.00–1.30	.20–.30		Silicon 1.10–1.40
Casting Steel	.40–.50	1.15–1.40	.050	.050		.90–1.20	.35–.45		Silicon .35–.45

tion. The same thing can be done with bar stock over a diameter equal to twice the thickness of the test section.

This material machines fairly well. It can be brazed or welded.

S.A.E. 1035. Here we have a medium carbon steel used for small or medium sized forgings not requiring great strength. It can be obtained in the cold-rolled or cold-drawn condition when it is to be machined without subsequent heat treatment. Hot-rolled or forged stock is usually subjected to heat treatment after fabrication. It is used for the fabrication of such standard parts as clevis ends, shackles, levers, hand operated shafts, and gears.

PHYSICAL PROPERTIES

	COLD FINISHED	HEAT TREATED
Ultimate tensile strength (lbs./sq. in.) ..	80,000	95,000
Yield strength (lbs./sq. in.)	50,000	60,000
Elongation (%).....................	15	15

This steel forges and machines well. It can be worked cold only with difficulty; it should not be welded.

S.A.E. 1045. This steel, obtainable as cold-drawn wire, is used for the fabrication of aircraft tie-rods. It is also procured as annealed bar for general machining and forging purposes in the manufacture of parts requiring greater strength than available in S.A.E. 1035 steel. Parts fabricated from the bar stock cannot be bent cold and must be heat treated after fabrication.

PHYSICAL PROPERTIES

	COLD-DRAWN WIRE	HEAT TREATED BAR
U. T. S. (lbs/sq. in.)..........	140,000	100,000
Yield str. "	......	70,000

The cold-drawn wire must withstand a reverse bend test in which it is bent back and forth 90° each way over a round surface with a radius three times the thickness of the wire. It must withstand seven of these 90° bends without failure. The cold-drawn wire may be cold swaged or cold drawn as required in the manufacture of tie-rods.

The bar stock machines well. It also has good surface hardness and wears well after heat treatment. Chain sprockets, hubs, and crankshafts are made from it.

S.A.E. 1095. This high carbon steel is obtainable in all of the following forms:

Spring steel (sheet or strip) annealed is used for flat springs which are heat treated after forming. As purchased the strip is cold rolled and uniformly annealed. The annealed material can be bent flat over a diameter equal to its thickness. It is universally used for flat springs in aircraft work.

Spring steel (wire) heat treated is a standard grade of music wire and is used in the fabrication of small springs. It is obtainable from .005 to .180 inch diameter, with a variation in tensile strength of 350,000 to 225,000 lbs./sq. in., respectively, for these two extreme sizes. It is purchased in the heat-treated state and can be coiled into springs as received. After coiling the spring should be strain relieved by heating for approximately one hour at a temperature of 325 to 375° F.

Steel wire, high strength is a cold-drawn wire from .032 to .306 inch diameter, with a tensile strength varying from 308,000 to 209,000 lbs./sq. in. for these two diameters. This wire is particularly good for hinge pins and other locations where music wire is ordinarily used.

Bar stock is used for parts subject to high shear or wear if casehardening is not desirable. It is sometimes referred to as drill rod since it is employed in the manufacture of drills, taps, and dies. Bar stock is purchased in the annealed state when it is to be machined and then heat treated. Drill rod is used for hard pins.

NICKEL STEELS

S.A.E. 2320. This is a carburizing steel with a moderately strong core. Its case has excellent wear and fatigue resisting characteristics, and its relatively low quenching temperature results in less distortion. Quenching in oil also reduces the distortion and gives a file hard case. Thin sections should not be manufactured from this steel because of its strong core. It is used to produce bushings, trunnions for mounting machine guns, and other parts requiring a wear-resisting surface combined with a shock-resistant core of moderate strength. The normal core strength is 80,000 lbs./sq. in.

This steel machines very well. It must, of course, be machined before casehardening. After casehardening it is ground to the finished dimensions.

S.A.E. 2330. This is the standard nickel steel and possesses good strength and great toughness. It can be purchased as bar stock in the forged, rolled, annealed, normalized and annealed, or heat-treated condition. If not purchased in the heat-treated condition, it is heat treated after fabrication. It is used for high grade machined parts, such as aircraft bolts, turnbuckle eyes and forks, and tie-rod terminals. When heat treated it has the following physical properties:

U. T. S. (lbs./sq. in.)	125,000	150,000
Yield str. "	100,000	120,000
Elongation (%)	17	15

Aircraft bolts are heat treated to 125,000 lbs./sq. in. ultimate strength.

This steel can be bent flat over a diameter equal to its thickness. It also has very good machining properties.

S.A.E. 2515. This is a carburizing steel with an extremely high strength core. The case is not so hard as that obtained with other carburizing steels. If extreme core toughness is desired, S.A.E. 2512 steel should be used. In this steel the carbon content is limited to .17% maximum. It is used for engine gears, knuckle pins, and other applications requiring a high strength core and good wearing qualities. By proper heat treatment, a core strength of 120,000 to 160,000 lbs./sq. in. is obtainable.

This steel machines fairly well but not so good as S.A.E. 2320.

NICKEL CHROMIUM STEELS

S.A.E. 3115. This is a carburizing steel with an exceedingly hard, wear-resisting surface and a tough core. Generally, it is used in engine construction for gear pins, piston pins, cam rings, push rod ends, and rollers. It has a core strength of 85,000 lbs./sq. in.

This steel machines well.

S.A.E. 3140. This steel heat treats exceptionally well and, consequently, is used for many structural parts requiring high strength and good fatigue qualities. It also has good creep resistance up to 1000° F. Wing hinge fittings, lift wire trunnions, engine bolts and studs are its chief uses. For these applications it is usually heat treated to 125,000 or 150,000 lbs./sq. in.

PHYSICAL PROPERTIES

U. T. S. (lbs./sq. in.)	125,000	150,000	180,000
Yield str. "	100,000	120,000	150,000
Elongation (%)	19	17	12

This steel machines well at heat treatments up to 150,000 lbs./sq. in.

S.A.E. 3250. This is a high carbon chrome-nickel steel used for high strength machined or forged parts subject to severe wear. But casehardened steels are employed to a large extent instead of this steel, because they wear better and crack less in heat treatment. S.A.E. 3250 is used, however, for axle shafts, gears, spline shafts, and other parts for heavy duty work. It has high strength and is very hard, and can be heat treated to a tensile strength as high as 220,000 lbs./sq. in., with a yield strength of 200,000 lbs./sq. in.

S.A.E. 3312. This is a carburizing steel with a strong, tough core similar to S.A.E. 2512. It is used for wrist pins, starter jaws, timing gears, rear axles and transmission gears for heavy duty trucks.

Its core strength is 100,000 lbs./sq. in.

MOLYBDENUM STEELS

S.A.E. X4130. This is chrome-molybdenum steel which has been generally adopted in aircraft construction for practically all parts made of sheet and tubing. Bar stock of this material is also used for small forgings under ½ inch in thickness. The general use of this steel is due to its excellent welding characteristics, its ease of forming, its response to heat treatment, and its availability in all sizes of sheet and seamless drawn tubing. The standard sizes of round and streamline tubing are given in the Appendix.

It is customary to specify this steel for all parts of an airplane fabricated from steel unless some special property possessed by one of the other steels is required. Chrome-molybdenum steel is used for all welded assemblies, for sheet fittings, and for landing gear axles. Fuselages and landing gears are common examples of welded assemblies made of chrome-molybdenum steel. Sheet metal fittings can be readily fabricated from it because of its excellent forming characteristics. The landing gear axles are formed from chrome-molybdenum tubing heat treated to 180,000 lbs./sq. in.

Sheet and tubing are usually purchased in the normalized state. In this condition the following physical properties can be expected:

SHEET

U. T. S. (lbs./sq. in.)....................	90,000
Yield str. "	70,000
Elongations: over 3/16 in. thick..........	20%
1/8 to 3/16 in.............	15%
1/16 to 1/8 in.............	12%
Less than 1/16 in...........	10%

TUBING

	WALL THICKNESS		
	Up to .035	.036 to .186	Over .186
U. T. S. (lbs./sq. in.)..........	95,000	95,000	90,000
Yield str. "	75,000	75,000	70,000
Elongation: full tube..........	10%	12%	15%
strip.............	5%	7%	10%

When heat treated this material has the following physical properties:

U. T. S.	YIELD STRENGTH	SHEAR	BEARING
125,000	100,000	80,000	175,000
150,000	125,000	100,000	190,000
175,000	140,000	115,000	200,000
200,000	150,000	125,000	210,000

Only 80% of these values should be taken if the part has been welded.

The following tabulation gives the minimum acceptable elongation for heat treated chrome-molybdenum steel of various thicknesses:

MINIMUM % ELONGATION IN TWO INCHES

DIAMETER OR THICKNESS INCHES	ULTIMATE TENSILE STRENGTH			
	125,000	150,000	175,000	200,000
Up to .028...................	2.0	1.5	1.0	1.0
.029–.067...................	4.0	2.5	1.5	1.0
.068–.124...................	6.5	5.0	3.0	2.0
.125–.254...................	9.0	7.0	5.0	4.0
Over .254...................	10.5	8.5	5.5	4.5

An examination of the elongation table will show that material .065 inch thick or less has a very low elongation when heat treated above 150,000 lbs./sq. in. This low elongation is a mark of brittleness. For this reason it is a good rule never to heat treat material .065 inch or less in thickness above 150,000. Parts subject to vibration, such as control system parts, should not be heat treated above 125,000. If heat treated above this value, under constant vibration any small flaws in the material will develop into cracks. It is customary to treat wing hinge fittings to 150,000 lbs./sq. in.; landing gear parts are heat treated to 180,000 lbs./sq. in.

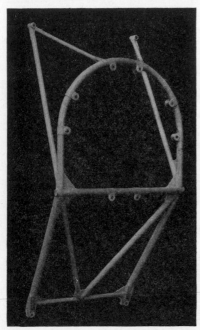

FIGURE 9. ENGINE MOUNT
Chrome-Molybdenum Sheet and
Tubing

Chrome-molybdenum welds readily with the oxyacetylene flame, and it may also be electric arc-welded when over $\frac{1}{16}$ inch thick. Heat-treated parts, however, cannot be welded without destroying the heat treatment. Welding will reduce the strength of normalized metal in the region adjacent to the weld that was heated to a temperature just below the critical range of the steel. It is desirable to normalize all welded parts after fabrication to regain the loss in strength and to relieve the internal stresses set up by the welding. These stresses are due to the fact that welding shrinks the metal. Rigid jigs must be used in welding up sheet or tubular assemblies to keep this shrinkage under control.

Chrome-molybdenum sheet may be bent cold through an angle of 180° over a diameter equal to its own thickness. The government specifications require this steel to pass this bend test either across or parallel to the grain of the metal. In fabricating fittings, however, bends should always be made across the grain, and the direction of greatest stress should be along the grain. If this is done, there is less likelihood of cracking or failure of the fitting in fabrication or due to fatigue stresses in service. When the fabrication processes involve severe forming, it is advisable to anneal the steel and then normalize or heat treat the finished assembly.

Chrome-molybdenum can be brazed, but this process is seldom used nowadays in aircraft construction.

S.A.E. 4140. This is a chrome-molybdenum steel containing a higher carbon and manganese content than X4130 steel. The higher carbon and manganese content improves the heat treating properties of the steel and enables great strength and hardness to be obtained with thick sections. This steel is used for structural machined and forged parts over ½ inch in thickness, and is obtainable as bar stock in any one of the following conditions: forged, rolled, annealed, normalized, or heat treated. It is, however, usually purchased in the normalized condition, machined to shape, and then heat treated. Forgings are always normalized or heat treated after fabrication.

S.A.E. 4140 is used for wing hinge fittings, flying wire trunnions, and other similar fittings in aircraft requiring great strength. Forgings of this steel are very commonly used. The physical properties of this material are the same as those given for S.A.E. X4130 sheet stock. Bars 1½ inch thick or over in the normalized condition have slightly less strength—ultimate tensile strength is 85,000 lbs./sq. in. and yield strength, 65,000 lbs./sq. in. It is generally heat treated to 150,000 lbs./sq. in.

This steel machines without difficulty at heat treatments up to 150,000 lbs./sq. in. It is seldom welded but can be if necessary although its high manganese content makes welding more difficult than is the case with S.A.E. X4130 steel.

S.A.E. X4340. This is a nickel-chromium-molybdenum steel with excellent properties. It has very good depth-hardening qualities, which make it ideal for large forgings requiring high strength and hardness throughout, and also has good impact and fatigue resistance at high strengths. It is machinable in the heat-treated state up to 180,000 lbs./sq. in. Propeller hubs, crankshafts, and other large forgings are made from this material. It is also used interchangeably with S.A.E. 3140.

As ordinarily employed this material has a tensile strength of 150,000 lbs./sq. in., a yield strength of 130,000 lbs./sq. in., and an elongation of 16%. It is sometimes heat treated as high as 200,000 lbs./sq. in. ultimate tensile strength.

S.A.E. 4615. This is one of the best of the carburizing steels. It has a very fine grain, and usually requires only one quench to develop satisfactory properties. Due to the single quenching operation it distorts less than other carburizing steels. It also machines nicely. Because of its good machining qualities it is used commercially for automatic machine production. It has a file hard case for resisting wear and is excellent for use in bushings, rollers, and other locations requiring wear resistance and accurate dimensions. A core strength of 80,000 to 100,000 lbs./sq. in. is obtainable with S.A.E. 4615. It has high fatigue resistance in addition to its other good properties.

CHROME-VANADIUM STEELS

S.A.E 6115. This is a carburizing steel with a core strength of 90,000 lbs./sq. in. It is a fine-grained type and may be used interchangeably with other carburizing steels.

S.A.E. 6135. This steel is strong, tough, and has high fatigue resistance. It is used for propeller hubs, welded steel propeller blades, and engine bolts and nuts. All these applications require a high fatigue resistance. This steel also machines well. Its physical properties as used in the manufacture of propeller hubs are: ultimate tensile strength, 135,000 lbs./sq. in.; yield strength, 115,000 lbs./sq. in.; elongation, 15%.

S.A.E. 6150. This steel has high strength and fatigue properties. It is used for all important coil springs in aircraft and is available in rod form from .180 to .500 inch in diameter. It is purchased in the annealed condition and heat treated after forming. In bar form this steel is used for propeller cones and snap rings which require good fatigue and machining properties. Rod for helical springs can be heat treated to develop the following properties: ultimate tensile strength, 200,000 lbs./sq. in.; yield strength, 150,000 lbs./sq. in.; elongation, 6%.

Bar stock is normally heat treated to develop an ultimate

tensile strength of 150,000 lbs./sq. in., a yield strength of 125,000 lbs./sq. in., and an elongation of 14%.

S.A.E. 6195. This is a high carbon chrome-vanadium steel which is used for parts subject to high bearing loads and requiring maximum hardness. Ball bearings, roller bearings, and races are made from it.

SPECIAL STEELS

Silicon-Chromium Steel. Important springs are manufactured from this high strength steel which may be obtained in rod form. For this purpose it is interchangeable with S.A.E. 6150 steel. It can be heat treated to an ultimate tensile strength of 200,000 lbs./sq. in., a yield strength of 150,000 lbs./sq. in., and an elongation of 6%.

Nitriding Steel. This is a special steel used only for nitrided parts. In the chapter on Surface Hardening its properties are discussed in detail. It is used for bushings and gears requiring great surface hardness and wear resistance.

Steel Castings. Steel castings are seldom used in aircraft construction. In the past they have been used extensively for tail skids and sometimes for landing gear fittings. The following properties are obtainable by heat treatment:

U. T. S.	100,000	150,000
Yield str.	70,000	110,000
Elongation	17%	5%

This material may be welded before heat treatment.

CHAPTER V

HEAT TREATMENT OF STEEL

It has long been known that a great variation in the properties of steel could be obtained by heating the metal to a high temperature and quenching quickly in a liquid, such as brine, water, or oil. Unfortunately, each alloy required a different treatment, and since the actual effects were not understood, the whole science of heat treatment was a hit or miss affair. Recently a new science known as "metallography," which deals with the internal structure of metals and the principles underlying changes in structure, has been developed. By means of etching and microscopic examination the internal structure of steel in all its various states has been studied. Due to these studies and the work of numerous investigators heat treatment is today an exact science.

Heat treatment of steel is based upon the fact that the metal is a crystalline structure which assumes different forms at various temperatures. The change in structure as the temperature decreases is normally slow, and it has been found that by rapid cooling, such as dropping the hot metal in a cold liquid, the normal structure at high temperatures can be retained at atmospheric temperatures. This new structure has totally different physical properties from the normal atmospheric structure. Numerous variations are possible, depending upon the temperature from which the metal is quenched and the speed of quenching. The practical terms which describe the heat treatments normally used are: annealing, normalizing, hardening, drawing. In addition to these we have special treatments called carburizing, cyaniding, and nitriding. To develop the desired properties all aircraft steels are subjected to one or more of these operations. This chapter will be devoted to the theory and practical applications of heat treating.

CRITICAL RANGE

Materials are said to be allotropic when they possess the property that permits them to exist in various forms without a change in chemical composition. Carbon which exists as diamond, graphite, and charcoal is a common allotropic substance. Pure iron is also allotropic, existing in three states: namely, *alpha, beta, and gamma iron*. In this case each of these states is only stable between very definite temperature limits—alpha iron up to 1400° F., beta iron from 1400° F. to 1652° F., and gamma iron above the latter temperature.

When molten iron solidifies and is permitted to cool at a uniform rate, it is found that at 1652° F. the cooling stops momentarily. At this point a change in the structure of the iron has taken place, in which gamma iron has been transformed into beta iron. This rearrangement of the structure has resulted in the evolution of heat, which accounts for the retardation of the cooling. This point is designated by the symbol Ar_3 and is called the *upper critical point*. As the cooling continues, it is found that a second retardation occurs at 1400° F. Obviously this is caused by the transformation of beta into alpha iron with the resultant evolution of heat. This point is indicated by Ar_2, the *second critical point*.

In heating pure iron similar points occur in which heat is absorbed without a rise in the metal temperature. These points are designated Ac_2 and Ac_3. These heat absorption points are some 20° F. higher than the respective Ar_2 and Ar_3 points. The critical range is the range of temperature between the lower and upper critical points.

Carbon steels have definite critical points and a critical range. The exact temperature at which these points occur and the number of points depend upon the carbon content of the steel. Low carbon steels have three critical points. In addition to the preceding two points described for iron, when a small amount of carbon is added to the iron another point designated as Ar_1 occurs at 1274° F. There is, of course, a similar point on a rising heat designated Ac_1. The point Ar_1 is called the *lowest critical point* or the *recalescent point* because the intense evolution of heat causes the metal to glow.

The "r" in the symbol Ar is derived from the French word

refroidissement, which means cooling. Similarly, the "c" in the symbol Ac is the first letter of *chauffage*—to heat.

Referring to Figure 10 it can be seen that the number of critical points and the scope of the critical range depend upon the carbon content. There are three critical points up to a little over .4% carbon. In this region the two upper critical points

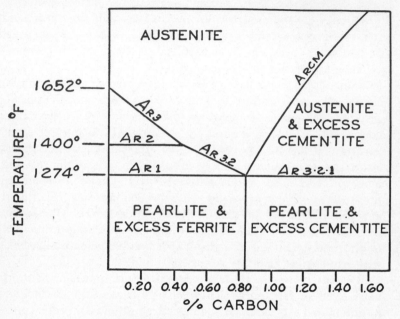

FIGURE 10. CRITICAL POINTS OF STEEL

merge, forming a single point, $Ar_{3.2}$. At .85% carbon all the critical points unite, and we have one point, Ar_{321}. Above .85% carbon a new point designated Ar_{cm} extends above the Ar_{321} point.

Alloy steels possess similar critical points, but they occur at different temperatures for each steel. Nickel and manganese have the property of materially lowering the critical range. In fact, the 13% manganese steel has a critical range below atmospheric temperatures.

INTERNAL STRUCTURE OF STEEL

The internal structure of steel is almost wholly dependent upon the exact relationship of the iron and carbon. The carbon is in chemical combination with the iron as iron carbide (Fe_3C), called *cementite*. In steels containing .85% carbon, the cementite forms a perfect mixture with the pure iron (called ferrite) present. This mixture is called *pearlite* because of its resemblance in appearance to mother-of-pearl. Pearlite is a mechanical mixture of six parts of ferrite to one part of cementite. Steels with less than .85% carbon are composed of pearlite and excess ferrite. Practically all aircraft steels are of this type. On the other hand, tool steels which contain more than .85% carbon are composed of pearlite and excess cementite.

In metallurgy the name *eutectic alloy* is given to that alloy of two substances which has the lowest fusing point. In every alloy there is one percentage combination of the two elements that will fuse at the lowest temperature. Variation of the percentage composition of either element, up or down, will increase the temperature of fusion. A similar condition exists in steel in the critical range, although here we are dealing with a solid solution. You will note in Figure 10 that the lowest temperature for the upper critical point occurs at .85% carbon content. This alloy has been named the *eutectoid*. Steel with less than .85% carbon is called *hypo-eutectoid* and with more than .85% *hyper-eutectoid*. Steels with excess ferrite are hypo-eutectoid, and steels with excess cementite are hyper-eutectoid.

Pearlite is normally a laminated structure consisting of alternate layers of ferrite and cementite. In some cases pearlite has a granulated appearance and is called granular pearlite. If steel is cooled very slowly through the critical range, laminated pearlite, which is the most stable form, will result. Pearlite is relatively strong, hard, and ductile. It has a tensile strength of over 100,000 pounds per square inch, an elongation of approximately 10%, and maximum hardening power. This latter point is extremely significant. It means that the greatest hardness from heat treatment is obtained by steel containing .85% carbon. It is also true that starting with low carbon steel, greater hardness is obtainable as the carbon content increases and approaches .85%. This point is important when selecting a steel to give great strength and hardness after heat treatment.

Ferrite is pure alpha iron in carbon steels. In alloy steels containing nickel, molybdenum, or vanadium these alloying elements are in solid solution in the ferrite. Ferrite is very ductile and has a tensile strength of about 40,000 pounds per square inch. It should be noted that it imparts these properties to low carbon steels of which it is the major constituent. Ferrite does not have any hardening properties.

Cementite is iron carbide (Fe_3C). It is very hard and brittle and produces a hardening quality on steels of which it is a part.

Austenite, the name given to steel when it is heated above the critical range, consists of a solid solution of cementite in gamma iron. It is only stable when maintained at a temperature above the critical range. It will, however, attain perfect homogeneity if sufficient time is allowed. The grain size of steel it has been found is smallest just above the critical range, and it is a known fact that the smallest grain size will give the strongest and best metal. For this reason when steel is heated for subsequent hardening or working, its temperature is kept just above the upper critical point for the time necessary to insure thorough heating of the material.

THEORY OF HEAT TREATMENT

When molten steel solidifies austenite is formed. As further cooling takes place, the critical range is reached and the austenite goes through a transition until at the lower critical limit the familiar pearlite with excess ferrite or cementite, depending upon the carbon content, is formed. The transition from austenite to pearlite through the critical range is normally a slow operation. It has been found that if this operation is speeded up by such means as dropping austenitic steel just above the critical range in cold water or oil, the transition can be arrested. By this means a structure can be produced at atmospheric temperature with different physical characteristics from those which normally would be obtained with slow cooling. This operation is so severe that an extremely hard, brittle material with shrinkage strains is obtained. By reheating the metal below the critical range the normal transition in the critical range is allowed to proceed a little further and shrinkage strains are reduced, thus creating a useful condition of moderate hardness and strength.

Hardening is the name given to the first operation described in the preceding paragraph. It consists in heating steel to just above the critical range, holding the metal at that temperature until thoroughly heated (called soaking), and then rapidly cooling (or quenching) by immersing the hot steel in cold water or oil.

Drawing or *tempering*, as it is sometimes called, consists in reheating the hardened steel to a temperature well below the critical range, followed by soaking and quenching.

Martensite is the main constituent of hardened steel. It is an intermediate form of cementite in alpha iron obtained when the transition from austenite to pearlite is arrested. Martensite is the hardest structure obtained in steel.

Troostite is another intermediate form, similar to martensite, which is often present in hardened steels. Troostite is also present in drawn or tempered steels whereas martensite is not.

Sorbite is the third intermediate form between austenite and pearlite. It is the main constituent of drawn steel and gives that type of steel maximum strength and ductility.

Hardened steel consists almost entirely of martensite with some troostite. When the steel is reheated, as in drawing, the martensitic structure breaks down and sorbite, with a small amount of troostite, remains. By varying the drawing temperature, different amounts of troostite and sorbite can be retained, and consequently a variation in physical properties is obtainable.

Heating through the critical range is absolutely necessary to obtain the best refinement of the grain. Fine grain steel has the best physical properties. As steel is heated above the critical range, the grain becomes coarser. There is a narrow limit of temperature just above the critical range within which steel must be heated if it is to retain its fine grain structure after quenching. It should be noted that a fine grain structure is obtained just above the critical range only on a rising heat. If liquid steel is solidified and cooled the finest grain is obtained on solidification and becomes coarser as cooling progresses.

As you will note by referring to Figure 10, it is absolutely necessary to know the chemical content of the steel to establish the critical range and the heat treatment temperature. Each steel, both carbon and alloy, has its individual critical range which must be definitely known if the best results are to be obtained from heat treatment.

The effects of heating to various temperatures and cooling at different rates may be summarized as follows:

1. When a piece of steel is heated to the upper critical point, Ac_3, it becomes as fine grained as possible no matter how coarse or distorted the grain was previously.

2. After it has been heated to Ac_3, if the steel is allowed to cool slowly, it retains the fine grained structure and is also soft and ductile.

3. After it has been heated to Ac_3, if the steel is cooled rapidly, as by quenching in cold water, it retains the fine grained structure and is fully hardened.

4. If steel is heated above Ac_3, permitted to cool to Ac_3, and then quenched, it will be fully hardened but more coarse grained than if it had only been heated to Ac_3 originally.

5. The higher the temperature above Ac_3 from which the steel is cooled, either slowly or rapidly, the coarser the grain. In this case slower cooling will result in coarser grain.

6. When a piece of hardened steel (which has been previously heated to Ac_3—or above—soaked, and quenched) is again heated to somewhere below Ac_1, it is softened but without change in grain size. The softening is greater as the temperature increases up to Ac_1.

Annealing. Annealing of steel is effected by heating the metal to just above Ac_3, soaking at that temperature for a definite time, and cooling very slowly in the furnace itself. This treatment corresponds to number 2 just above. The time of soaking is about one hour per inch thickness of material to make certain that all of the material is brought up to temperature. Slow cooling is usually obtained by shutting off the heat and allowing the furnace and metal to cool together. An alternate method to restrict the rate of cooling is to bury the heated steel in ashes or lime.

Annealed steel is fine grained, soft, ductile, and without internal stresses or strains. It is readily machinable and workable. In the annealed state steel has its lowest strength. For that reason it is often given a subsequent heat treatment so as to increase the strength after all machining and mechanical work are complete. The ductility of annealed steel is utilized in tube and wire drawing and in rolling sheet. After the steel has passed through the dies or rolls several times, re-annealing is necessary to relieve the stresses induced by the cold work and to prevent cracking. There are several modifications of the full annealing treatment used when all of the effects are not essential, and speed and economy are important.

Process annealing consists in heating below Ac_1 in the region between 1020° and 1200° F. This treatment is commonly used in the sheet and wire industries to restore ductility.

Spherodizing is a form of annealing applied particularly to high carbon steels to improve their machinability. As indicated by the name, a globular cementite structure is obtained. In this form the cementite can be pushed aside by the cutting tool instead of offering great resistance as when present in the laminated form. The operation of spherodizing consists in prolonged heating just slightly below the critical range, followed by slow cooling.

Shop annealing is the term used to describe the practice of heating steel with a welding torch to 900° to 1000° F. and dropping it into a pail of ashes or lime to restrict the cooling rate. This treatment will relieve internal strains. It is never used in aircraft work unless it is to be followed by a regular heat treatment.

In all annealing processes, due to prolonged heating at high temperatures and slow cooling from these temperatures, the surface of metal is prone to scale. This scale is iron oxide. Whenever possible annealing should be done in closed receptacles to exclude air from the metal. The receptacle should not be opened until it has cooled almost to room temperature. In the case of high carbon steels the prevention of scale formation is particularly important. Oxidation of the carbon at the surface will occur if not guarded against. This decarburization is injurious to the metal and must be avoided. When steel parts have not been annealed in a receptacle, the scale must be removed by a cleaning or pickling treatment. This treatment is described in the chapter on Corrosion.

Normalizing. Normalizing is a form of annealing which consists in heating the steel above Ac_3 and then cooling in still air. Due to the more rapid quenching obtained by air-cooling compared to furnace-cooling, the steel is harder and stronger but less ductile than annealed material. Normalizing is required whenever it is desired to obtain material of uniform physical characteristics. Forgings are generally normalized to relieve all internal stresses. Normalizing, too, will relieve stresses, refine the grain, and make steel more uniform just as annealing will, but, at the same time, improved physical properties are obtained. Because of the better physical properties, aircraft steels are often used in the normalized condition but seldom if ever in the annealed state. If annealed steel is used in fabrication for ease of working, it is subsequently normalized or heat treated to a higher strength.

Welded parts are frequently used in airplane construction. Welding causes strains to be set up in the adjacent material. In addition, the weld itself is a cast structure as opposed to the wrought structure of the rest of the material. These two types

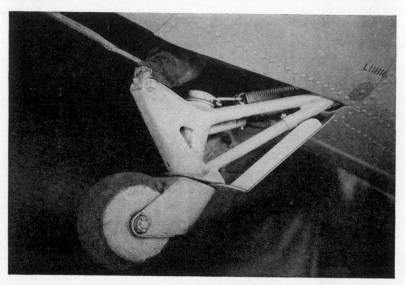

FIGURE 11. TAIL WHEEL ASSEMBLY
Heat Treated Chrome-Molybdenum Steel

of structure have different grain sizes, and to relieve the internal stresses and refine the grain, all welded parts should be normalized after fabrication. Such treatment will reduce the possibility of cracks and fatigue failures in service. Normalizing of welded parts is considered so important by one government department that it even requires this treatment for engine mounts. In many cases where large furnaces are not available, or the basic design of mount will not permit normalizing without too much warping, it is necessary to design an assembled mount made up of small sections. The sections can be normalized individually and bolted or riveted together.

Low carbon steels are often normalized to improve the machining qualities and to reduce distortion in subsequent heat-treating operations. In actual practice the aircraft manufacturer buys tubing, sheet, and bar in the normalized condition, performs the necessary machining or welding operations, and then normalizes or heat treats the finished article. In connection with the purchase of normalized material it is often necessary to specify the maximum tensile strength that is acceptable. This is particularly true of thin sheet which, when quenched in still air, will cool far more rapidly than heavier material. As a result, thin sheet will be composed of sorbite as well as pearlite—the usual constituent of normalized steel. The sorbite makes the steel stronger but also more brittle. Chrome-molybdenum sheet steel, as purchased in the normalized state, will often run from 110,000 to 125,000 pounds per square inch ultimate tensile strength. Where severe bending is to be done, the purchase order should specify a maximum of 95,000 pounds per square inch which is the accepted strength for normalized chrome-molybdenum steel.

Medium and high carbon steels should be normalized and then annealed before machining or fabrication. This sequence of operations is sometimes called double annealing. The resultant structure is similar to that obtained by spherodizing, as described previously. In aircraft work the amount of machining done is usually small and the annealing is often omitted.

Some alloy steels cannot be satisfactorily hardened without first being normalized. This is especially true of alloys containing chromium. The accepted explanation of this phenomenon is the necessity for the complete solution of the chromium and iron carbides in the gamma iron. Solution is effected by normalizing prior to hardening.

Hardening. Hardening is the first of two operations required for the development of high strength steels by heat treatment. Hardening consists of heating above Ac_3, soaking at that temperature until the mass is uniformly heated, and then quenching in brine, water, or oil. This treatment produces a fine grain, maximum hardness and tensile strength, minimum ductility, and internal strains. In this condition the material is too hard and brittle for practical use. A light blow, as from a hammer, would shatter the material.

Heating is conducted as little above Ac_3 as practical in order to reduce warping and the possibility of cracking when the ma-

terial is quenched. On the other hand, large objects are heated
to the upper limit of the hardening range in order to assure

FIGURE 12. GRUMMAN RETRACTABLE LANDING GEAR
Heat Treated Chrome-Molybdenum Tubing

thorough heating. For the materials and sections used in aircraft work quenching in oil is invariably the method employed.
The heat absorption of oil is slower than water or brine, and

consequently the cooling operation is more gentle. Less warping and cracking occurs and sufficient hardness is obtained.

As explained previously under Theory of Heat Treatment, the rapid quenching from a temperature above the critical range arrests the transition from austenite to pearlite, and results in the formation of martensite and some troostite. Martensite is the hardest form of steel and is responsible for the extreme hardness and brittleness of hardened steel.

Drawing (Tempering). Drawing (or, as it is sometimes called, tempering) is the second operation required to develop high strength, heat-treated steel. It consists of heating hardened steel to a temperature well below Ac_1, soaking at that temperature, and then quenching in brine, water, oil, or air. This treatment relieves the strains in hardened steel, decreases the brittleness, and restores ductility. In addition, the strength and hardness are somewhat reduced. The strength, hardness, and ductility obtained depend upon the temperature to which the steel was reheated. The higher the temperature, the lower the strength and hardness but the greater the ductility. By decreasing the brittleness of hardened steel, tempered steel is made tough and still retains adequate strength. Tempered steels, as used in aircraft work, have from 125,000 to 200,000 pounds per square inch ultimate tensile strength.

When hardened steel is reheated as in tempering, the transition from austenite to pearlite is continued further, and the martensite is converted to troostite and then sorbite. Tempered steel is composed largely of sorbite, which gives it toughness. Hardened steel, reheated to a low temperature and quenched, is composed of troostite and sorbite, and is still very hard and strong but more ductile than hardened steel; hardened steel reheated to a higher temperature and quenched is composed of sorbite and some pearlite, and is tougher and more ductile but still retains considerable strength and hardness.

PRACTICAL HEAT TREATMENT

The first important consideration in the heat treatment of a piece of steel is to know its chemical composition which, in turn, determines its critical range. When the critical temperature is known the next consideration is the rate of heating and cooling to be employed to insure completion of transition or retardation of transition as the case may be. The carrying out of these operations is beset with practical problems. These involve the use of furnaces for uniform heating, pyrometers for controlling temperatures, handling of hot metal, and quenching in suitable mediums. Some notes on the more vital considerations in heating, soaking, and quenching are given below.

Heating. The aim in heating is to transform pearlite to austenite as the critical range is passed through. This transition takes time; so a relatively slow rate of heating is employed. It is customary to insert the cold steel in the furnace when it is from 300° to 400° F. below the hardening temperature. In this way too rapid heating of the cold steel through the critical range is prevented. It is cheaper to keep a furnace up to the hardening temperature and remove heated steel and insert new cold steel periodically without permitting the temperature to drop several hundred degrees before inserting the new cold work. This is sometimes done where the work is not extremely important, but it does not guarantee complete and thorough transition to austenite. There is also the possibility of cracking, depending on the shape of the material, due to rapid heating and expansion.

In reheating for tempering, the furnace should not be above 800° to 1000° F. when the work is inserted and, in any case, not above the tempering temperature of the steel which is being treated. If the tempering temperature is too high, the transition from martensite to sorbite will be accelerated beyond control of the heat treater.

Several types of furnace are employed in heating. The common type is a "dry heat" furnace and is fired by oil, gas, or electricity. A uniform temperature must be maintained throughout the furnace, and the work must be properly placed to insure uniform heating. The work must not be placed too close to the wall of the furnace; otherwise radiated heat from the wall will heat one face of the work beyond the rest, with resultant uneven heating. In a dry furnace it is desirable to maintain a neutral atmosphere, so that the heated steel will neither oxidize nor decarburize. Practically, however, this is difficult to realize, and considerable scaling of the work results. In this respect the electric furnace is the most satisfactory because only a slight amount of scaling takes place. An atmosphere free of oxygen is maintained in one type of electric furnace by feeding a carbon vapor into it during heating operations. The carbon vapor is generated by "cracking" an oil in a smaller subsidiary furnace. There is practically no scaling of the work in this type furnace. Special paint coatings, such as "Galvo Anti-scale," are sometimes used to minimize scaling during the heating operation when atmospheric control is not available.

A "liquid heat" furnace is invariably used for parts which have been finished-machined before heat treatment. In this type furnace parts are heated in a molten salt bath. Here there are several advantages, the most important being the complete elimination of scaling. In addition, better temperature regulation and more uniform heating are attainable. For production work where speed is essential, faster heating is possible with the liquid bath than with dry heat. Numerous other advantages are claimed for the liquid bath, but those just given are the most important.

Soaking. During the soaking period the temperature of the furnace must be held constant. It is in this period that rearrangement of the internal structure is completed. The time of soaking depends upon the nature of the steel and the size of the part. Heavier parts require longer soaking to insure equal heating throughout. In specifying hardening temperatures, it is customary to give a range of from 50° to 75° F. within which the material must be soaked. Light parts are soaked in the lower part of this range and heavy parts in the upper part of the range. For the steels and sizes normally used in aircraft construction a soaking period of from 30 to 45 minutes is sufficient. During the tempering operation the steel is soaked from 30 minutes to one hour, depending on the thickness of the material.

Quenching. The rate of cooling through the critical range determines the form that the steel will retain. In annealing, the heated steel must be furnace-cooled to 900° F.; then it may be air-cooled to room temperature. Exceptionally slow cooling to 900° F., which is below the critical range, provides sufficient time for complete transition from austenite to pearlite which is the normal, stable condition of steel at atmospheric temperatures.

In normalizing, the heated steel is removed from the furnace and allowed to cool in still air. The cooling is more rapid than in annealing, and complete transition to pearlite is not attained. Some sorbite remains in normalized steel, which accounts for the improvement in physical properties over annealed material. Air-cooling is a very mild form of quench.

In order to harden steels, it is necessary to use a more rapid quenching medium. There are three mediums commonly used— brine, water, and oil. Brine is the most severe quenching medium, water is next, and oil the least severe. In other words, oil does not cool the heated steel through the critical range as rapidly as water or brine. However, oil does cool rapidly enough to develop sufficient hardness for all practical purposes. In aircraft work high carbon and alloy steels are oil quenched. Medium carbon steel are water quenched and mild carbon steel (S.A.E. 1025) is quenched in either brine or water. A severe quench is required for steels with relatively low carbon contents in order to develop the required hardness. This agrees with the comments previously made in the paragraphs under "Internal Structure of Steel" relative to the importance of the carbon content on the hardening properties of steel.

Oil quenching is preferred to water or brine when sufficient hardness is obtainable because of the reduced strain, warpage, and cracking of the steel when cooled more slowly. When the structure changes from austenite to martensite, the volume is increased; and if the change is too sudden, cracking will occur. Cracking occurs particularly in the lower temperature ranges when the steel is no longer plastic enough to readjust itself to expansion and contraction. The shape of a part is extremely important if excessive warping and cracks are to be avoided. Thin flanges on heavy sections are especially bad. When tubular parts are quenched, they should be immersed with the long axis vertical to reduce warpage.

Small parts when quenched cool more rapidly and harden more uniformly throughout. In large parts the inside core is usually softer and weaker than the rest of the material. This fact must be given consideration in design in calculating the cross-sectional strength. Values obtained from heat-treated parts of small sections cannot be applied directly to larger sections. Strength values normally quoted are based on heat-treated sections 1 to 1½ inches in diameter. As explained in the chapter on Steel and Its Alloys many alloys possess the property known as penetration hardness. These alloys harden quite uniformly throughout when heat treated and quenched, and no allowance need be made for a soft core unless the section is excessively large. Such sections are seldom used in aircraft work.

The quenching medium is normally maintained at about 70° F., and provision is incorporated to prevent the temperature from changing more than ± 20° F. This involves a large reservoir of liquid and some method of providing circulation and cooling. The rate of cooling through the critical range is governed by the temperature maintained in the quenching medium. Inasmuch as slight variations in this temperature have an appreciable effect on the rate of cooling, it is obvious that the quenching medium temperature must be held within narrow limits if consistent results are to be obtained.

After steel is reheated and soaked for tempering, it is quenched in either air or oil. Chrome-nickel steels, however, must be quenched in oil—not air—after tempering in order to avoid "temper brittleness" to which this particular group of steels is subject if air quenched.

Heat Treatments for Aircraft Steels

As previously explained, each type of steel has different hardening qualities which are governed by its composition. For this reason the practical heat treatments of various steels differ somewhat as to heating temperatures, soaking periods, and quenching methods. In the following pages an effort has been made to describe the heat treatment operations commonly used on aircraft steels. Since these data are presented purely for the general information of the reader, and not as a reference for the practical heat treater, there has been no hesitancy to discuss an interesting point right in the body of the description. For more specific information on the steels listed, or on others not listed, the steel manufacturer should be consulted and he will gladly furnish the required data.

The heat treatments listed in the following pages do not conform wholly to the Army or Navy specifications or S.A.E. recommendations but are an average of the three. Due to slight variations in the chemical composition of steel made by different manufacturers, in heat-treating equipment, in the size of average parts, and in the technique of heat treaters, a definite, narrow range for hardening and tempering temperatures cannot be laid down. The figures given will satisfy average conditions, but the individual heat treater may have to vary them a little to obtain satisfactory results.

The range of hardness numbers for a given tensile strength is also an average figure. Each factory should establish its own correlation between tensile strength and hardness numbers by heat-treating tensile test specimens, recording their hardness, and then testing to determine their ultimate tensile strength. For important work tension specimens should be heat treated along with the work and tested. Absolute faith should not be placed in hardness readings alone.

It will be noted under Item 4 of S.A.E. 2330 steel that there is a discussion of the relationship between the tempering temperature to be used and the actual hardness of the steel after the hardness operation. Use of the suggested proportion on material above or below average may save time and labor, particularly where too soft tempered material would otherwise be obtained, thus requiring both re-hardening and re-tempering.

The lower part of the heating ranges should be used for material less than ¼ inch thick. A majority of airplane parts fall in this category. Prolonged heating of this material should also be avoided to prevent grain growth.

S.A.E. 1025

MILD CARBON STEEL

Normalizing

1. The temperature of the furnace should not exceed 1100° F. when the work is inserted.

2. The temperature should be increased to 1625-1675° F. gradually and held at that temperature for 30 to 45 minutes depending on the thickness of the part.

3. The parts should be removed from the furnace and allowed to cool in still air.

Final hardness should be as follows: Rockwell B-62 to B-74, Brinell 105 to 130.

Ultimate tensile strength: 55,000–67,000 pounds per square inch.

Heat Treatment

1. The temperature of the furnace should not exceed 1650° F. when the work is inserted.

2. The temperature should be held from 1575–1650° F. for 15 minutes or longer, if required, to insure uniform heating.

3. The parts should be removed from the furnace and quenched in water at 70° F.

4. The hardened parts should then be inserted in a furnace whose temperature is not over 1150° F.

5. The furnace temperature should then be increased to 1150–1200° F. (the temperature will have dropped when the parts were inserted) and held for 30 minutes to one hour, depending on the thickness of the material.

6. The parts should then be removed from the furnace and allowed to cool in still air.

Final hardness should be as follows: Rockwell B-77 to B-85, Brinell 140 to 165.

Ultimate tensile strength: 70,000–82,000 pounds per square inch.

This heat treatment is used for S.A.E. 1025 steel when used in the manufacture of nuts. AN Standard steel nuts, which are used exclusively in aircraft construction, fall in this category.

S.A.E. 1035

MEDIUM CARBON STEEL

Heat Treatment

1. The temperature of the steel and furnace should be increased gradually over a period of one hour until a temperature of 1525–1575° F. is attained. This temperature should be held for ten minutes or more.

2. The parts should be removed from the furnace and quenched in water if over 3/8 inch diameter or in oil if smaller than 3/8 inch. Quenching small parts in water will cause fractures.

3. The hardened parts should be reheated slowly for a period of 45 minutes or more until a temperature of 950–975° F. is reached. This temperature should be held for at least 45 minutes.

4. The parts should then be removed from the furnace and allowed to cool in still air.

Final hardness should be as follows: Rockwell B-85 to B-100, Brinell 160 to 250.

Ultimate tensile strength: 80,000–118,000 pounds per square inch.

S.A.E. 1045

MEDIUM CARBON STEEL

Heat Treatment. (Similar technique to that described for S.A.E. 1035. Temperatures differ.)

1. Hardening temperature 1500-1550° F.
2. Quench in oil.
3. Tempering temperature 1000° F.
4. Cooled in still air.

Final hardness should be as follows: Rockwell B-92 to B-102, Brinell 193 to 259.

Ultimate tensile strength: 95,000–124,000 pounds per square inch.

S.A.E. 1095

HIGH CARBON STEEL

Heat Treatment. (Similar technique as described for Mild Carbon Steel.)

1. Hardening temperature 1450-1500° F.
2. Quench in oil. (High carbon steels are sometimes quenched in water until they have cooled to the temperature of boiling water when they are transferred to oil at 75° F. This method results in rapid cooling through the critical range and slower cooling at low temperatures where cracking occurs.)
3. Tempering temperature 800–850° F.
4. Cooled in still air.

Final hardness should be as follows: Rockwell C-42 to C-45, Brinell 400 to 430.

Ultimate tensile strength: 195,000–213,000 pounds per square inch.

This heat treatment is applied to S.A.E. 1095 steel when it is to be used for structural parts or springs. Leaf springs made from this material are commonly used in aircraft construction.

S.A.E. 2330

NICKEL STEEL

Heat Treatment

1. The temperature of the furnace should not exceed 1100° F. when the work is inserted.
2. The temperature should be increased gradually to 1450–1500° F. and held for 20 minutes.
3. The parts should be removed from the furnace and quenched in oil.

4. At this stage the Brinell hardness should be checked to ascertain that it is approximately 500. If it is over 500 the tempering temperatures given below should be increased somewhat; if below 500 the tempering temperatures should be reduced somewhat. The tempering temperatures should be increased or decreased about in the same proportion that the actual Brinell number bears to 500.

5. As previously explained in the paragraphs under Tempering, the final ultimate tensile strength and hardness of a piece of steel depends on the temperature to which hardened steel is reheated and drawn. Thus different tempering temperatures must be used if different strength values are to be obtained for the same type of steel. S.A.E. 2330 steel is commonly used in two different strengths; the tempering temperatures to obtain these conditions are:

Ultimate Tensile Strength	Tempering Temp.
125,000	950° F.
150,000	800° F.

Parts should be held at the tempering temperature for a minimum of 30 minutes.

6. Parts should then be removed from the furnace and allowed to cool in still air.

Final hardness should be as follows:

	125,000	150,000
Rockwell	C-25 to C-32	C-33 to C-37
Brinell	250 to 300	310 to 360

S.A.E. 2330 steel heat treated to 125,000 pounds per square inch is used for a great many AN Standard parts, particularly aircraft bolts.

S.A.E. 3140

CHROME-NICKEL STEEL

Heat Treatment

1. The temperature of the furnace should not exceed 1100° F. when the work is inserted.

2. The temperature should be increased gradually to 1475–1525° F. and held for 15 minutes or longer, if necessary, to insure uniform heating.

3. The parts should be removed from the furnace and quenched in oil.

4. The furnace temperature should not exceed 800° F. when parts are inserted for tempering.

5. The temperature should be raised to the required value for the strength desired and held for 30 minutes to one hour, depending on the thickness of the material.

Ultimate Tensile Strength	Tempering Temp.
125,000	1050° F.
150,000	950° F.
180,000	800° F.

6. Parts should be removed from the furnace and cooled by quenching in oil. An oil quench is mandatory for chrome-nickel steels to avoid temper brittleness.

Final hardness should be as follows:

	Rockwell	Brinell
125,000	C-25 to C-32	250 to 300
150,000	C-33 to C-37	310 to 360
180,000	C-38 to C-42	360 to 400

S.A.E. X4130

CHROME-MOLYBDENUM STEEL

Annealing

1. The temperature of the furnace should not exceed 1100° F. when the work is inserted.

2. The temperature should be increased to 1550-1650° F. gradually and held at that temperature for 15 minutes or longer to insure uniform heating throughout.

3. The furnace should then be shut down and the work and the furnace allowed to cool slowly to at least 900° F. at which point the work may be removed and allowed to cool in still air.

Ultimate tensile strength: 78,000 pounds per square inch approx.

Normalizing

1. and 2. Identical with annealing process.

3. The work should be removed from the furnace and allowed to cool slowly in still air.

Final hardness should be as follows: Rockwell B-89 to B-99, Brinell 180 to 240.

Ultimate tensile strength: 90,000–110,000 pounds per square inch.

Heat Treatment

1. The temperature of the furnace should not exceed 1100° F. when the work is inserted.

2. The temperature should be gradually increased to 1550–1650° F. and held for 15 minutes or longer, if necessary, for thorough heating. For sections under $\frac{1}{4}$ inch thickness the lower part of the temperature range should be used.

3. The parts should be removed from the furnace and quenched in oil at approximately 70° F.

4. The hardened parts should be inserted in a furnace whose temperature is not above the desired tempering temperature and in no case above 800° F.

5. The temperature of the furnace should then be raised to the tempering temperature required to obtain the desired physical condition. These temperatures for the tensile strengths used in aircraft construction are as follows:

Ultimate Tensile Strength	Tempering Temp.
125,000	1075° F.
150,000	900° F.
180,000	700° F.
200,000	575° F.

Parts should be held at the tempering temperature for 30 minutes to one hour depending on the thickness.

6. Parts should be removed from the furnace and allowed to cool in still air.

Final hardness should be as follows:

	Rockwell	Brinell
125,000	C-25 to C-32	250 to 300
150,000	C-33 to C-37	310 to 360
180,000	C-38 to C-42	360 to 400
200,000	C-42 to C-46	400 to 440

S.A.E. 4140

CHROME-MOLYBDENUM STEEL

(High Carbon)

Due to its higher carbon content this steel responds to heat treatment better than X4130 steel. For heavy parts machined from bar or forging stock it has replaced X4130 steel entirely. The heat treatment process is practically identical with that given for X4130 steel, excepting that the hardening range is 25° F. lower, making it 1525–1625° F. This change is due, of course, to the higher carbon content.

S.A.E. X4340

CHROME-NICKEL-MOLYBDENUM STEEL

Heat Treatment

1. The temperature of the furnace should not exceed 1100° F. when the parts are inserted.

2. The temperature should be increased gradually to 1475–1525° F. and held for 15 minutes or longer, if necessary, to insure thorough heating.

3. The parts should be removed from the furnace and quenched in oil.

4. The hardened parts should be inserted in a furnace whose temperature is not above the desired tempering temperature and in no case above 1000° F.

5. The temperature of the furnace should then be raised to the tempering temperature required to develop the desired physical properties.

Ultimate Tensile Strength	Tempering Temp.
125,000	1200° F.
150,000	1050° F.
180,000	950° F.
200,000	850° F.

Parts should be held at the tempering temperature for 30 minutes to one hour, depending on the thickness.

6. Parts should be removed from the furnace and quenched in oil.

Final hardness should be the same as recorded for X4130—chrome-molybdenum steel—for equivalent tensile strengths.

It should be noted that this steel is one of the chrome-nickel series and must be quenched in oil ofter tempering to avoid temper brittleness.

S.A.E. 6135

CHROME-VANADIUM STEEL

(Medium Carbon)

Heat Treatment

1. The temperature of the furnace should not exceed 1100° F. when the work is inserted.

2. The temperature should be increased gradually to 1550–1575° F. and held for 15 minutes or longer, if necessary, to insure thorough heating.

3. The parts should be removed from the furnace and quenched in oil.

4. The hardened parts should be inserted in a furnace whose temperature is not above 800° F.

5. The temperature of the furnace should then be raised to the required tempering temperature which depends on the tensile strength desired in the finished part.

Ultimate Tensile Strength	Tempering Temp.
125,000	1050° F.
150,000	925° F.

Parts should be held at the tempering temperature for 30 minutes to one hour, depending on the thickness.

6. Parts should be cooled in still air.

Final hardness should be as follows:

	Rockwell	Brinell
125,000	C-25 to C-32	250 to 300
150,000	C-33 to C-37	310 to 360

S.A.E. 6150

CHROME-VANADIUM STEEL

(Springs)

Heat Treatment

1. The temperature of the furnace should not exceed 1100° F. when the parts are inserted.

2. The temperature should be increased gradually to 1525-1550° F. and held for 15 minutes or longer, if necessary, to insure thorough heating.

3. The parts should be removed from the furnace and quenched in oil.

4. The hardened parts should be inserted in a furnace whose temperature is not above 700° F.

5. The temperature of the furnace should then be raised to 700-850° F. and held for 30 minutes to one hour, depending on the diameter of the spring material.

6. Parts should be allowed to cool in still air.

Final hardness should be as follows: Rockwell C-42 to C-47, Brinell 400 to 444.

Ultimate tensile strength: 200,000 pounds per square inch approx.

CHAPTER VI

SURFACE HARDENING

For some design purposes it is necessary to have a hard, wear-resisting surface and a strong, tough core. This condition can be obtained in steel by a number of methods. Heat treating alone, as discussed in the previous chapter, will give a uniform condition, either extremely hard and strong, or moderately hard and tough, throughout the entire cross section of the metal. By the methods of surface hardening described in this chapter, it is possible to obtain a surface or case harder than the highest obtainable by heat treatment, combined with a tough core. Since any depth from a mere skin to over ⅛ inch can be produced, the case thickness can be varied to suit the design requirements. The hard case resists wear and abrasion, and the soft tough core resists shock stresses. This combination of properties is essential in the design of gears, pinions, wrist pins, trunnions, and other parts subject to abrasion and shock loads.

The methods commonly used for surface hardening are known as carburizing, cyaniding, and nitriding. The combination of carburizing and the subsequent heat treatment which always follows this operation is called casehardening. Casehardening is used more often than the other methods in aircraft work.

CASEHARDENING

As commonly practiced, casehardening consists of carburizing a piece of steel, quenching either mildly or rapidly, reheating to refine the core, quenching rapidly, reheating again to refine and harden the case, quenching rapidly, tempering at a low temperature and cooling slowly. For unimportant parts and with some steels one or more of these operations can be eliminated. A detailed discussion of the theory and practical application of each of these operations follows.

72

Carburizing. Carburizing steels may be either carbon or alloy steels but must be within the low carbon range. The carburizing process consists in heating these steels in contact with a carbonaceous material. This material may be either solid, liquid, or gaseous. Above the critical range the iron carbide in steel passes into solution in the gamma iron, as explained under Heat Treatment. Low carbon steels are weak solutions and will absorb free carbon. The carbon-rich carbonaceous materials when heated give off a gas containing carbon which diffuses into the steel surface. The depth of penetration depends upon the carbonaceous material, the temperature, and the time allowed.

The absorption of carbon at the surface will greatly increase the carbon content in this region. This carbon content will range from .80-1.25% at the surface and will taper off towards the center with the core remaining at the original content. Subsequent heat treatment will harden the case and toughen the core. This is to be expected from the explanation made under Heat Treatment where it was shown greater hardness could be obtained from high carbon steels.

Solid Carburizing. The oldest and most commonly used method of carburizing is with a solid carbonaceous material. This material is usually bone, charred leather, wood charcoal, or coke. These materials are used singly or mixed together and usually contain an energizer to increase the formation of carburizing gases when heated.

The parts to be carburized are packed in a metal box (usually nichrome) with at least two inch legs, so that the furnace gases may circulate freely around the entire box. All surfaces of the parts must be covered with at least ½-inch of the carburizing material. The box must have a lid which can be sealed tight. A common seal is moist fire clay to which a little salt has been added to prevent cracking. When the box is properly packed and sealed it is ready for insertion in the furnace.

The furnace should be brought up to 1600–1700° F. as quickly as possible. The range of some carburizing steels is 1600–1650° F., others 1625–1675° F., and still others 1650–1700° F. All fall under 1700° F. More rapid penetration can be obtained at higher temperatures, but grain growth will increase rapidly and affect the quality of the steel. The temperature should be kept as close to the critical range as possible to avoid grain growth. It should be borne in mind, however, that due to the size of the box and the packing, the enclosed parts will lag about 100° F. behind the furnace when being heated. The furnace must be kept at the carburizing temperature somewhat longer to allow for this lag.

The carburizing temperature is held until the desired depth of case is obtained. The time required varies for the different carburizing steels. For S.A.E. 1020 carbon steel, which is often used for casehardened parts, the variation of depth of case with time at temperature is as follows:

DEPTH OF CASE	TIME AT 1650° F.
1/64 inch	One hour
1/32 "	Two hours
3/64 "	Four hours
1/16 "	Six hours
1/8 "	Sixteen hours

In aircraft work a case depth of 1/64 or 1/32 inch is commonly used since the abrasion is seldom great and shock resistance is important. Thick cases are liable to crack under shock loads.

After carburizing the box is removed from the furnace and allowed to cool in air, or the parts removed and quenched in oil from the carburizing temperature. The slower method of cooling is employed when warpage must be avoided. This cooling completes the carburizing process, and the parts are then ready for grain refinement, hardening, and tempering.

Liquid Carburizing. Carburizing in a liquid salt bath has recently been successfully developed. This method is applicable to small parts where a depth of case not greater than .040 inch is satisfactory. Liquid carburizing has the advantage of forming a case uniform in depth and carbon content. In the use of solid carburizers it is often impossible to obtain uniform results on small parts packed in a box since those near the sides differ from those in the center. Furthermore, liquid carburizing is faster than solid carburizing because laborious packing is eliminated.

A salt that melts several hundred degrees below the carburizing temperature is used as the liquid heat. An amorphous carbon is added to the bath to furnish the required carbon. Periodically, additional carbon is added to keep the bath saturated. A layer of carbon covers the top of the bath to reduce volatilization loss.

As with the solid material the depth of case obtained is dependent on the time and temperature. The following are typical figures for S.A.E. 1020 steel:

DEPTH OF CASE		TIME
1600° F.	1675° F.	
.006 inch	.006 inch	1/3 hour
.010 "	.012 "	2/3 hour
.016 "	.018 "	One hour
.020 "	.024 "	Two hours
.026 "	.030 "	Three hours
.035 "	.040 "	Four hours

After carburizing, the parts may be quenched in water or oil. They are then ready for refinement, hardening, and tempering.

Gas Carburizing. Gas carburizing is becoming more generally used. One process consists in exposing small parts in a rotating retort to gas as a carburizing medium. Solid carburizer is sometimes added in the retort to enrich the carburizing atmosphere. Parts in the rotating retort are tumbled about, with resultant damage to corners and edges.

The latest improved process is done in the electric furnace with a carbon atmosphere as mentioned in the chapter on Heat Treatment. When carburizing, about twice as much carbon vapor is admitted to the furnace as when heat treating. In this process the parts remain stationary

Refining the Core. Due to the fact that the carburizing temperature is well above the critical range and is held for a long period of time, an excessive grain growth takes place in the steel. In order to obtain a fine, ductile grain in the core, it is necessary to reheat the steel to just above the upper critical point, soak until the metal is uniformly heated, and then quench in oil.

In actual practice the following typical procedure is used for S.A.E. 1020 steel:

The furnace is preheated to 1200° F., and after the parts are inserted, it is brought up to 1600° F. in 45 to 60 minutes. A longer time is taken for complex parts. The parts are soaked for 10 minutes or longer, if necessary, and then quenched in oil.

Hardening the Case. Since the case of a carburized steel part has a high carbon content, the temperature required above to refine the low carbon core is considerably above the critical range of the case. This high temperature results in grain growth and embrittlement of the case. It is, therefore, necessary to reheat the steel to just above the critical range of the high carbon case and then quench in oil. This treatment refines the grain and hardens the case. The hardening temperature for the high carbon case is well below the upper critical point for the low carbon core. The only effect this reheating has on the core is a tempering action.

For S.A.E. 1020 steel the hardening procedure is as follows:

The furnace is preheated to 1000° F., and after the parts are inserted, it is brought up to 1400-1430° F. fairly rapidly. The parts are soaked for ten minutes and then quenched immediately in oil.

Tempering. In order to relieve hardening strains, carburized steel parts are tempered by heating in the region of 300-400° F. This tempering should be done immediately after the hardening quench. The furnace or oil bath should be at the tempering temperature when the parts are inserted. The low part of the tempering range should be used if extreme hardness is desired since hardness decreases as the tempering temperature increases. The parts should be soaked until uniformly heated and then removed and cooled slowly in still air.

SELECTIVE CASEHARDENING

In many designs it is desired to harden only that portion of the part subject to severe wear. Methods have been evolved to protect the other portions of the part from carburizing. The best method is to copper plate the sections to be left soft. A few thousandths of an inch of good dense copper plate will resist the penetration of carbon, providing too much energizer is not present in the carbonaceous material. Before copper plating, the sections to be hardened are Japanned to protect them from being plated. The Japan is removed after plating but before carburizing.

It is customary to finish hardened carburized parts by grinding. In some cases, where soft sections are desired, sufficient material is left on in the original machining to allow for grinding. By this method the case is completely removed by grinding where a soft section is desired. This method is slow and expensive.

Sometimes a portion of a carburized part is threaded. It is essential that the threads be true and soft while the remainder of the part must be hard to resist wear. If the threads are cut and then carburized and hardened, the threads will be warped and thrown out of center with the hardened ground surface. To avoid this condition the following procedure is recommended:

1. Machine for carburizing, leaving ¼ inch of stock on the section to be threaded.
2. Carburize for the desired depth of case.
3. Turn off all but 1/64 inch of stock on the section to be threaded. All the high carbon case will thus be removed from the threaded portion.
4. Heat treat to refine the core and harden the case, and temper to remove strains.
5. Finish-grind the hardened surface, turn the threaded section to size true to the ground surface, and then thread. Machining operations are possible on the threaded section even after the hardening treatment because its low carbon content will not permit appreciable hardening.

Warpage and Cracking. Warpage of carburized parts is very common and is caused by improper packing or severe quenching. It is customary to finish-grind casehardened parts to reduce the distortion.

Cracking of parts occurs in the hardening quench. It is absolutely necessary to avoid all sharp corners, notches, or sudden changes of section in parts to be hardened. In some cases it is preferable to design a part in two or more pieces to avoid hardening cracks.

Some carburizing steels require a less severe quench than others and are not as subject to warping and cracking. Where absolute accuracy is necessary the proper steel should be selected with minimum distortion properties. S.A.E. 4615 is generally recommended.

Carburizing Steels. Carburizing steels are either plain carbon or alloy steels but are invariably in the low carbon range. A low carbon content is necessary to retain a tough core after the heat treatment. In special cases steel with a carbon content as high as .55% has been successfully carburized. Normally, however, the carbon content is restricted to a maximum of .25%. For light parts requiring extremely tough cores, .18% carbon is the maximum that should be permitted. For heavy parts requiring strong cores, the carbon content of the steel should be .15%-.25%.

Since the carbon content is limited in these steels, an increase in strength cannot be obtained by merely using a higher carbon steel. In order to obtain greater strength without a decrease in toughness after heat treatment, it is necessary to use an alloy steel. The alloy steels commonly used are nickel, nickel-chromium, and molybdenum steels. The greatest core strength is obtained by using a nickel steel, S.A.E. 2515.

A good case is also extremely important. The plain carbon steel S.A.E. 1020 gives a file-hard case that is slightly better than that obtained with the alloy steels. Alloys decrease the hardness of the case somewhat. An increase in the nickel content decreases the case hardness. S.A.E. 2515 steel has the softest case of the carburizing steels.

The following listed steels are used most frequently for carburized parts. Their core strengths are also given:

S.A.E. 1020	60,000 lbs./sq. in.
2320	80,000 "
2515	120,000–160,000
3115	85,000
3312	100,000
4615	80,000–100,000
6115	90,000

CYANIDING

Cyaniding is a surface hardening of steel obtained by heating it in contact with a cyanide salt, followed by quenching. Only a superficial casehardening is obtained by this method, and consequently it is seldom used in aircraft work. It has the advantage of speed and cheapness, however, and may be used to advantage on relatively unimportant parts.

The cyanide bath, which is usually sodium or potassium cyanide, is maintained at 1550–1600° F. The work to be hardened is preheated to 750° F. and then immersed in the bath for from 10 to 20 minutes. It is then withdrawn and quenched in water until cold. A superficial case of $\frac{1}{64}$ inch maximum depth is obtained. The case is hard but not homogeneous. Great care must be taken to remove all scale before cyaniding and to insure uniform cooling, or soft spots will be present in the case. Immersing the work for over 20 minutes does not increase the case materially but results in high carbon spots and brittleness. In cyaniding it is also important to use a closed pot since the fumes are extremely poisonous.

The hard case obtained from cyaniding is not due wholly to a high carbon content. As a matter of fact, the carbon content is relatively low. Chemical analysis shows the presence of nitrogen in the form of iron nitride in the case. It is this constituent which imparts the hardness as well as brittleness to the case. It should be noted that the core is also hard and brittle after cyaniding, which is, of course, undesirable.

NITRIDING

Nitriding is the surface hardening of special alloy steels by heating the metal in contact with ammonia gas or other nitrogenous material. The process of nitriding was only developed a few years ago and is still in the course of development. It has great possibilities, however, and should eventually supersede casehardening by carburizing on all important work. A harder case is obtainable by nitriding than by carburizing. In addition there is no distortion or cracking associated with nitriding and the case obtained appears to be corrosion resistant in most mediums, including salt water.

Nitriding can only be done with special steels. The essential constituent in nitriding steels or *nitralloy,* as they are sometimes called, is aluminum. The chemical analysis of a typical nitriding steel frequently used in this country is as follows:

Carbon............	0.30–0.40	Nickel............	0.50 max.
Aluminum.........	0.90–1.50	Manganese........	0.40–0.60
Chromium.........	0.90–1.50	Phosphorus........	0.045 max.
Molybdenum........	0.15–0.25	Sulphur...........	0.04 max.

When heated in the presence of ammonia gas the aluminum and iron combine with nitrogen to form aluminum and iron nitrides, which form an exceptionally hard skin. From 1% to 1.50% aluminum is necessary to produce the best results.

The physical condition of nitriding steel before the hardening treatment is very important. It has been found that if the material is in the annealed state, the nitrogen will penetrate the boundaries of the relatively large grains and cause a brittle, non-uniform casehardening. To avoid this condition the steel is hardened and tempered to obtain a sorbitic grain structure. The actual heat treatment given Nitralloy G is as follows:

Hardening temperature—1725-1750° F.
Quench in oil
Tempering temperature
    950° F. for 1 hour. This treatment will result in maximum hardness of the case after nitriding and a core strength of 150,000 lbs. per square inch.
    1200° F. for 1 hour. This treatment is used when the part is to be machined before nitriding. A core strength of 125,000 lbs. per square inch is obtained.

When no distortion is permissible in the nitrided part, it is necessary to normalize the steel prior to nitriding to remove all strains resulting from the forging, quenching, or machining.

The nitriding operation consists of heating the steel to 950° F. in the presence of ammonia gas for from 48 to 72 hours. The container in which the work and ammonia gas are brought in contact must be airtight and equipped with a fan to maintain good circulation and an even temperature throughout. The depth of the case obtained by nitriding is about 0.020 inch and has a Vickers Brinell hardness number of over 950. The nitriding process does not affect the physical state of the core if the preceding tempering temperature was 950° or over. This is usually the case.

The molybdenum present in nitriding steels imparts ductility to both case and core. In spite of this fact, however, the case is still very brittle. It is possible to improve its ductility by increasing the nitriding temperature to 1150° F. for a period of two hours at the end of the regular treatment. The increased ductility is gained at the expense of 100 points in hardness.

It should be noted that there is no quenching associated with the process of nitriding. As a result there is no distortion or cracking of the work. This is particularly true of properly normalized material without internal strains as explained above. Due to the brittleness of the case, care must be taken in the design to avoid sharp corners. This is necessary because nitrides are formed on both sides as well as the edge, which makes a brittle corner or edge that is easily chipped.

No scaling of the work occurs during the nitriding operation.

The slight oxide film formed is easily removed by buffing or by using emery paper.

Tinning of any surface will prevent it from being nitrided. This fact is utilized when a piece of work is to be partially treated only.

Nitrided surfaces can be reheated to 950° F. without losing any of their hardness. If heated above that temperature, they lose their hardness rapidly and cannot be retreated to regain the lost hardness.

Gas welding of nitriding steels is not practical since a large part of the aluminum is burnt away and the remaining metal will not nitride properly. Spot welding after nitriding has been successful.

Care must be taken to remove all the decarburized metal caused by preliminary heat treatment prior to nitriding. If the decarburized metal is not removed, the nitride case will flake. Nitriding steels decarburize more than other steels during heat treatment. They also are increased in size slightly by the nitriding process. This increase is of the order of .002 inch for a piece 12 inches in diameter.

As previously stated nitrided steels are reputed to be corrosion resistant in fresh or salt water as well as under ordinary atmospheric conditions. The steel, however, has not been in use long enough to make a definite statement on its corrosion resistance.

CHAPTER VII

SHAPING OF STEEL

In order to fully utilize steel, or any structural material for that matter, it is essential that it be available in a usable shape. When newly made steel is removed from the furnace, it is in a molten condition. This molten steel is poured into a large ingot before being subjected to other processes required to obtain the necessary form. In rare cases the molten steel is poured directly into a mold of the shape of the finished piece. The steel ingot is reduced to material of the desired shape by one of several processes which have been developed. These processes may be classified broadly as mechanical treatment or casting. The mechanical treatment in turn may be sub-divided into hot or cold working, and these in turn into rolling, forging, and drawing. This chapter will be devoted to describing these processes and the results obtained from each. In addition, the defects found in steel after fabrication, whether introduced in the furnace or during the working, will be described.

MECHANICAL TREATMENT

In determining whether a desired shape is to be cast or formed by mechanical working, several things must be considered. If the shape is very complicated, casting will be mandatory if expensive machining of mechanically formed parts is to be avoided. On the other hand, if strength and quality of material is the prime consideration of a given part, a casting will not be satisfactory. For this reason steel castings are seldom used in aircraft work.

As previously explained in the chapter on Heat Treatment of Steel, the grain size increases as molten steel solidifies and cools down to the critical temperature. When steel is worked mechanically above the critical range, the growth of the grain is prevented and a fine-grained, dense steel is the result. Gas cavities and blowholes are also eliminated by the pressure of mechanical working. The resultant steel is the best quality of steel obtainable from the physical viewpoint.

Hot Working

Almost all steel is hot worked from the ingot into some intermediate form from which it is either hot or cold worked to the finished shape. When an ingot is stripped from its mold after about one hour of solidification, its surface is solid but the interior is still molten. The ingot is then placed in a soaking pit which prevents loss of heat, and the molten interior of the ingot gradually solidifies while reheating the partially cooled surface. After about one hour of soaking, the temperature of the ingot is equalized throughout and is reduced by rolling to intermediate sizes which may be more readily handled.

The rolled shape is called a *bloom* when its sectional dimension is 6 x 6 inches, or larger, and approximately square. The section is called a *billet* when it is approximately square and less than 6 x 6 inches. Rectangular sections in which the width is greater than twice the thickness are called *slabs*. Slabs are the intermediate shape from which sheets are rolled.

Hot working is done either by rolling or forging. Simple sections required in large quantities are rolled; more complicated sections are forged. Because it is possible to control the pressure and temperature more closely in forging then in rolling, a forged part is of better quality. This difference is not marked however.

Hot Rolling. Blooms, billets, or slabs are heated above the critical range and rolled into a variety of shapes of uniform cross section. The more common of these rolled shapes are sheet, bar, channels, angles, I-beams, railroad rails, etc. In aircraft work we are especially interested in sheet, bar, and rod rolled from steel. It is extremely important that the rolling should end just above the critical range in order to obtain the finest grained metal. If the rolling ends while the steel is well above the critical range, grain growth will occur until the critical range is reached; if rolling should continue below the critical range, the grain of the metal will be crushed and distorted. It is frequently necessary to reheat the steel between rolling operations when all the work cannot be done before the steel has cooled down to the critical range.

There are many types of rolling mills to serve different purposes but the principle of operation is the same. The section to be rolled is fed between two rollers which are somewhat closer together than the original section. By this means the cross section· is diminished. The operation is repeated until the desired thickness and shape is obtained. In the operation of rolling mills there is a strong temptation to keep the metal extremely hot and plastic to reduce the forces necessary for reduction of the cross section. If this is done and the finishing temperature is far above the critical range, a very coarse grained structure will result. Coarse grains lack the cohesion of fine grains, and consequently the metal is not as strong. In hot rolling a scale is always formed on the surface of the metal since it is impossible to keep oxygen away from the hot surface during the rolling operations. This scale may be removed by pickling in acid after completion of the rolling operations.

Steel shapes to be rolled are heated to approximately 2300° F. before rolling. Inasmuch as the rolling is finished somewhere above 1400° F., it is difficult to predict the exact thickness since contraction will occur during cooling. In addition, the surface scale must be removed, particularly in material intended for aircraft work. As will be explained later in this chapter, hot-rolled material is frequently finished by cold rolling or drawing to obtain accurate finish dimensions and a bright, smooth surface.

Forging. Complicated sections which cannot be rolled, or sections of which only a small quantity are required, are usually forged. In many cases in aircraft work the first set of parts for the experimental airplane are machined out of solid bar stock, although the intention is to forge the particular parts for production. The reason for this is the expense and delay involved in making the necessary die and obtaining the forging. Most parts are cheaper to machine out of bar stock if only a few are required. A comparison of costs should be made in every case before the decision is made to forge or machine a part. It should be borne in mind that the forged part will require some finish machining, and this expense should be included in the comparative cost of the forging. On the other hand, unless parts are machined out of forging stock, the machined parts will not be so good as the forging insofar as the physical condition of the metal is concerned. The tendency at the present time is to forge as many parts as possible, thereby relieving the usually overworked machine department. Once a standard part is forged it is possible to use it on subsequent models without having to write off the cost of the die against the later contracts. There is a definite saving here.

Forging of steel is a mechanical working above the critical range to shape the metal as desired. Due to the pressure exerted the grain of the metal is refined, and the metal is made more dense and homogeneous. The best quality of metal is thus obtained. As previously explained, however, it is necessary to finish forging the steel just above the critical range in order to prevent grain growth or distortion. Working of the metal while hot breaks up the crystalline structure and prevents grain growth, so that the finest grain and best mechanical properties are procured if forging ends just above the critical range. Forging is done either by pressing or hammering the heated steel until the desired shape is obtained.

Pressing is used when the parts to be forged are large and heavy. It is also superseding hammering where high grade steel is required. Since the press is slow acting, its force is transmitted uniformly to the center of the section, and thus the interior grain structure is affected as well as the exterior, giving the best possible structure throughout.

Hammering can only be used on relatively small pieces. Since the hammer transmits its force almost instantly, its effect is limited to a small depth. It is necessary to use a very heavy hammer or to subject the part to repeated beatings to insure complete working of the section. If the force applied has been insufficient to penetrate to the center, the finished forging surface will be concave. If the center has been properly worked, the surface of the forging will be convex or bulged. The advantage of hammering is that the operator has control over the amount of pressure applied and the finishing temperature, and is able to produce metal of the highest grade.

This type of forging is usually referred to as smith forging. Smith forging is extensively used when only a small number of parts are required. Considerable machining and material is saved when a part is smith forged to approximately the finished shape.

Upsetting is a forging operation in which a hot piece of metal is increased in thickness and decreased in length by hammering on the end. This is the manner in which heads are put on bolts. An upset head is stronger than a machined head because the grain direction is ideal to resist pulling off stresses. In the case of the machined head the plane of cleavage would parallel the grain and would be weak. With the upset head the grain is perpendicular to the force and will resist shearing forces. The question of grain direction is extremely important in all metal fittings. In laying out forgings, care must be taken to insure

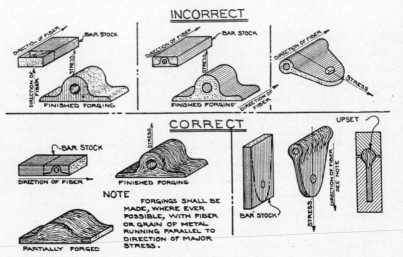

FIGURE 13. CORRECT AND INCORRECT DIRECTIONS OF GRAIN IN FORGINGS
Courtesy of Horace C. Knerr

proper direction of grain relative to the major stress. Figure 13 shows the right and wrong methods of laying out forgings from this viewpoint.

Swaging is a forging operation which may be done either hot or cold. It consists of reducing the cross section and shaping a bar, rod, or tube. It is done by subjecting a revolving die, which shapes the work, to a large number of repeated blows.

Drop Forging. Drop forging is a modification of forging by hammering. Two dies are used, one of which is attached to the hammer and the other to the anvil. When brought together the shape inside these dies is that of the part required. At the intersection of the two dies there is a relieved section all around the edge to take care of surplus metal squeezed out when the dies are brought together. In the actual operation a heated billet is placed on the lower die and the hammer and upper die are dropped. The operation is repeated until the hot billet has assumed the shape of the dies. During the forging operation the dies are kept clean with a high pressure steam or air hose to prevent scale being forged into the part. The surplus metal which has been squeezed out into the relieved section is called the *fin* or *flash*. This fin is trimmed off the finished part.

Drop forging is used for the production of individual pieces in large quantities. Fairly intricate sections can be made by this method. Aircraft fittings are drop forged quite extensively. The fitting should be forged as close to finished dimensions as possible to save on machining. In some fittings only drilling and reaming of holes is necessary. Other fittings may require extensive machining if they are complex and cannot be forged to the finished shape. In laying out forging dies it is necessary to slope the inside faces from 7 to 15 degrees to permit drawing out the finished part. This sloping of the sides is referred to as the *draft*.

Drop forgings are small relative to the hammer used and are satisfactorily worked throughout. Because of their small size and the indefinite time required for forming, it is difficult to obtain the proper finishing temperature. Practice and experience must be relied on in this instance.

Chrome-molybdenum and chrome-nickel-molybdenum steels are commonly used for aircraft forgings. Where corrosion resistance is important, 18-8 corrosion resisting steel is used.

COLD WORKING

When steel is worked above the critical range as previously described it is referred to as hot working. Cold working of steel is done at atmospheric temperatures; it can be either cold rolling or cold drawing. Sheet steel, and bars ¾ inch in diameter or larger are rolled; smaller bars, wire, and tubing are drawn to size.

Cold-worked material increases in strength, elastic limit, and hardness but loses its ductility. The increase in brittleness is very marked. A good surface finish is obtained by cold working, and the material can be held to accurate dimensions. These last two points are very important since hot-rolled material lacks both of these properties.

A more compact and better metal is obtained by cold working. The crystals are broken into smaller masses and distorted along the direction of working to such an extent that their cleavage planes all but disappear. In order to relieve the internal strains set up by this condition, it is customary to anneal or normalize cold-worked material after fabrication.

Cold Rolling. Whenever bar or sheet with a smooth surface and accurate dimension is required cold-rolled material should be ordered. The material is actually hot rolled to near the required size, pickled to remove the oxidized scale, and then passed through chilled finishing rolls to impart a smooth surface and reduce it to accurate dimensions.

The amount of cold work done in rolling is relatively little, so that no appreciable increase in strength is obtained. In the case of bar stock only the surface is hardened. It is advisable to purchase all material in the normalized state, however, to insure relief of all internal strains.

Cold Drawing. Wire is manufactured from hot-rolled rods of ⅛ to ¾ inch in diameter. These rods are pickled in acid to remove scale, then dipped in lime water, and finally dried in a

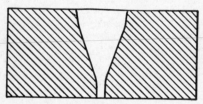

FIGURE 14.   WIRE DRAWING DIE

steam drying room where they remain until drawn. To reduce the cross section of the rod, it is drawn cold through a die shaped as shown in Figure 14. The end of the rod is filed or hammered to fit through the die, where it is fastened to the drawing block which proceeds to pull the rest of the wire through. The force necessary is approximately 50% of the breaking strength of the wire. The rod cross section is reduced gradually, and repeated drawings are necessary to attain the desired wire size. Each drawing reduces the ductility of the wire, so that after several drawings it is necessary to anneal the wire before further drawing. Wire annealing is done in a closed pot to prevent oxidation of the surface during the heating operation. The wire is not removed from the pot until near atmospheric temperature.

Cold drawing of wire increases the tensile strength tremendously but greatly reduces the ductility. Music wire is drawn to small diameters with a tensile strength of 300,000 pounds per square inch. By proper selection of the reduction to be made in each draw, and the number of draws to be made after annealing, it is possible to obtain any strength wire desired. The reduction in cross-sectional area for each draw may be as high as 30%. When dead soft wire is required, it is annealed after the final drawing operation.

In aircraft work large quantities of seamless steel tubing are used. This tubing must be accurate in outside diameter, and the thin wall must be uniform in thickness and free from defects. All aircraft tubing is finished to size by cold drawing. The operations required in the manufacture of seamless steel tubing are as follows:

1. A steel billet is hot rolled to form a round bar of the necessary length and diameter.

2. The round bar is heated to 2200° F. and passed through the piercing rolls. These rolls spin the bar and force it forward over a conical shaped forged mandrel. The mandrel pierces a large hole longitudinally through the bar and at the same time lengthens it from two to four times its original length. The tube formed by this operation is not uniform in diameter and has a wavy surface.

3. To obtain a uniform diameter and the desired thickness of wall, the pierced tube, which is still hot, is passed through two grooved rolls of the desired diameter. As the tube is forced through the rolls, it also passes over a fixed mandrel of the required internal diameter. Several passes through the rolls over the fixed mandrel are usually necessary to reduce the outside diameter to the proper size.

4. After cooling the tube is pickled to remove all scale. It is then cold drawn through dies and over mandrels of varying sizes until reduced to the finished dimensions. The set-up for this operation is shown in Figure 15. One end of the hot-rolled tube is hammered to a point, inserted through the die, and gripped by a pair of tongs. These tongs are attached to a traveling chain through which the drawing force is exerted. A mandrel is inserted through the open end of the tube and is positioned just between the faces of the die. As can be seen from the illustration, the outside and inside diameters and, necessarily, the wall thickness, are definitely fixed as the tube is drawn through the die and mandrel. The sectional area is reduced from 15% to 25% by each draw. It is necessary to anneal and pickle the tube after

each draw in order to soften it sufficiently for the next draw. Sometimes as many as ten draws are required to obtain a tube of the desired diameter and wall thickness. Some tubing manufacturers have developed long, cylindrical, airtight retorts in which smaller diameter tubing is enclosed during annealing. By this method pickling after each annealing operation is eliminated.

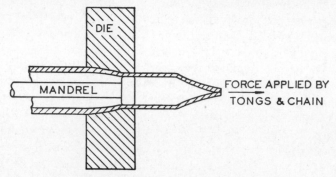

FIGURE 15.   COLD DRAWING OF TUBING

Aircraft tubing is invariably purchased in the normalized condition. Tubing manufacturers are equipped for normalizing all tubing, so that all evidences of the cold-working may be removed.

It is obvious that the manufacture of dies and mandrels is an art in itself. Also special lubricants must be used for all cold-drawing operations. These items are not within the scope of this book, but for those interested tubing manufacturers are only too glad to demonstrate how seamless tubing is made.

STEEL CASTINGS

Steel castings are relatively heavy and are seldom used in aircraft construction. Aluminum alloy castings, which will be described in a later chapter, are frequently used because of their light weight. There are occasions, however, when a steel fitting too complicated for forging must be used. The steel casting will solve this problem but the quality of this steel is not so good as forged metal. The manufacture of a casting involves, in turn, the making of a pattern, the preparation of the mold, the pouring of the molten metal, and the finishing of the casting. When used in aircraft work the casting is also heat treated after fabrication to develop its full properties.

Patterns are made of wood or metal depending upon the amount of service expected of them. Patterns are exact duplicates of the designed parts, except for the fact their dimensions are slightly greater to allow for the shrinkage of the molten metal as it cools. Steel shrinks $\frac{1}{4}$ inch per foot. To allow for this shrinkage the pattern maker lays out the pattern with a shrink rule on which all the dimensions are expanded in the proportion of $\frac{1}{4}$ inch to the foot. Thus, although the rule reads 12 inches, it is actually $12\frac{1}{4}$ inches long. By the use of a shrink rule the pattern maker avoids the necessity of increasing each dimension with the attendant possibility of error. In addition to the shrinkage allowance sufficient metal should be allowed on the casting to permit finish machining if required. As cast the surface will be quite rough. In order to remove the pattern from the mold it is customary to "rap" it to break it loose and then lift it out. Rapping slightly increases the size of the mold and will result in additional metal on the surface of the casting, which must be machined or filed off if a definite dimension is to be held.

Molds for steel castings are made with dry sand in iron containers. The surface of the mold is treated with a sticky substance to bind the sand and then sprinkled with ground quartz or similar material to make a highly refractory surface. The mold must be designed with the following considerations in mind:

1. The pattern must be readily removable. It is necessary to build the mold in two or more parts to permit the removal of the pattern. When the pattern is complicated, it is often necessary to build it in several parts held together with dowel pins, so that it may be removed piecemeal without disturbing the mold.

2. An adequate number of gates of sufficient size must be provided for pouring the molten metal into the mold. Gates must be close enough, so that metal poured in adjacent gates will meet and blend together before either has cooled. A surplus of molten metal must be kept in the gates to furnish metal to the casting as it cools and shrinks.

3. A riser must be provided leading from every high part of the mold. The risers allow the escape of air as the mold is filled, and also provide a place for loose sand and impurities to float clear of the casting proper. In addition the risers furnish a reservoir of hot metal to feed the casting as it shrinks.

4. Small vent holes are also provided for the escape of gases and steam.

5. The material of which the mold is built must resist burning by the molten metal and distortion due to the static pressure of the metal.

Steel made by the electric furnace is commonly used for high grade castings, alloy steel being chiefly used. Electric furnace steel is of better quality and may be heated higher, thus permitting it to be poured into thinner and more intricate sections than is possible with other steel. After cooling, the gates and risers are removed from the casting by sawing or burning off, and filing.

Castings are invariably composed of heavy and light sections. In cooling, severe internal strains are set up due to the unevenness with which sections of different thickness cool. To remove these strains all steel castings should be annealed. In aircraft construction greater strength is usually desired, and the castings are heat treated to develop a strength as high as 125,000 pounds per square inch.

Many defects are found in castings if proper precautions are not taken; they are similar to the defects found in ingots described in detail later in this chapter. In many cases it is possible to repair cracks or small holes in castings by plugging or welding. If welding is resorted to, it must, of course, be done before heat treatment.

Manganese Steel Castings. Manganese steel has been used in aircraft construction in the past for tail skid shoes. It has exceptional resistance to wear and abrasion and is extremely hard. It is practically impossible to machine this steel, and as a consequence, it must be cast and finished by grinding if it is necessary. Manganese steel has no particular application in aircraft construction nowadays but may serve some purpose in the future. For that reason it is mentioned here. This particular manganese steel is composed of about 13% manganese and slightly over 1% carbon.

DEFECTS IN STEEL

In every stage of the manufacture or shaping of steel there is a possibility of defects creeping into the metal. These defects are the direct cause of many material failures. They seriously reduce the strength of the steel, particularly the fatigue strength, and destroy the reliability of the metal. In aircraft work where one failure may cost several lives and expensive property loss, every precaution is taken to eliminate these defects. It is customary for aircraft manufacturers to maintain inspection staffs and special equipment to catch any flaws in material or workmanship. A short description of the most common defects found in steel follows.

Defects in Ingots. Gas cavities in the ingot, called *blowholes*, are caused by the trapping of dissolved or occluded gases as the ingot cools. Carbon monoxide gas is the most common cause of blowholes which may be as large as 1 inch in diameter. In carbon steels if blowholes are not oxidized, they will weld when hot worked and not cause any trouble. In alloy steels or when oxidized, they will not weld and will form internal cracks, seams, or hair lines when rolled. These are serious defects.

Impurities collect at the top of the ingot as it cools. These impurities are slag, oxides, and often particles of the furnace or ladle lining—all of which enter the steel during its manufacture. When the ingot has formed and been given a preliminary rolling, the top 15% to 30% is discarded or cropped. Cropping removes the impurities bodily.

Segregation is the concentration of many of the chemical compounds found in steel at the center of the ingot, thus destroying the homogeneity of the material. These compounds have solidification points that differ from the main portion of the ingot and collect at the hottest section of the ingot which is the center. Segregation produces material which is not uniform in strength and quality.

Piping is the cavity formed at the upper center section of the ingot caused by contraction in cooling. The surface of the ingot cools and solidifies first, and as the interior cools, it is attracted to the already solid surface. This effect and gravity produce the pipe or cavity in the upper center section of the ingot. For this reason ingots are cast on end. The pipe is removed when the ingot is cropped.

Cracks are caused on the surface of the ingot if it is removed from the mold while very hot and exposed to chilly air. Cracks may also be caused by rupture of the thin solidified surface of the ingot just after pouring due to internal pressure or a rough mold. If cracks are not numerous, they may be chipped out smoothly and all traces removed in rolling. But if they are not chipped out, rolling will close the crack but not weld it together.

Scabs or *cold shuts* are caused by molten metal splashing against the mold wall in pouring, and solidifying, and they either freeze there or drop into the molten metal. If not remelted because the molten metal is relatively cool, these drops of solidified metal remain separate. Should they appear on the surface, these scabs are not serious and may be chipped off before rolling.

Ingotism is the formation of large crystals caused by pouring the steel too hot and cooling it too slowly. Large crystals have poor cohesion and produce weak steel. The large crystallization may be broken up by reheating and hot rolling the metal.

Defects Caused by Rolling. Small cracks known as *seams* are formed by the elongation of blowholes in rolling.

Hair lines are very minute seams caused by rolling small blowholes. They have no measurable depth and range in length up to ½ inch, but it is important to note that they may be the starting place of a fatigue failure.

Slivers are small pieces of metal that are rolled into the surface. These slivers may be scabs or cold shuts that were not removed from the ingot.

Laminations are produced by the failure of the metal to weld together because of piping, blowholes, slag, or the rolling of chilled metal into the surface.

Fins and laps are caused by improper rolling when a small amount of metal or fin is forced out between the rolls and is then rolled into the surface when the bar is rolled the next time, thus forming a lap.

Snakes are made by slag or chilled metal due to a delay in filling the ingot mold. They show as a mark across the surface of a rolled piece. Small surface cracks caused by rolling surface cracks in the ingot are also called snakes.

Hard spots are formed by segregated material or chilled metal striking the side of the ingot mold in pouring.

Pits and scale marks are caused by failure to keep the rolls or the rolled material clean during the rolling.

Defects in Cold Drawn Seamless Tubes. Thin fins of metal, called *laps*, are folded over the adjacent metal of the tube. They are formed in the piercing operation.

Pits are small depressions. They may be formed by rolling grit into the tube surface or by overpickling the tube when cleaning scale off preparatory to drawing.

Tears are ragged openings in the interior or exterior surface of the tube which are caused by the mandrel or die picking up hard or weak spots in the metal during drawing operations. Small tears are referred to as "checks."

Scratches are made by rough dies or mandrels, or by grit in the lubricant, or by insufficient lubrication.

Sinks are depressions or collars extending around the inside of the tube caused by a displaced mandrel, which permit drawing the tube to a smaller inside diameter than desired.

Rings are transverse corrugations in the wall of the tubing produced by insufficient lubrication and subsequent jumping of the tube during drawing.

Wall thickness variation is brought about by inaccurate piercing or worn mandrels or dies. Government specifications permit a variation of wall thickness of 10% of the nominal wall thickness. Aircraft tubing as purchased readily meets this requirement.

CHAPTER VIII

CORROSION-RESISTING STEELS

Corrosion-resisting steels are often popularly called "stainless steels." They were first developed about 1910 but were not commercially available until after the World War. This delay was due to the fact that chromium, their main constituent, was restricted to wartime uses. Since then many hundred types of corrosion-resisting steels have been developed and many of these are available commercially. Slight variations of the chemical composition of these steels result in marked changes in properties. It is due to this sensitivity to change in chemical composition that so many types of corrosion-resisting steel have been developed. By the same token great care must be exercised in the selection and use of a given type to insure obtaining the desired physical properties.

Corrosion-resisting steels are normally classified into three groups:

Group 1. Chrome-Nickel Steels. This group composes those steels containing 0.20% carbon or less, 17% to 25% chromium, and 7% to 13% nickel. The well known "18-8" corrosion-resisting steel is one of this group; in fact, this steel with minor modifications, is most often used in aircraft construction. A distinctive property of this group is that the strength cannot be increased by heat treatment but only by cold working.

Group 2. Hardenable Chromium Steels. These steels contain from 12% to 18% chromium, with varying amounts of carbon up to as high as 1.00%. As indicated by the name, they are hardenable by heat treatment. This type steel is commonly used for the manufacture of cutlery, such as "stainless steel" knives and forks. It is also used in one form for the manufacture of aircraft bolts and fittings requiring good corrosion resistance.

Group 3. Nonhardenable Chromium Steels. These steels contain from 15% to 30% chromium and up to 35% carbon. They are not hardenable by heat treatment. They may be used for special applications, but as yet have not been used in aircraft construction.

For aircraft purposes no attention is paid to the above grouping. It is customary to think of the corrosion-resisting steels in relation to their uses in aircraft construction. The two main uses are: (1) nonstructural, such as the manufacture of exhaust collectors, which are dependent upon the excellent corrosion and heat resisting qualities of the steel; and (2) structural, which depend on the high strength and ease of fabrication, as well as the corrosion resistance. In the latter part of this chapter the corrosion-resisting steels commonly used in aircraft work are grouped and described under these headings. A further division of structural steels is made into general structure, such as sheet and tubing, machined parts produced from bar or forgings, and castings.

An ultimate tensile strength of 80,000-300,000 lbs. per square inch is obtainable, the lower value from annealed stock and the latter in cold-drawn wire. Structural sheet is procurable with a strength of 185,000 lbs. per square inch. Round or streamline tubing may also be secured with this same strength value. As will be explained later, these great strengths are obtained by cold working—by rolling or drawing—and will be lost if heat is applied to the steel. This fact immediately eliminates the possibility of using heat in the fabrication or joining of this high strength material and limits its use to a certain extent. Electric spot welding is used almost exclusively for joining this material.

CORROSION

Corrosion-resisting steels are not fully resistant to all corrosive agents. Their corrosion resistance depends upon their own physical state as well as the temperature and concentration of the particular corrosive agent. In aircraft design the most severe corrosive agent to be guarded against is salt water. Generally, the steels described in this chapter are resistant to salt water corrosion but in varying degrees.

It is customary for aircraft specifications to require the material to pass a salt spray test which is a quick means of determining the relative corrosion resistance of a specimen. Specimens are rated A, B, C, or D—A representing the best resistance and D an unacceptable condition. A more detailed description of these ratings is given after the description of the salt spray test.

The corrosion resistance of corrosion-resisting steels depends almost wholly on the surface condition of the metal. The formation of a tough, passive, invisible oxide film on the surface prevents further corrosion of the metal. It is important to have a clean surface free of impurities or particles of foreign matter, and this condition is obtained by either pickling or polishing, both of which are described in this chapter. When the surface is clean, it has been found advantageous to dip the metal in a solution of nitric acid to accelerate the formation of the protective oxide coating. This operation is called *passivating*.

Corrosion-resistant steels may be purchased in a variety of finishes, depending upon the use to which they will be put. It must be remembered, however, that any fabricating, and more particularly welding, will destroy the surface finish, which must be restored after completion.

INTERGRANULAR CORROSION

Intergranular corrosion is a phenomenon of 18-8 corrosion-resistant steels. It occurs when this type steel is heated as in welding. It results in embrittlement and subsequent cracking of the steel in the vicinity of the weld. Since this type steel is welded in the fabrication of exhaust collectors for aircraft, an understanding of the phenomenon and the means of avoiding it are necessary.

All 18-8 corrosion-resisting steels are austenitic in character. It will be remembered that standard steels are austenitic when heated above their critical range. In this state the constituents of the steel are in solid solution and the steel is nonmagnetic. At atmospheric temperatures 18-8 corrosion-resisting steel is in this state. It is found, however, that when heated within the range of 1000-1550° F., carbides will be precipitated at the grain boundaries unless the carbon content is very low. These carbides are believed to be iron carbides or iron-chromium carbides. Carbide precipitation is not instantaneous but requires an interval of time in which to occur. During oxyacetylene welding operations there is a zone just outboard of the weld that falls within the dangerous temperature zone, and carbides are precipitated.

The precipitated carbides do not cause failure until exposed to an active electrolytic agent (such as salt air, spray, or water

FIGURE 16. HULL AND BODY COVERING
18–8 Steel-Fleetwings' Amphibian

in the case of the airplane). The electrolytic attack on the carbide zone results in extreme brittleness and subsequent cracking. Intergranular corrosion is not evident on the surface of the steel prior to failure.

In cases where 18-8 steel is to be welded it is customary to specify a maximum carbon content of 0.07% to reduce or prevent the precipitation of carbides. It has also been found that the addition of certain elements—titanium, columbium, or molybdenum—will prevent the formation of carbides. Such precipitation as does occur can be corrected by an annealing heat treatment when these special elements are present. In the case of steels containing titanium, columbium, or molybdenum the heat treatment is referred to as a stabilizing treatment and is performed at a much lower temperature than the annealing treatment. Stabilizing is so-called because it results in the formation of stable carbides which will not precipitate out of solid solution.

Embrittlement Test. In order to determine the extent of carbide precipitation and possible embrittlement, government specifications usually provide for an embrittlement test. In this test samples of the material are handled as follows:

The samples are heated for 2 hours at a temperature of 1200° F. and cooled in air. They are then boiled for 48 hours in a solution containing 10% H_2SO_4, 10% $CuSO_4$, and water. A reflux condenser (or similar device) must be used to prevent any change in the concentration of the solution. When removed from the solution, the samples must not crack when bent 180 degrees over a diameter equal to twice the thickness of the material. In addition, the sample must ring when dropped on a hard surface.

Metallographic Examination. Government specifications require a metallographic examination to be made when the quality of the material is important. This examination is both macroscopic and microscopic.

The *macroscopic* examination is performed as follows:

The sample must be the full cross section of the material to be examined. The surface must be either machined or ground smooth and flat. The samples are boiled for 60 minutes in an etching solution of 50 per cent hydrochloric acid to secure a deep etch. They are then dipped in cold concentrated nitric acid, washed in running water, and scrubbed clean. Examination of the surface must show the material to be dense and sound and free from pipe, fissures, gas cavities, sponginess, abnormal inclusions or segregation, or too many pinholes.

The *microscopic* examination is performed as follows:

The sample should be 3 inches long by ½ inch wide by ⅛ of an inch thick. It is prepared for examination by subjecting it to an electrolytic etch. The electrolyte consists of 10 grams of sodium cyanide, containing not more than .20% chlorides dissolved in 90 milliliters of water. The sample is the anode, and a piece of the same or similar material is the cathode. These electrodes are spaced about 1 inch apart. A 5-6 volt direct current is passed for 5 minutes or until the structure is well developed. The presence of precipitated carbides may then be determined.

HEAT TREATMENT

As previously stated, the strength or hardness of the 18-8 steels cannot be increased by heat treatment. It is practical, however, to anneal or stabilize these steels to eliminate carbide precipitation, or to remove strains due to cold working. In the case of the hardenable chromium steels it is possible to harden and temper the steel as is done with the standard steels. In the following descriptions the annealing and stabilizing operations apply to 18-8 steels; the hardening, to the chromium steel discussed in the latter part of this chapter.

Annealing. Corrosion-resisting steel is annealed to soften the metal, relieve fabricating strains, and reduce carbide precipitation. It is extremely important that the steel be heated and cooled rapidly through the carbide temperature range of 1000-1550° F. if further precipitation is to be avoided. Annealing is done at a temperature of 1940-1960° F. Unlike standard steels the quench from this temperature must be rapid. Heavy parts are water quenched but light parts, such as are used in aircraft work, are air quenched.

Stabilizing. Stabilizing treatment is a treatment used exclusively to dissolve precipitated carbides and prevent intergranular corrosion. It is applied only to 18-8 steels containing titanium or molybdenum as stabilizing agents. Columbium bearing 18-8 does not require stabilization if the columbium/carbon ratio is 10 or more. The treatment consists of heating the steel at 1550-1625° F. for from 2 to 4 hours and quenching as in annealing. This treatment is given exhaust collectors after they are completely fabricated and welded. Some metallurgists prefer the straight annealing treatment to this special stabilizing treatment. Either treatment will dissolve precipitated carbides.

Hardening. The chromium steel, in accordance with Navy Specification M-286 described later, is hardened by heating to 1780-1820° F., quenching in oil, and tempering to the desired strength. An ultimate tensile strength of 175,000 lbs. per square inch is commonly specified for this steel.

SALT SPRAY CORROSION TEST

This test consists in subjecting a specimen of the material to prolonged exposure in an intense salt atmosphere in a closed box. After being cut the specimen is passivated and thoroughly cleaned by immersion in a suitable solvent, such as petrolic ether and alcohol. After drying it is carefully suspended vertically from a glass rod in a closed box, about 3 feet long by 2 feet wide and 2 feet deep. This box must be constructed of a nonmetallic, neutral material such as glass, slate, or stone. By the use of compressed air and a nozzle arrangement with one end submerged in a salt water solution, the box can be filled with spray. Baffles are installed to prevent direct impingement of the spray on the specimens, and the box is so designed that condensed liquid cannot drip on the specimens.

The salt water solution varies for different materials from a 4% to a 20% solution. The latter solution is becoming standard. It consists of 20 parts by weight of salt (sodium chloride) in 80 parts of distilled water. The specific gravity of this solution is 1.151 at 60° F. The salt should be a commercially pure grade, low in magnesium and calcium chloride content. The solution should be carefully filtered before using. The concentration of the salt solution should be checked every 24 hours and adjusted, as necessary, by the addition of salt or water.

The test is conducted at a temperature of 35° C. and as continuously as possible. Interruptions for regulation or adjustment are permitted. The duration of the test required for any particular material is set forth in the specification. It varies from 24 to 700 hours. The latter time applies to aircraft tie-rods.

Rating Salt Spray Test Specimens. After completion of the salt spray test the specimens are carefully removed and washed in running tap water. They are then examined visually for evidences of corrosion and rated on the following basis:

"*A*" *Rating*—An ideal condition in which no pitting, or scaling, and little (if any) staining is present.

"*B*" *Rating*—A good condition with very little pitting, scaling, or staining and practically no progressive corrosion.

"*C*" *Rating*—A fair condition without excessive pitting, scaling, or progressive corrosion.

"*D*" *Rating*—An unsatisfactory condition showing excessive progressive corrosion.

The strength of a material is adversely affected by corrosion. In comparing the strength of corroded material with that of the original, the average strength of not less than three corroded specimens should be compared with the strength of two or more of the original material.

PICKLING

When corrosion-resistant steel is annealed or welded a tenacious scale is formed on the surface which can only be removed by sandblasting or pickling. The usual practice is to sandblast the surface lightly and then complete removal of the scale by pickling. Pickling is the immersion of the material in an acid bath, usually for the purpose of cleaning the surface. The following acid bath is generally used to remove the scale from exhaust collectors which have been welded and then stabilized and quenched in air:

50% solution by weight of hydrochloric acid at 130-140° F.

Even when a light sandblast precedes this pickling, it is necessary to leave the material immersed in the bath about one hour to obtain satisfactory removal of the scale. The surface, however, will still be dark and dull looking.

A bright silvery finish may be obtained by pickling in a 10 per cent nitric acid and 3 per cent hydrochloric acid solution heated to 160° F. In extreme cases scale is removed by immersing the work in a solution made up of equal parts of nitric and hydrochloric acid. This solution is extremely powerful and will eat the metal away if immersed for more than a few minutes.

After immersion in the pickling solution the work must always be thoroughly rinsed in hot water to insure removal of the acid. When scale is particularly tenacious, the material is sometimes removed from the pickling solution, scrubbed with a wire brush to loosen the scale, and then repickled. By this method the danger of over pickling, which may result in hydrogen absorption and embrittlement of the metal, is avoided. All corrosion-resisting steel must be passivated after pickling. This operation will be described presently.

POLISHING

The best corrosion resistance may be obtained from 18-8 steel if the surface is highly polished. This operation is very slow and expensive. It is rarely required nowadays in aircraft construction since a sandblasted or pickled surface is found to possess satisfactory corrosion resistance.

Polishing is performed on surfaces which have been sand-blasted lightly to remove the scale. A series of buffing operations, using cloth and cotton wheels and very fine buffing compounds, will gradually develop a highly polished surface. It is important that no steel or wire brushes be used in order to avoid leaving steel particles imbedded in the surface of the polished metal.

PASSIVATING

Passivating is the final operation on corrosion-resisting steel after it has been sandblasted, pickled, or polished. It consists in immersing the material for 20 minutes in a solution containing from 15% to 20% nitric acid, at a temperature between 120-150° F. The material must then be washed thoroughly in warm water. Passivating does not affect the appearance of a polished surface. It is good practice to passivate corrosion-resisting steel after machining, fabrication, or severe handling since it restores the corrosion resistance.

Corrosion-resisting steels owe that property to their alloy content, which aids in the formation of a tough, passive oxide film on the surface of the metal. The formation of this film is accelerated by the passivation treatment. Other than the formation of this film, nitric acid has little or no effect on corrosion-resisting steel. It will, however, remove any particles of foreign matter from the surface, thus eliminating a direct cause of corrosion due to the electric potential existing between dissimilar metals.

WORKING PROPERTIES

In general, corrosion-resisting steels are very difficult to forge or machine. Free machining varieties of this steel have been developed by the addition of sulphur, but this element causes "red shortness" or brittleness at high temperatures and makes forging more difficult. Annealed sheet or tubing stock may be readily formed or drawn but work hardens rapidly. Intermediate anneals may be necessary to complete forming operations. Note the specific comments made about each operation.

Forging. The forging of corrosion-resisting steels requires pressures from two to three times as great as those used for forging ordinary steels. The temperature range is also higher and varies with slight changes in the constituents. For one standard grade of 18-8 steel the temperature range for forging is 2150-1800° F. Forging below 1800° F. might cause a cold check and result in the rejection of the part. Corrosion-resisting steel, in accordance with Navy Specification 46S18 or Air Corps Specification 10079, is normally used for forged parts in aircraft construction when corrosion resistance is essential. This material is described in detail at the end of this chapter.

Forming and Drawing. The steels used in the manufacture of exhaust collectors are readily formed and drawn. This material is always bought in the annealed state and can be hammered and bent to the required shape without difficulty. In exceptional cases where severe working of a part is necessary to obtain the required form, it is necessary to anneal the steel before completing the operation. This annealing should be done at a temperature of 1900-1950° F., followed by an air cool. Welded and seamless tubing are available for the manufacture of exhaust collectors. Welded tubing is usually considered satisfactory for this purpose, in view of all the welding that is going to be done anyway in the fabrication of the collector. The elbows of exhaust collectors have been bent around a radius equal to $2\frac{1}{2}$ times the diameter of the tubing, although slightly greater radii are desirable. Special tube bending machines are required to do this bending properly.

Structural corrosion-resisting steel sheet or tubing is cold rolled or drawn to the desired temper. A tensile strength of 185,000 pounds per square inch is obtainable by full cold working. It is common practice to further draw or roll cold rolled strip into "U" or other sections for rib capstrips (or other structural purposes), particularly in connection with spot welding.

Machining. Corrosion-resisting steels are difficult to machine because the chips cling to the tip of the cutting tool, and the cut work hardens the surface, thus making the next cut more difficult. Free machining varieties of corrosion-resisting steel have been developed by the addition of sulphur. This grade of steel is not quite as resistant to corrosion, however, as the standard grade of corrosion-resisting steel. When corrosion resistance is paramount, steel in accordance with Grade 1 of Navy Department Specification 46S18, in the annealed condition is used. This steel is difficult to machine, but a satisfactory job can be done.

In drilling, only a very light center punch should be made, and the drill should not be allowed to ride on the metal without cutting. It is obvious that these precautions are necessary to prevent hardening of the metal by cold working. Similar precautions are necessary in milling and sawing.

In punching, this steel must be cut throughout its entire thickness. A close fit between punch and die is essential.

WELDING AND SOLDERING

Corrosion-resisting steels are commonly joined by one of three methods of welding: gas welding by means of oxyacetylene, electric arc welding, or electric spot welding. In aircraft work nonstructural steel, such as used in the fabrication of exhaust collectors, is always gas welded. Electric arc welding is not practical on material below $\frac{1}{16}$ inch thick and for that reason is seldom used in aircraft work. Work hardened structural steel can be spot welded without affecting its physical properties. This method is commonly used to attach parts fabricated from sheet or strip.

These steels can also be soft soldered or silver soldered readily. Soldering is not used for structural purposes in aircraft, but may be used occasionally for sealing seams or in the preparation of cable terminals.

Gas Welding. In aircraft factories oxyacetylenc welding equipment is always available for welding chrome-molybdenum steel. This same apparatus is used for welding nonstructural corrosion-resisting steel. A weld can be obtained by this method that can be bent flat on itself without cracking. Gas welded material is susceptible to intergranular corrosion, however, and must always be annealed or stabilized after fabrication.

FIGURE 17. HULL FRAMING—18–8 STEEL

The type of welding flame used in gas welding corrosion-resisting steel is very important. If an excess of oxygen is used the metal will bubble and a porous weld will result. On the other hand, if a reducing flame (too much acetylene) is used, the metal will absorb carbon, the weld will be brittle, and the corrosion resistance of the metal will be lowered. A neutral flame is therefore best, but because of the impracticability of maintaining this condition in practice, a slightly reducing flame is used to avoid porosity and oxidation. It has been determined that even a slightly reducing flame will increase the carbon content of the deposited weld metal about 15 points, whereas a full reducing flame will increase it 50 to 60 points.

There are many types of welding rods on the market for use with 18–8 steel. In general, the rod diameter should be the same as the thickness of the material being welded. The welding rod should also be of similar chemical composition to the welded material. Where the welded material will be subjected to high temperatures in service, as in exhaust collectors, it is advisable to use a welding rod containing columbium. A welding rod containing titanium is not practical, as most of the titanium is burnt away during the welding operation. A flux is universally used in conjunction with the above welding rod. The flux makes the metal flow more freely and aids in securing deeper penetration.

In the actual welding operation the flame is directed forward in order to preheat the metal ahead of the spot being welded. The torch is held close to the work, so as to push the flame down into the weld. The rod, on the other hand, is held just above the weld, so that it will melt and drop down in place as the work progresses. A relatively small tip is used on the torch to permit slow, careful welding without danger of obtaining a porous weld. Due to the fact that 18–8 steel expands about 50% more than ordinary steel when heated but has only about one half the heat conductivity, there is great danger of warpage from welding. To avoid this warpage, it is necessary to clamp the parts to be welded in a rigid jig.

Electric Arc Welding. As stated above, it is not practical commercially to weld metal less than $\frac{1}{16}$ inch thick by the electric arc method. This method does give better welds than gas welding on heavier material. In aircraft construction the heaviest 18–8 steel welded is about .049 inch thick, so that metallic arc welding is not practical.

In electric arc welding the following practice is followed:

1. The material to be welded is made the negative electrode, the welding wire positive. This is just the opposite to the method used in welding mild steel.
2. The material is thoroughly cleaned and freed of grease.
3. A flux-coated filler rod is used with a chemical composition similar to the material being welded. The flux must not contain any carbonaceous compound in order to avoid increasing the carbon content of the weld.
4. The use of a short arc is recommended to enable the flux to function. The flux cleans the weld puddle and escapes to the surface, carrying with it the impurities in the weld. It then forms a glassy film over the top of the weld.

5. When a filler rod has been all used up, a small crater will mark the termination of the weld. Before proceeding with the next rod, it is necessary to clean the flux from the surface of the crater so as to avoid obtaining a porous spot.

Like gas welded material, electric arc welded material is subject to carbide precipitation and intercrystalline corrosion. It is essential that all welded material be annealed or stabilized after fabrication.

Spot Welding. Spot welding or shot welding, as it is sometimes called, consists essentially in holding two pieces of material in close contact between two electrodes and passing a low voltage, high amperage current through them for a very short period of time. Fusion immediately takes place between the two sheets. Corrosion-resisting steel is particularly adapted to spot welding because of its clean surface, its high electrical resistance, and its poor heat conductivity. The importance of these properties is explained in the following paragraph.

The heat energy generated in a weld is measured by

$$\text{Resistance} \times (\text{current})^2 \times \text{time}$$

The resistance is made up of three parts: namely—

1. The contact resistance between the sheets to be welded
2. The contact resistance between the electrodes and the sheets to be welded
3. The electrical resistance of the sheets themselves

It is obvious that the first resistance is directly dependent upon a clean surface. The uniformity of the weld also depends upon accurate control of the electrode pressure upon which both the first and second resistances are dependent. If the third resistance, which is a property of the material and therefore constant, is large relative to the first and second resistances, then satisfactory welds can be obtained without perfect pressure control. For this reason thin 18–8 steel can be better welded than other metals. The relatively high electrical resistance of 18–8 steel also reduces the amount of current required to make a weld. Its poor heat conductivity aids in welding by preventing undue dissipation of the heat generated.

In studying the distribution of energy delivered to a weld, it has been found that only about 5% goes to produce fusion, while the remainder is dissipated through the surrounding cold metal and electrodes. It immediately becomes apparent that any small variation in the dissipated energy results in a large percentage

FIGURE 18.   SKELETON TAIL ASSEMBLY
18–8 Steel Spot Welded

variation in the fusion energy. Very accurate control of all elements entering into a weld are therefore essential. This fact has necessitated the development of precision machines and improved apparatus to guarantee uniform welds. The high initial cost of this apparatus has greatly retarded the use of spot welding in aircraft construction.

An extremely high heat is developed in spot welding at the instant of fusing, and this heat then dissipates rapidly. In the case of corrosion-resisting steels this rapid cooling or quenching leaves the weld soft and ductile. It is similar to the annealing process, previously described, wherein quenching is done in air or water. It is interesting to note that an effort was made to adapt spot welding to chrome-molybdenum steel but without success. With this steel the rapid cooling of the weld was a hardening process which resulted in a very brittle weld that broke like glass. An attempt was made to overcome this trouble by normalizing after welding, but many of the welds failed during the heat treatment. These failures were probably due to expansion strains causing rupture before the normalizing temperature could be reached.

Due to the high temperature of spot welding, the surface along the weld will be turned blue by oxidation. This oxide will slowly turn brown, resembling rust, if exposed to the weather. The change, however, is a surface condition which affects only the original oxide. The oxide may be readily removed by pickling or polishing. Polished spot welds are as corrosion resistant as the original metal. In the occasional case where a spot weld has failed by corrosion (or for some other reason), it has been drilled out and a stainless steel machine screw inserted to fill the hole. This practice has been used, particularly in stainless steel seaplane floats where watertightness was necessary. Very few spot welds failed in this application.

Spot welds may be placed at the rate of 960 per minute by means of roller electrodes. By this same means it is possible to seam weld where watertightness is required. Seam welding is somewhat more difficult than spot welding since all traces of dirt must be removed between the contact surfaces if a satisfactory, continuous weld is to be obtained. The diameter of spot welds can be varied for different types of work, but in general a ⅛ inch spot is used. Spot welds may be spaced any desired distance apart. Automatic machines provide for overlapping spots up to ¾ inch spacing.

Some of the numerous advantages claimed for spot welding are as follows:

Spot welded joints can be designed to attain 100% of the strength of the material.

They are faster than riveting, since no layout and drilling of holes is necessary. Numerous spot welds can also be made in the time required to insert and head one rivet.

The pitch of spot welds may be much closer than rivets. In addition, only a small flange need be turned up for spot welding because the spot is small and little or no edge clearance is required.

Seam welded watertight joints do not require the insertion of tape and a sealing compound. Thus weight and expense are saved.

The drag of rivet heads is eliminated in exterior covering.

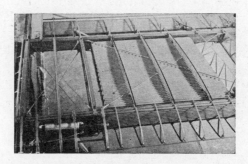

FIGURE 19. SEAM WELDED FUEL TANK—18–8 STEEL

Spot welded stainless steel construction has found many applications in aircraft already and is constantly being put to new uses. A summary of structures in which corrosion-resisting steel was used wholly or partially is as follows: wing beams, wing ribs, wing covering, monocoque fuselage, seaplane floats, fuel and oil tanks, ailerons, tail surfaces. It is apparent that with the use of corrosion-resisting steel tubing and wire for controls, landing gear, and wing bracing, it is possible at the present stage of development to construct an entire airplane of corrosion-resisting steel. As a matter of fact such a plane has recently been completed by Fleetwings, Incorporated. It is shown in Figure 21. Most of the illustrations in this chapter are taken from this plane.

Soldering. Corrosion-resisting steels are readily soldered with either soft or hard solder. Repairs to tanks can be made by soldering on a patching plate. Soldering corrosion-resisting steel will not cause carbide precipitation because of the low temperature employed, and consequently no heat treatment is required. The physical properties of cold worked material will not be seriously affected by soldering either. Prior to the development of seam welding, joints were often spot welded and then soldered to obtain tightness.

FIGURE 20. BODY PANEL CONSTRUCTION
18–8 Steel Spot Welded

A silver brazing alloy in accordance with Navy Department Specification M-221 is reputed to have excellent properties. Its chemical composition is as follows: silver 50%, copper 15.5%, zinc 16.5%, cadmium 18%. This solder may be obtained in the form of strip, or wire, or granulated. Its melting point is 1175° F.

A soft solder containing 75% tin and 25% lead has been found satisfactory for use with 18–8 steel. Many other solders, both soft and hard, are also available.

The following practice is recommended for soldering 18–8 steel:

Roughen the edges to be soldered with sandpaper, particularly when the surface is highly polished. Paint the edges with a soldering flux or fluid, which may be either plain hydrochloric acid or a prepared brand available on the market. Bring the metal up to a heat sufficient to accept the solder in a liquid condition. This is done by heating the soldering iron well above the normal soldering temperature in order to compensate for the low heat conductivity of 18–8 steel. Sufficient heat must be maintained at all times to permit the solder to flow into the joint.

FIGURE 21. FLEETWINGS' AMPHIBIAN

Progress should be slow to avoid the necessity of going over the joint a second time. In order to remove all traces of flux or acid from the joint or adjoining metal, the finished work is washed with a solution of 1 part nitric acid in 3 parts of water. After ten minutes this solution is washed off with clear water. This treatment removes all acid from the work and passivates it.

Brazing of 18–8 steel should be avoided because of the electrolytic corrosion set up due to dissimilar metals.

PROPERTIES OF CORROSION-RESISTING STEELS

In Table 5 the corrosion-resisting steels commonly used in aircraft construction have been grouped according to their use. The Army or Navy Specification number has been listed when applicable. Immediately following this table the properties of each group are given in detail. The properties of corrosion-resisting tie-rods and cable are given in the Appendix.

TABLE 5
SUMMARY OF CORROSION-RESISTING STEELS

General Use	Form	Specification		
		Navy	Army	AN Aero
Exhaust collectors	Sheet	47S19	57–136–9	AN–QQ–S–757
	Tubing—seamless	44T25	57–180–3	AN–WW–T–858
	Tubing—welded	44T26	57–180–4	AN–WW–T–861
Structural	Sheet	47S21	11068	AN–QQ–S–772
	Tubing—round	44T27	57–180–3	AN–WW–T–855
	Tubing—streamline	44T29		
	Wire	22W13	48–37	
Machined parts	Bar	46S18	10079	AN–QQ–S–771
	Bar	S–80		
	Bar	M–286		
Springs	Bar	S–64		
Castings		46S27		
Tie-rods	Streamline	49T9	29–60	
	Round or square	49T10	29–61	
Cable	Extra flexible	22C4	48–36	AN–RR–C–48

Corrosion-Resisting Steel for Exhaust Collectors

Material for this purpose must have good forming qualities and be readily weldable. It must also be free from intergranular corrosion after welding, and for that reason a stabilized material containing titanium is used.

Chemical Composition

Carbon	0.08 max.	Nickel	7.0–12.0
Manganese	0.20–2.50	Silicon	1.50 max.
Phosphorus	0.030 max.	Copper	0.50 max.
Sulphur	0.040 max.	Columbium *	10×Carbon Content
Chromium	17.0–20.0		

*Titanium may be substituted for the Columbium. (Titanium = 5 × Carbon Content.)

The maximum carbon limitation of 0.08% is very important if the material is to be welded in order to reduce carbide precipitation to a minimum. The presence of a substantially larger amount of columbium or titanium than carbon reduces the danger of intergranular corrosion.

Physical Properties

Density	0.284 lb./cu. in.
Melting point	2550° F.
Modulus of elasticity	28,000,000 lbs./sq. in.
Ultimate tensile strength	80,000 lbs./sq. in.
Yield point	35,000 lbs./sq. in.
Elongation	40%

Heat Treatment. This material cannot be increased in strength by heat treatment. It is customary to stabilize it by holding it at 1550-1625° F. for 2 to 4 hours after severe forming or welding. Material below $\frac{1}{16}$ inch thickness as used in aircraft is quenched in air. Heavier material may be water-quenched.

Working Properties. All fabrication operations necessary for the manufacture of exhaust collectors can be done cold with this material. These operations consist of belling and bending tubing, and forming, cupping, or bending sheet. The material hardens as it is worked, but the operations are seldom severe enough to require intermediate annealing for softening the metal to permit further working.

Sheet may be bent cold, without cracking, through an angle of 180° over a diameter equal to the sheet thickness. Government

FIGURE 22. EXHAUST COLLECTOR
18–8 Corrosion-Resistant Steel

specifications require bend tests to demonstrate this property both across the grain and parallel to the grain. In shop work it is always preferable to bend sheet across the grain, since there is less tendency to crack when this is done, and slightly greater fatigue strength is obtained.

Tubing for exhaust collectors is usually from 2 to 4 inches in diameter and has a wall thickness of .035 to .049 inch. This tubing can be bent to an inside radius as small as two diameters, but a somewhat larger radius is preferable for ease of bending and to reduce the back pressure of the exhaust. Special bending jigs are necessary to obtain a smooth job. It is customary to sublet this job to a company that specializes in bending tubing.

Welding. This material is readily weldable with the oxyacetylene torch. A neutral to slightly reducing flame must be used to prevent a porous or carbonized weld. A welding rod containing columbium or molybdenum should be used. There are a number of fluxes on the market that will give satisfactory results.

Corrosion. A very tenacious scale is formed on the surface of this material by the welding or heat-treatment operation. This scale must be removed by sandblasting, pickling, or polishing, followed by passivating, to obtain full corrosion resistance. The quickest and cheapest method is to sandblast the surface lightly until clean, and then passivate. Exhaust collectors treated by this method are quite satisfactory.

Available Shapes. This material may be obtained in sheet form and as welded or seamless tubing. Welded tubing is cheaper than seamless tubing and is often employed in the manufacture of exhaust collectors. Sheet and tubing with a thickness of .035 to .049 inch have been found to be adequate for this purpose.

Uses. The primary use for this material is in the manufacture of exhaust collectors, stacks, manifolds and fire walls. It is not used for structural purposes because of its relatively low strength and great elongation under load. This material has an austenitic structure and, as a consequence, is practically nonmagnetic in the annealed state. Its magnetic permeability increases with cold work, and there is some evidence that it also increases in service due possibly to vibration or temperature changes. Because of its low magnetic permeability, it is sometimes used for special purposes, such as in the vicinity of a compass.

Corrosion-Resisting Steel for Structural Purposes

This material has high strength properties which are obtained by cold working. No heat can be applied to aid in forming this material without destroying its physical properties. Consequently, only spot welding, or riveting, can be used in joining

FIGURE 23.   SKELETON FUSELAGE—18–8 STEEL

this material. It is obtainable in a number of tempers which depend upon the amount of cold work done on it. These tempers are called ¼ hard, ½ hard, ¾ hard, and hard. Annealed material is also available but seldom used.

Chemical Composition

Carbon *	0.12 max.	Chromium	17.0 min.
Manganese	2.00 max.	Nickel	7.0 min.
Phosphorus	0.03 max.	Silicon	0.70 max.
Sulphur	0.03 max.	Copper	0.50 max., or
		Molybdenum	2.00 min.

* Carbon content may be 0.15 max. up to and including 0.050 in.

Physical Properties

Density.................. 0.291 lb./cu. in.
Modulus of elasticity...... 28,000,000 lbs./sq. in.

STRENGTH PROPERTIES

TEMPER	U. T. S.	YIELD STRENGTH	% ELONGATION	BEND DIAMETER
		(Sheet and Strip)		
A	80,000	30,000	40	1 thickness
¼ H	125,000	75,000	25	1 "
½ H	150,000	110,000	10	2 "
¾ H	175,000	135,000	5	4 "
H	185,000	140,000	4	6 "

TEMPER	U. T. S.	YIELD STRENGTH	% ELONGATION
		(Tubing—Round or Streamline)	
A	80,000	35,000	35
¼ H	120,000	75,000	15
½ H	150,000	110,000	7
¾ H	175,000	135,000	3
H	185,000	140,000	2

TEMPER	DIAMETER	U. T. S. (lbs./sq. in.)
	(Wire)	
A	0.029–0.180	85,000
H	0.005–0.026	250,000
	0.047	240,000
	0.080	225,000
	0.146	200,000
	0.180	180,000

Heat Treatment. This material will not respond to heat treatment. Its properties are due wholly to cold working.

Working Properties. This material is regularly rolled, drawn, or bent to any number of structural forms. The most common of these sections is the simple "U" which is used in rib construction. Corrugated sheet is also readily formed and used where stiffness is required. Forming of this material requires special technique due to its "springiness" and low elongation.

The bend diameters for the various tempers of sheet are listed above under the Strength Properties. It will be noted that material above ½ hard temper requires a very generous bending radius. It is advisable to make all bends across the grain to reduce the possibility of cracking.

Tubing of ½ hard temper has been successfully bent to a radius of five diameters, but the operation required special care and was expensive. This particular application was for the control stick of an airplane. Bending of this tubing is not recommended. It should be remembered that heat cannot be applied to aid the forming operation without destroying the physical properties.

Drilling this material is very difficult due to its hardness and the increase in the surface hardness caused by the rotating drill.

Welding. Only spot welding is permissible with this material. Due to the rapidity with which the heat of spot welding is dissipated, there is no reduction in the physical properties of

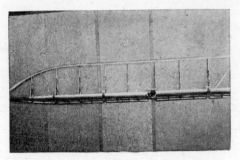

FIGURE 24. AILERON CONSTRUCTION
18–8 Steel Spot Welded

the metal. This material is almost invariably joined by spot welding.

Corrosion. The material has excellent corrosion-resisting properties if it has been pickled or polished, followed by passivating. It is normally purchased in one of these conditions and does not require any further treatment by the purchaser.

Available Shapes. This material is available commercially as sheet or strip, round or streamline tubing, and wire. It may be obtained in any desired temper, but ½ hard and hard are most often used. Sheet and strip may be obtained in thicknesses from .005 inch up to about $\frac{1}{16}$ inch. The upper limit of thickness is determined by the impossibility of obtaining the harder tempers by cold rolling thick material.

FIGURE 25.   WING CONSTRUCTION—18-8 STEEL SPOT WELDED

Standard tubing sizes and gauges are listed in the Appendix.

Uses. This material has been used in the construction of every part of an airplane's structure. Its most popular use has been as wing ribs and spars. Ailerons and tail surfaces have also been fabricated. Spot welding facilities, the necessity for corrosion resistance, and the strength/weight possibilities should all be taken into account in deciding whether to use this material. It is bad practice to employ it jointly with aluminum alloy in one assembly, because an electrolytic action will be set up that will eat away the aluminum alloy. This is especially true where wing ribs are one material and wing beams another. Each assembly should be composed, as nearly as possible, of the same material.

CORROSION-RESISTING STEEL
FOR MACHINED PARTS

There are numerous varieties of this steel. Slight differences in chemical composition result in different machining and forging properties. The specification numbers have been used for identification.

CORROSION-RESISTING STEELS FOR MACHINED PARTS

CHEMICAL COMPOSITIONS

ELEMENT	SPEC. 46S18 GRADE 1			SPEC. 46S18 GRADE 7	SPEC. 10079	SPEC. S-80	SPEC. M-286
	CRS1-A	CRS1	CRS1-H	CRS7-A CRS7			
Carbon (max.)	.07	.10	.12	.10	.20	.20	.15
Manganese	.20–2.50	.20–2.50	.20–2.50	.30–2.50	.20–2.50	.30–1.20	.30–.75
Phosphorus (max.)	.03	.03	.03	.17*	.03	.17*	.03
Sulphur (max.)	.04	.04	.04	.60*	.04	.60*	.04
Silicon (max.)	.50	.50	.50	.70	.70	.70	.20–.60
Chromium (min.)	18.0	18.0	18.0	18.0	17.0	18.0	15.5–17.5
Nickel (min.)	8.0	8.0	8.0	8.0	7.0	8.0	1.50–2.50
Copper (max.)	.50	.50	.50	.50	.50	.50	
Selenium	......	......	......	.15–.30, or	......	.15–.30, or	
Molybdenum	......	......	......	.75 max., or	......	.75 max., or	
Zirconium	......	......	......	.75 max.	......	.75 max.	

* If phosphorus exceeds .04, sulphur may not exceed .06.

Physical Properties

TYPE	SIZE (Inches)	U. T. S.	YIELD STRENGTH	% ELON-GATION	RED. AREA %
46S18(CRS1-A)... 10079 (1A)........ S-80 (A).........	All	80,000	35,000	35	50
46S18 (CRS1)	Up to 1½ Over 1½–3	100,000 95,000	50,000 45,000	28 28	45 45
46S18 (CRS1-H).. 10079 (1H)....... S-80 (H)........	Up to ¾ Over ¾–1 Over 1–1¼	125,000 120,000 105,000	100,000 85,000 65,000	12 15 20	35 35 35
46S18 (CRS7-A)....	All	80,000	35,000	35	45
46S18 (CRS7)	Up to 1½ Over 1½–3	100,000 95,000	50,000 45,000	28 28	45 45
M-286 (Ht. treated)	Class I Class II	175,000 115,000	135,000 90,000	13 15	

Material of the following types: CRS1-A, 1A, A, CRS7-A are in the fully softened, annealed condition. This material is austenitic steel and cannot be heat treated to obtain higher physical properties.

Material of the following types: CRS1, CRS7 are obtained by forging or rolling hot material at a temperature below that at which complete annealing occurs. Forgings of nonuniform section will not have uniform physical properties due to the difficulty of working all parts at the same temperature.

Material of the following types: CRS1-H, 1H, H are obtained by cold working.

Material of Specification M-286 is not austenitic and can be heat treated to obtain desirable physical properties.

Heat Treatment. All the steels listed above, except M-286, are austenitic and cannot be heat treated to improve their physical properties. They can be annealed as described earlier.

M-286 material is heat treated by soaking at 1780-1820° F. for 2 hours, quenching in oil, and then tempering to the desired properties. Class I material (175,000 U.T.S.) is obtained by quenching at 525° F.; Class II material (115,000 U.T.S.) is obtained by quenching at 1200° F. This material should not be heat treated to give strength values other than 175,000 or 115,000 lbs./sq. in. because of the danger of obtaining poor impact strength and corrosion resistance.

Working Properties. The austenitic steels are all difficult to machine because of the tendency to harden when cold worked. The addition of sulphur and selenium greatly improves the machinability. Material in accordance with Specification S-80 is known as a free machining, non-seizing steel. M-286 material also machines readily.

Welding. These steels can be welded if necessary. This operation is not applicable to these materials when used as machined parts in aircraft construction. Welding will, of course, destroy the physical properties of all but the annealed material.

Corrosion. Other than CRS7 and CRS7-A material, all the steels listed above will merit an "A" rating if subject to a salt spray test. M-286 material must be heat treated to develop this corrosion resistance. CRS7 and CRS7-A material have a "B" rating in the salt spray test.

CRS1-A is the most corrosion resistant of the materials under specification 46S18 and should be used where severe corrosion conditions will be met. This type of material is also free from intergranular corrosion even if welded and not subsequently annealed.

Due to the fact that the hot work performed on CRS1 and CRS7 material is in the carbide precipitation temperature zone, it is customary to require this material to pass an embrittlement test if its carbon content is greater than .07%.

Available Shapes. This material may be obtained as bar or rod, or forged to any required shape. The limits in size for the various types of materials is given in the table of physical properties above.

Uses. 46S18 (CRS1-A) material has the greatest corrosion resistance and is used for seaplane fittings which are immersed in salt water a great deal. It is very difficult to forge and machine and is only selected when absolutely necessary for corrosion resistance.

46S18 (CRS7 or CRS7-A) material is used for machine screws and nuts. The screws are either machined or upset. This material has non-seizing properties. Only one of a pair of mated parts need be made of this material to prevent seizing.

S-80 (H) material is used for small fittings requiring moderate strength and corrosion resistance. It is only obtainable up to 1¼ inch diameter or thickness.

M-286 material is used for aircraft bolts, tie-rod terminals, and other parts requiring high strength and corrosion resistance. This material will seize if threaded to similar material, but not when threaded to 46S18 material.   (18-8.)

CORROSION-RESISTING STEEL FOR SPRINGS

The material recommended for this purpose is a straight chromium steel, with a tensile strength of 200,000 lbs. per square inch after heat treatment and excellent corrosion resistance.

Chemical Composition

Carbon............	0.35–0.40	Manganese........	0.30–0.50
Chromium........	12.5–14.0	Silicon............	0.50 max.

Physical Properties

Modulus of elasticity..............	29,000,000 lbs./sq. in.
Ultimate tensile strength..........	200,000 lbs./sq. in.
Yield point......................	175,000 lbs./sq. in.
Elongation......................	5%
Rockwell hardness................	C-42

Heat Treatment. The physical properties listed above are obtained by heat treating the material to 1825° F., followed by an oil quench, and then tempering at about 1100° F.

Working Properties. Material is purchased in the fully annealed condition and heat treated after forming. In the annealed condition the material can be bent cold through an angle of 180°, without cracking, over a diameter equal to its own.

Corrosion. After heat treatment, pickling, and passivating, this material will withstand a 100-hour salt spray test without pitting or corrosion.

Available Shapes. Material may be purchased as round bar up to 1 inch diameter.

Uses. This material is recommended for springs requiring good corrosion resistance.

CORROSION-RESISTING CASTINGS

Corrosion-resisting casting material has considerably less strength than forgings or bar stock, but may be useful for special purposes where a complicated shape and corrosion resistance are the criterions.

Chemical Composition

Carbon*	0.20 max.	Chromium	18.0 min.
Phosphorus	0.05 max.	Nickel	8.0 min.
Sulphur	0.05 max.		

* Carbon of 0.30 max. is permissible if chromium is over 20.0 and nickel over 10.0.

Physical Properties

Ultimate tensile strength	70,000 lbs./sq. in.
Yield point	32,000 lbs./sq. in.
Elongation	30%

Heat Treatment. All castings should be annealed at not less than 1800° F. and quenched rapidly in cold water.

Welding. Minor defects in the casting can be welded prior to the final heat treatment. The defects must be thoroughly cleaned out to sound metal before welding.

Working Properties. Light finish machining can be done without difficulty. A bend test specimen ½ inch thick can be bent cold through 150° over a ¾ inch pin.

Corrosion. This material will show practically no scaling pitting or staining after a 24-hour salt spray test. It should be passivated after removal of the annealing scale by pickling or sandblasting.

CHAPTER IX

NICKEL ALLOYS

Nickel is the chief constituent of a number of nonferrous alloys which are used in special applications in aircraft work. The main feature common to all of these alloys is their exceptionally good corrosion resistance. In this respect they are equal to or better than corrosion-resistant steel. These nickel alloys work fairly easily and are obtainable commercially in most of the standard forms. Their use is gradually increasing in aircraft construction, as more designers realize how well they fulfill specialized needs.

Three nickel alloys are of special interest to the aircraft designer: Inconel, Monel, and K Monel. *Inconel* is a nickel-chromium alloy with good corrosion resistance and strength at normal and elevated temperatures. These properties are ideal for airplane engine exhaust collectors, which are frequently constructed of Inconel. *Monel* is a nickel-copper alloy with high corrosion resistance, reasonably good strength, and good working properties. *K Monel* is a nickel-copper-aluminum alloy with high corrosion resistance, exceptionally good strength (inherent as well as developed by heat treatment), and the property of being nonmagnetic. This latter property creates a use for this material as structural members in the vicinity of compasses.

The following pages describe these three alloys in as much detail as the aircraft designer is likely to require. There may be some occasional gaps in the data, due to the fact that two of these alloys are recent discoveries and have not yet been exhaustively tested.

INCONEL

Inconel is a nickel-chromium alloy classified as nonferrous because the iron content is negligible. The relatively small amount of contained iron and carbon do not impart any of the characteristics of steel, such as transformation ranges and hardening by heat treatment. Inconel is a corrosion and heat resisting metal. In aircraft work it is used more especially for exhaust collectors but is rapidly acquiring new uses.

Chemical Properties. The approximate composition of Inconel is:

Nickel..........................	78. %
Chromium.....................	13.5 %
Iron...........................	6.9 %
Manganese....................	0.35%
Carbon........................	0.08%
Copper........................	0.4 %
Silicon........................	0.35%

Chromium is added in the form of ferro-chrome, which also accounts for the iron present. The high nickel content gives the metal good workability and corrosion resistance, while the chromium contributes strength and a "stainless" or tarnish resistant surface. An increase of iron up to approximately 20% has little effect on the properties, but above that percentage rusting occurs and the welding properties change. Inconel was selected from a series of experimental alloys (in which the constituent ranges had been varied and the properties investigated) as the alloy combining the best corrosion resistance, strength, and working properties.

Physical Properties

Density (grams per cubic centimeter).........	8.55
Weight per cubic foot....................	533.5 pounds
Weight per cubic inch....................	0.309 pound
Melting point.............................	2540° F. (1395° C.)
Modulus of elasticity (pounds per square inch).	31,000,000 to 32,000,000
Modulus of torsion (pounds per square inch)..	10,000,000 to 11,000,000

STRENGTH PROPERTIES

	TENSILE STRENGTH, lbs./sq. in.	YIELD POINT, lbs./sq. in.	ELONGATION % in 2"
SHEET			
Annealed...........	80– 95,000	30– 40,000	55–35
Full hard..........	125,000	100,000	7
STRIP			
Annealed...........	80– 95,000	30– 40,000	55–35
¼ hard.............	100–115,000	60,000	30–20
½ hard.............	115–130,000	....	28–18
¾ hard.............	120–140,000	....	24–12
Hard	130–150,000	....	17–7
Full hard..........	145–170,000	....	10–2
ROD			
Annealed...........	80– 95,000	30– 40,000	55–35
Cold drawn.........	100–130,000	80–105,000	30–20
WIRE			
Annealed...........	80– 95,000	30– 40,000	55–35
Spring temper.......	175–200,000	....	10–2

Inconel has the property of retaining high strength at elevated temperatures. This property is particularly important when the metal is used in heating systems or for exhaust collectors. The tensile properties of annealed Inconel at elevated temperatures are shown in Figure 26.

Impact toughness tests on a Charpy testing machine give an average reading of 200 foot-pounds without fracture of the specimen. Excellent toughness is indicated with a much higher value than steel and nonferrous alloys.

Wire up to ⅝ inch diameter can be cold drawn and given

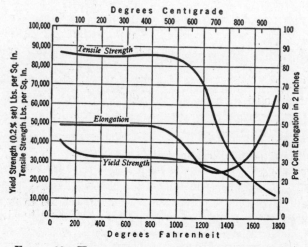

FIGURE 26. HIGH-TEMPERATURE PROPERTIES OF INCONEL

spring temper. After coiling the springs should be treated at 800° F. to release coiling strains, a necessary treatment if springs are to operate at elevated temperatures up to 750° F. The torsional elastic limit of Inconel spring wire is 100,000 pounds per square inch.

Annealing and Stress Relieving. The heat treatment of Inconel consists only of annealing processes which will relieve internal stresses due to cold working and for the purpose of softening the metal. Inconel cannot be hardened by heat treatment; it is only hardenable by cold working.

Internal stresses set up during cold rolling or during fabrication may be relieved without appreciable softening by heating the metal for 1½ hours at 1400° F. Cooling may be effected either by furnace cooling or quenching in air, water, or very dilute alcohol-water solution without changing the physical properties. Water or alcohol quench is preferable to reduce the amount of surface oxidation.

Softening of Inconel is obtained by heating the metal at 1800° F. for 10 to 15 minutes and quenching by any of the above methods. This softening treatment would be employed, for example, between draws where an excessive amount of cold work is to be done in the making of deep drawn articles.

In heating Inconel to temperatures above 700° F. the furnace atmosphere should be free from sulphur and active oxygen to avoid surface scaling. The chromium oxide which forms is removable with difficulty only by grinding or pickling.

Working Properties. As indicated by the elongation values given under Strength Properties, Inconel is very ductile and can be readily formed in the annealed state. It hardens from cold working, not as rapidly as 18–8 corrosion-resisting steel but more rapidly than copper, aluminum, or Monel.

Forging must be done between 2300° F. and 1850° F. As mentioned under heat treatment, all heating should take place in sulphur free or very low sulphur nonoxidizing atmospheres. Shapes similar to those forged in steel may be readily produced.

Hot and cold rolling of sheets and strips is accomplished in a manner similar to that employed for steel. Rods are also hot rolled or cold drawn, and tubing—either welded or seamless—is cold drawn. Steel practice is in general followed in these operations.

Inconel castings can be made but suffer from high shrinkage. The metal must be poured fast and at as low a temperature as will permit free running, and still completely fill the mold.

Machining of Inconel is difficult and must be done at low speeds with carefully treated and sharpened tools. Considerable heat is generated in machining. Inconel machines uniformly with sulphur base oils, and does not drag or stick badly.

Inconel bends readily. Government specifications require that test pieces must withstand cold bending, any direction of the sheet, without cracking, through an angle of 180° on a diameter equal to the thickness of the test specimen. For shop work it would be advisable to call for bend radii equal to one thickness of the material.

Welding. Inconel welds readily and gives a strong, sound, ductile weld which resists corrosion. Welding may be done by electric arc, electric spot or seam (resistance welding), or with the oxyacetylene flame.

Oxyacetylene welding is used exclusively on engine exhaust manifolds and collectors because of the lightness of the gauge. In this type of welding an Inconel rod coated with Inconel Gas Welding Flux is recommended. The joint is also coated with a water paste of this flux on both surfaces to prevent oxidation. When a slightly reducing flame is used to avoid oxidation a uniform weld with excellent penetration is easily obtained. It is advisable when finishing off an Inconel gas weld to withdraw the flame slowly, as this permits slower freezing of the crater and so avoids any porosity at the finish of the weld.

Welded joints in the annealed metal develop the strength of the base metal. As evidence of ductility welded sheet may be bent flat on itself, at right angles to the weld or along the welded seam, without the cracking of the weld.

There is no limitation on the thinness of sheet which can be welded with oxyacetylene other than the skill of the welder. It is also permissible to touch-up an imperfection in a weld without affecting the general soundness.

Metallic arc welding of material heavier than 18 gauge (0.050 in.) is practical.

Welded tubing is produced from strip Inconel by automatic oxyacetylene and automatic atomic hydrogen welding. This type of tubing approaches the soundness of seamless tubing (which is much more expensive) and can be annealed, drawn, swaged, and bent without failure. Welded tubing is superior in uniformity of wall thickness, surface finish, and freedom from die scratches.

Welded joints in Inconel are not subject to intergranular deterioration, nor do they suffer any metallurgical change other than a normal very slight softening. They do not require heat treatment to improve their corrosion resistance.

Soldering and Brazing. Silver soldering or brazing are used where the strength of a welded joint is not required, or the heat of welding would cause buckling. Both operations are performed with the oxyacetylene torch, but because of the lower flow points of silver solders (1175° F.), naturally a much smaller flame is required than for welding. In silver soldering Handy Flux and Handy & Harman's Easy-Flo Brazing Alloy are recommended. Silver solders must have a low flow point to avoid cracking of the Inconel which is hot short around 1400° F. The recommended silver solder is of sufficiently low melting point to clear this range by an ample margin.

Soft soldering of Inconel is also possible, but care must be taken to insure a thorough bond with the metal. "Tinning" with an iron and the use of an active flux is recommended.

Corrosion Resistance. Inconel is practically corrosion resistant in normal atmosphere or in the presence of salt water. It is believed to be somewhat better than corrosion-resistant steel in this respect, but sufficient evidence is not at hand for a definite comparison.

Inconel welds are slightly more corrosion resistant than the parent metal. Due to the small amount of iron in Inconel, there is no trouble with carbide precipitation or intercrystalline corrosion as experienced with 18-8 corrosion-resistant steel after welding. Inconel welds should be cleaned after fabrication by immersing in a 50%, by weight, cold nitric acid solution for 5 to 10 minutes. This should be followed by a thorough water rinse.

Electrolytic corrosion or pitting of Inconel is almost negligible because of the high nickel content. Inconel is rated galvanically as a passive metal.

When heated above 700° F. in an oxidizing atmosphere chromium oxide is produced on the surface. This oxide can be removed only by grinding or pickling. For exhaust collectors there is no point in removing this surface oxide, as it will simply reform as soon as the engine is run and the exhaust gets hot.

Available Shapes. Inconel is available commercially in the following forms:

    Sheet; Strip; Rod—hot rolled or cold drawn;
    Tube—Cold drawn seamless, Welded;
    Castings

Uses. Inconel is ideally suited for use in the construction of exhaust manifolds or collectors. Its ease of forming and welding, combined with its strength at high temperatures and corrosion resistance, make a perfect combination of properties for this purpose. Its slightly greater weight, compared to corrosion-resistant steel, is one disadvantage, but this is compensated by the use of lighter material. Inconel exhaust collectors are usually made of .042 inch sheet and steel collectors of .049 sheet, which makes the weights about equal.

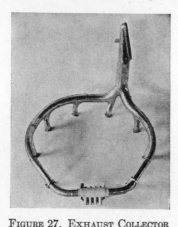

FIGURE 27. EXHAUST COLLECTOR
AND HOTSPOT—INCONEL

Manufactured by Solar Aircraft
Company

Inconel is also suited for locations requiring corrosion-resistance or nonmagnetic qualities. An example of the latter is windshield framework or ammunition chutes which are located within two feet of a compass. Aluminum alloy is not suitable for these locations because of the bulky joints required in the case of the windshield and the poor wearing qualities of the ammunition chute. No doubt other applications will be found for this relatively new material.

MONEL

Monel is a high nickel-copper alloy. It has an interesting combination of properties including high strength and excellent resistance to corrosion. Monel cannot be hardened by heat treatment, only by cold working. It is not used generally in aircraft construction but is used very generally for industrial and chemical applications.

Chemical Properties. The chemical composition for standard wrought Monel products is as follows:

Nickel	68. %
Copper	29. %
Iron	1.5 %
Manganese	1.1 %
Silicon	0.1 %
Carbon	0.15%

Spring wire has a higher manganese content up to 2.50 max.
Castings have a higher silicon content up to 2.0% max.

Physical Properties

Density (grams per cubic centimeter)—cast...... 8.80
Density—rolled.............................. 8.90
Melting point............................... 2370–2460° F.
                                            (1300–1350° C.)
Modulus of elasticity tension................. 25,000,000–26,000,000
Modulus in torsion.......................... 9,000,000– 9,500,000
Weight per cubic inch—cast.................. 0.318 pound
Weight per cubic inch—rolled................ 0.323 pound

STRENGTH PROPERTIES

	TENSILE STRENGTH, lbs./sq. in.	YIELD POINT, lbs./sq. in.	ELONGA-TION %
SHEET AND STRIP			
Cold rolled			
Annealed...	70,000– 85,000	25,000– 45,000	40–20
Full hard...	100,000–120,000	90,000–110,000	8–2
TUBING			
Cold drawn			
Annealed...	65,000– 80,000	25,000– 35,000	35–25
As drawn...	90,000–105,000	60,000– 75,000	20–15
ROD AND BAR			
Cold drawn			
Annealed...	70,000– 85,000	25,000– 35,000	50–35
As drawn...	85,000 125,000	60,000– 95,000	35–15
Hot rolled....	80,000– 95,000	40,000– 65,000	45–30
WIRE			
Cold drawn			
Annealed...	70,000– 85,000	25,000– 35,000	45–25
Spring......	140,000 (B&S Gage 0–2)		8
	160,000 (B&S Gage 15–19)		2
CASTINGS.......	65,000	32,500	25

The magnetic transformation point of Monel is affected considerably by slight variations in composition and by mechanical and thermal treatment. Ordinarily a horseshoe magnet will attract Monel, but the pull of the magnet varies with temperatures and with the metal itself.

Annealing. Annealing for softening and the relief of cold-working strains is the only heat treatment for Monel metal. Hardening cannot be done by heat treatment, only by cold working.

Box annealing of small parts is accomplished by heating to 1400° F., holding for two to six hours at temperature, and quenching in water containing 2% denatured alcohol. This alcohol-water quench will reduce the surface oxidation that takes place when the work is removed from the furnace. A silvery white surface results. A pink color after the quench indicates oxidation in the furnace, improper heating conditions, or delay in quenching which permits excessive oxidation.

Open annealing of material is done by heating to 1700° F., holding for 3 to 7 minutes, depending on the severity of cold work that is to be performed, and quenching in alcohol-water solution.

Working Properties. Monel is similar to mild steel in its cold working properties, such as cupping, drawing, bending, and forming. Due to its higher elastic limit, greater power is required than for steel; and for excessive working, it is necessary to anneal frequently.

Hot working, such as forging and hot rolling, must be done between 2150° F. to 1850° F. Heating for all high nickel alloys should be done in sulphur-free atmospheres. These are obtainable by using gas or oil fuels, the latter carrying a specification of 0.5% (maximum) sulphur content. Coke or coal are not recommended because of their offending sulphur content. The combustion of the gases should be complete before these gases reach the surface of the metal. For that reason, combustion spaces must be large enough. Atmospheres should be maintained reducing. Cold rolled or drawn material is obtained by cold working hot-rolled material after pickling and annealing.

Sheet can be bent about a radius equal to one thickness of the material. The cold ductility of the metal is demonstrated in its ability to make sylphon type bellows and corrugated flexible tubing.

Machining of Monel can be done without difficulty. For automatic screw machine work a machining quality rod is available. Because of the great toughness of the metal, cutting speeds are slower and cuts are lighter than for mild steel. Tools should be of tough, high speed steel, ground with sharper angles than for steel, and honed. Sulphurized oil should be used abundantly as a lubricant for boring, drilling, and so on. It is preferred for all work, though water soluble oils suffice for lathe work. "R"

Monel is available for automatic machine work where high cutting speeds must be maintained.

Welding. Monel can be readily welded by any of the methods commonly used for steel, among them, oxyacetylene, carbon arc and metallic arc, spot, seam, butt, and flash welding. The method to use depends on the gauge of material to be joined and the type of equipment to be made. Sound, strong, ductile welds are regularly made.

When oxyacetylene welding Monel, a slightly reducing flame neither harsh nor mild is maintained. A flux (Inco Gas Welding & Brazing Flux) in the form of water paste is painted on parts to be welded and on the welding rod. The pool of weld metal should not be puddled or boiled, but kept quiet; otherwise the "life" of the metal may be burned out.

The metallic arc welding of Monel is carried out by using a flux coated Monel wire of the shielded arc type capable of producing X-ray perfect welds. Reversed polarity is used. Single and multiple head welds are made, but, of course, in the latter case the flux and slag must be removed before laying down subsequent beads.

Carbon arc welding is similar to acetylene welding in that a source of heat in the form of an arm flame is used instead of an oxyacetylene flame. Small diameter pointed carbons (⅛″-¼″) are used, together with a lightly fluxed Monel filler wire.

Soldering. Soft soldering is a convenient easy means of joining where corrosion and contamination are not troublesome and where strength is not required. Soft solder is inherently weak and must not be used where finished equipment will be subjected to vibration or high stresses. Pretinning of the edges prior to forming is desirable. Either high or low tin solders are satisfactory, the 50-50 lead-tin is the more widely used with zinc chloride base fluxes.

Silver solders are also used for joining Monel, the procedure outlined under Inconel, being applicable.

K MONEL

K Monel is a nonferrous alloy composed mainly of nickel, copper, and aluminum. It is produced by the addition of a small amount of aluminum to Monel. It is corrosion resistant and can be hardened by heat treatment—two properties which are very important. K Monel has been successfully used for gears, chains, and structural members in aircraft subject to corrosive attack. K Monel being nonmagnetic is sometimes used for structural members in the vicinity of a compass.

Chemical Properties. The approximate composition of K Monel is:

Nickel	63–70%
Copper	22–30%
Aluminum	2–4 %
Carbon	0.25 max.
Iron	2.0 max.
Manganese	1.0 max.
Silicon	0.50 max.

Physical Properties

Density (grams per cubic centimeter)	8.47
Melting point	2400–2460° F.
	(1315–1350° C.)
Modulus of elasticity (tension)	25,000,000–26,000,000
Modulus of torsion	9,000,000– 9,500,000
Weight per cubic inch	0.31 pound

STRENGTH PROPERTIES

	TENSILE STRENGTH lbs./sq. in.	YIELD POINT lbs./sq. in.	ELON- GATION %
STRIP			
Cold-rolled, soft	105,000*		25
Cold-rolled, soft, heat treated	130,000	90,000	10
Cold-rolled, half hard	125,000	85,000	5
Cold-rolled, half hard, heat treated	150,000	110,000	3
Cold-rolled, full hard	145,000	105,000	3
Cold-rolled, full hard, heat treated	170,000	125,000	2
RODS AND FORGINGS			
Hot rolled or forged	110,000*		30
Hot rolled or forged, heat treated	140,000	100,000	20
Cold drawn ($\frac{3}{8}$ to 1)	135,000*		13
Cold drawn (1 to 3)	125,000*		13
Cold drawn ($\frac{3}{8}$ to 1), heat treated	145,000	110,000	15
Cold drawn (1 to 3), heat treated	140,000	100,000	17
WIRE			
Cold drawn	155,000*		4
Cold drawn, heat treated	165,000		5

* Maximum

Cold-rolled, soft material is obtained by a softening heat treatment. It should be specified where great softness is necessary for fabricating operations. Structural parts made from this material should normally be hardened by heat treatment after fabrication. Secondary parts are often left in the soft state. It should be noted that the strength values given for the soft material are maximum values.

Cold drawn material is the strongest grade that can be machined reasonably well. For this reason it is usually specified for machined parts that are to be used without further heat treatment.

The heat treated materials are cold worked followed by full heat treatment which makes them hardest and strongest. These grades can be machined only with difficulty. They should be specified only for parts that can be purchased finished or can be finished by grinding.

Wire up to ¼ inch can be cold drawn and heat treated to above 175,000 lbs./sq. in. for use as springs. This is full hard material. The wire must be in the cold-drawn condition when coiled if maximum strength is desired after heat treatment. If the spring is made from soft wire or formed hot, subsequent heat treatment will only develop intermediate properties. The reason for this action is explained under heat treatment.

K Monel is nonmagnetic at all normal temperatures. Its magnetic permeability is 1.0, which is the same as air. This property is extremely important for parts located in the vicinity of a compass.

Heat Treatment. Annealing or softening of K Monel is obtained by soaking at one of the following temperatures for the time specified:

1400° F.	2 hours
1500° F.	1 hour
1600° F.	2 to 5 min.
1800° F.	1/2 to 2 min.

Quenching must be done in water for sections over ½ inch thick, or oil for smaller sections. K Monel will not soften, if cooled in air as it requires a rapid quench.

The maximum hardness that can be attained by heat treatment alone, starting with soft K Monel, is equivalent to about

300 Brinell. However, if the hardness of soft material is increased by cold working and then heat treated, the additional hardness developed by the heat treatment is superimposed on the cold-worked hardness. Thus, cold-worked metal with a Brinell hardness of about 250 can be further hardened by heat treatment to 350-400 Brinell.

Hardening by heat treatment is obtained by following the procedure outlined below, depending on the initial hardness of material:

MATERIAL CONDITION	TEMP. °F.	TIME AT TEMP.
Soft: 140 to 180 Brinell	1200–1250	1 hr.
	or	
	1080–1100	16 hrs.
Moderately cold worked: 175 to 250 Brinell	1080–1100	8 to 16 hrs.
Fully cold worked: over 250 Brinell	980–1000	6 to 10 hrs.

The longest time should be used for the softest material. For best possible hardness, the material should be cooled not faster than 15° F. per hour down to 900° F. Furnace cooling is essential.

K Monel can be stress relief annealed after cold working by heating to 525° F. and quenching. No softening occurs due to this treatment.

In heating K Monel the fuel should be free from sulphur and a reducing atmosphere maintained in the furnace to avoid excessive oxidation. K Monel should not be placed in a cold furnace and heated gradually, but should be charged into the hot furnace.

Working Properties. K Monel can be worked quite readily in the shop in the annealed form. Working above this grade is difficult due to the greater hardness.

Hot working of K Monel should only be done between 2175-1700° F. The metal should be quenched in water from the finishing temperature above 1700° F. Annealed soft material will then be obtained.

Cold drawn rod is produced from hot rolled rod that is annealed, pickled, and cold drawn to size in two or more operations through chromium-plated hardened steel dies.

Cold rolled strip or sheet is produced from hot rolled material by annealing, pickling, and cold rolling to the desired hardness. The maximum hardness obtainable by cold rolling without subsequent heat treatment is known as the full hard condition.

Wire is cold drawn in the same manner as rod but the percentage of cold reduction is greater. Spring wire is cold drawn to 25% of the original cross-sectional area. As noted under heat treatment, in order not to anneal out any of the effect of cold working this grade material is not heated as high as the softer materials. Heat treatment at 980-1000° F. will give a tensile strength of 175,000 to 200,000 lbs./sq. in.

Hot rolled or cold drawn rod can be machined satisfactorily. Heat treated material can only be machined with difficulty. A special free machining grade, known as "KR" Monel, is available for high production parts on screw machines, turrets, etc. The mechanical properties are slightly lower than for K Monel.

Welding. K Monel sheet has been successfully welded by oxyacetylene. A rod of the same material and a flux composed of half sodium fluoride and half Inco (a welding and brazing flux prepared by the International Nickel Company) mixed with water to form a paste can be used. Another satisfactory flux consists of 5 to 6 parts of chromalloy flux mixed with 1 part of fluorspar powder. A slightly reducing flame should be used. The weld obtained is ductile and can be bent flat on itself without cracking. The welding of K Monel by oxyacetylene has only recently been developed. No data are available of the effect of welding on the strength of heat treatment of the sheet.

Electric arc welding of K Monel is readily accomplished.

Brazing. K Monel can be brazed readily and with good results by the use of Handy & Harman's Easy-Flo Brazing Alloy and Handy Flux. Care should be taken to have the edges of the sheets perfectly smooth or cracking will result because of hardness of the metal. The minimum amount of heat necessary to completely flow out the silver solder should be supplied to the joint.

Corrosion. K Monel is naturally corrosion resistant and does not rely upon a protective film, such as oxide formed on the surface. It is resistant to corrosion in normal atmospheres or in salt water.

Electrolytic corrosion does not affect K Monel since it is high in the galvanic series, but if coupled with steel or aluminum, it may cause corrosion of these metals.

As purchased, K Monel will usually be received in an non-tarnished condition. If subsequent heat treatment is performed, the metal surface will oxidize. This oxide can be removed by pickling. The manufacturer will gladly furnish the proper pickling solution that should be used for any given set of conditions.

Available Shapes. K Monel is commercially available as strip, wire, rod, and forgings. Forged stock can be obtained to suit any possible requirements in aircraft work.

Uses. K Monel is used for structural parts in the vicinity of compasses because of its nonmagnetic quality. The corrosion resistance and excellent strength qualities of this material make it practical for machined parts that are subject to corrosion. Specific examples of this use are gears and chains for operating retractable landing gears on amphibian airplanes.

Specifications.

Inconel:

    Aeronautical Spec. AN-QQ-N-271
        (Nickel-chromium-iron alloy; sheet and strip)

Monel:

    Aeronautical Spec. AN-QQ-N-281
        (Nickel-copper alloy; forgings, rods, sheet, strip, wire)

K Monel:

    Aeronautical Spec. AN-QQ-N-286
        (Nickel-copper-aluminum alloy; forgings, rods, strips, wire)

CHAPTER X

COPPER AND ITS ALLOYS

Copper, brass, and bronze have a limited use in aircraft construction. They do have important specialized applications, however, such as bearings and fuel and oil lines. Copper wire is used throughout the electrical system. In general these metals are corrosion resistant, nonmagnetic, fairly strong, and good conductors of electricity.

COPPER

Copper Tubing. Copper tubing is very generally used for fuel and oil lines. The copper used in the manufacture of this tubing must contain at least 99.90% copper. The tubing is purchased in the soft annealed condition and it is seamless drawn. In the purchased condition or after annealing it has the following physical properties:

U. T. S.	32,000 lbs./sq. in.
Yield point	6,000 "
Elongation	52%
Rockwell hardness	63 (B-⅛-100)

This tubing can be annealed by heating it in an air furnace at 1100-1200° F. and quenching it in water. To obtain the maximum softness and ductility the tubing should not be held at temperature longer than 5 minutes.

Copper tubing is available in sizes ranging from ⅛ to 1⅛ inches outside diameter. A wall thickness of 0.035 inch is used up to ⅝ inch diameter and 0.049 inch for larger diameters. These sizes cover the standard requirements for aircraft fuel, oil, and water lines. For high pressure oxygen lines a special high pressure copper tubing is used.

Copper-Silicon-Bronze Tubing. This tubing is considerably stronger than pure copper tubing and has largely superseded it for fuel, oil, water, and air lines.

CHEMICAL COMPOSITION

Silicon	1.00–5.00	Iron (max.)	2.50
Manganese (max.)	1.50	Impurities (max.)	.50
Zinc (max.)	2.50	Copper	remainder

This tubing has a tensile strength of 50,000 lbs./sq. in. and an elongation of 35%. It is used in the following standard sizes: ⅛ × 0.035, 3/16 × 0.035, ¼ × 0.035, 5/16 × 0.035, ⅜ × 0.035, 7/16 × 0.035, ½ × 0.035, ⅝ × 0.035, ¾ × 0.049, ⅞ × 0.049, 1 × 0.049, 1⅛ × 0.049.

This tubing can be annealed at a temperature of 1000-1100° F. if required after severe forming and bending.

Copper Wire. A soft copper wire is used as a locking wire in aircraft construction. It is drawn from pure copper and has a tensile strength approaching 40,000 lbs./sq. in. and an elongation of 25%.

Beryllium Copper. This material is a high strength, heat-treatable, non-magnetic alloy available as bar, rod, sheet, strip, and wire.

Density = 0.298 lbs./cu. in.

CHEMICAL COMPOSITION

Beryllium...	2.00–2.25
Elements added to obtain special properties............	0.50 max.
Metals (impurities) other than above.................	0.50 max.
Copper..	remainder

PHYSICAL PROPERTIES

	U. T. S. lbs./sq. in.	YIELD POINT lbs./sq. in.	ELONGATION %
BARS, RODS, FORGINGS			
Annealed (over ¾″)......	80,000 max.	....	35
Cold drawn (over ¾″)....	80,000 min.	....	5
Annealed (⅜ to ¾″).....	80,000 max.	....	35
Cold drawn (⅜ to ¾″)...	95,000 min.	....	5
Annealed, heat-treated....	150,000 min.	85,000	10
Cold drawn, heat-treated..	175,000 min.	88,000	3.5
SHEET AND STRIP (cold rolled)			
Soft annealed............	80,000 max.	....	35
" " , heat-treated	150,000	90,000	7.5
¼ hard................	80,000	....	10
¼ " , heat-treated.....	160,000	92,000	5
½ hard................	90,000	....	5
½ " , heat-treated.....	170,000	93,000	2.5
Full hard...............	100,000	....	2
" " , heat-treated....	180,000	95,000	2
WIRE			
Soft annealed............	80,000 max.	....	35
" " , heat-treated	150,000	....	5
¼ hard................	90,000	....	5
¼ " , heat-treated.....	160,000	....	3
½ hard................	100,000	....	2
½ " , heat-treated.....	180,000	....	1.5

This material is annealed by heating at 1440° F. for ½ to 3 hours and quenching. Hardening is accomplished by holding at 525-575° F. up to 3 hours, depending on the properties required.

Heat-treated material is considered to have more stable and uniform properties and is preferred for aircraft work.

BRASS

Brass is a copper alloy consisting of a solid solution of zinc in copper. In addition to zinc and copper, brasses sometimes contain a small amount of aluminum, iron, lead, manganese, magnesium, nickel, phosphorus, or tin. Brass with a zinc content of 30% to 35% is very ductile, and with 45% zinc content it has a relatively high strength. Brasses with a zinc content up to 37% are in so-called "alpha solution," while above that percentage a "beta solution" condition exists. It is the difference between these two conditions that accounts for the ductility of the low zinc brass and the strength of the high zinc brass. Alpha solution brass can only be annealed, but beta solution brass can be increased in strength by heat treatment.

Muntz Metal. Muntz Metal is a brass composed of 60% copper and 40% zinc. It has excellent corrosion resisting qualities in contact with salt water. It can be increased in strength by heat treatment. When heated to 1500° F. the beta solution absorbs the alpha solution. If quenched in water from this temperature, the homogeneous beta condition is retained and the strength increased about 50%. If the heated metal is cooled slowly as in air, the absorbed alpha is reprecipitated and the properties of annealed material are obtained.

PHYSICAL PROPERTIES

	HEAT TREATED	ANNEALED
U. T. S. (lbs./sq. in.)	80,000	57,000
Yield point "	......	20,000
Elongation (%)	9.5	48
Hardness (Brinell 10 mm, 500 kg)	158	80
Weight (lbs./cu. in.)	0.303	0.303

As cast this metal has an ultimate tensile strength of 50,000 lbs./sq. in. and an elongation of 18%. It is used in the manufacture of bolts and nuts, as well as parts in contact with salt water.

Manganese Bronze (Brass). Manganese bronze is really a high zinc brass. It is exceptionally strong, tough, and corrosion resistant.

CHEMICAL COMPOSITION

Copper	57–60	Manganese (max.)	0.50
Tin	0.5–1.5	Aluminum (max.)	0.25
Iron	0.8–2.0	Lead (max.)	0.20
Zinc	remainder	Impurities (max.)	0.10

Sand castings of this metal develop an ultimate tensile strength of 65,000 lbs./sq. in. and an elongation of 20%. As sand cast the metal contains a maximum of 1.5% aluminum and 3.5% manganese. The increased aluminum content is essential for the production of sound sand castings.

PHYSICAL PROPERTIES OF WROUGHT MANGANESE BRONZE

	U. T. S. lbs./sq. in.	YIELD POINT lbs./sq. in.	ELONGATION %
Rods and bars, half-hard	72,000	36,000	20
Rods and bars, hard	85,000	60,000	5
Shapes, soft	55,000	22,000	25
Plates, soft	57,000	22,000	20
Plates, half-hard	60,000	24,000	18

This metal can be forged, extruded, drawn, or rolled to any desired shape. It is generally used in rod form for machined parts when used at all in aircraft construction.

Hy-Ten-Sl Bronze. This is the trade name of a very high strength copper alloy resembling manganese bronze in chemical composition.

PHYSICAL PROPERTIES

	SAND CAST	FORGED, ROLLED, EXTRUDED
U. T. S. (lbs./sq. in.)	115,000	120,000
Yield point "	70,000	73,000
Elongation (%)	10	8
Weight (lbs./cu. in.)	0.280	0.280

With lower strength but higher elongation this alloy is also available in four other grades. It is reputed to be extremely hard, wear-resistant, noncorrosive, and readily machinable, and is recommended for bearings or bushings subject to heavy loads.

Naval Brass (Tobin Bronze). Naval brass is often called Tobin bronze. It is not so strong as manganese bronze but has greater strength, toughness, and corrosion resistance than commercial brass. It is used for turnbuckle barrels, bolts, studs, nuts, and parts in contact with salt water.

CHEMICAL COMPOSITION

Copper..............	59.0–62.0	Iron (max.)...............	.10
Tin...............	0.5–1.5	Lead (max.)...............	.30
Zinc..............	remainder	Impurities (max.)..........	.10

PHYSICAL PROPERTIES

	U. T. S. lbs./sq. in.	YIELD POINT lbs./sq. in.	ELONGATION %
Rods and bars, soft............	54,000	20,000	30
Rods and bars, half-hard.......	60,000	27,000	25
Rods and bars, hard..........	67,000	45,000	22
Shapes, soft..................	56,000	22,000	30
Plates, soft..................	52,000	20,000	30
Plates, half-hard..............	56,000	28,000	25
Sheets and strips, soft..........	50,000	20,000	20
Sheets and strips, half-hard.....	60,000	25,000	15
Castings.....................	30,000	......	15

Naval brass has excellent machining qualities and is used for screw machine parts. Turnbuckle barrels are made of this material.

Red Brass. Red brass is sometimes classified as a bronze because of its tin content. Castings made from red brass are used in the manufacture of fuel and oil line fittings. It has good casting and finishing properties and machines freely.

CHEMICAL COMPOSITION

Copper..............	84.0–86.0	Iron (max.)............	0.25
Tin.................	4.0–6.0	Phosphorus (max.)......	0.75
Lead...............	4.0–6.0	Antimony (max.).......	0.25
Zinc................	4.0–6.0	Impurities (max.).......	0.15

Red brass castings have an ultimate tensile strength of 26,000 lbs./sq. in., a yield point of 12,000 lbs./sq. in., and an elongation of 15%.

BRONZE

Bronzes are copper alloys containing tin. Lead, zinc, and phosphorus are also present in some bronzes but do not total more than 15%. There is also an aluminum bronze in which aluminum is the major alloying element. The true bronzes have up to 25% tin, but those containing below 11% tin are the most useful. Bronzes have excellent bearing qualities due to the fact that the tin is in a hard delta solid solution in the copper. This hard delta solution distributed through the alpha metal gives ideal bearing properties. Delta solution is only present in bronzes with over 9% tin content. When less tin is present, it is in alpha solution. It is possible to improve the strength of copper-tin bronzes through heat treatment. The exact response to heat treatment depends upon the state of solution of the tin. The bearing qualities are impaired if the delta solution is removed or changed by heat treatment.

Gun Metal. Gun metal is a hard bronze casting material. Its shrinkage is not great and it has fair machinability. It is recommended for use under severe working conditions and heavy pressures as in gears and bearings.

CHEMICAL COMPOSITION

Copper	86.0–89.0	Lead (max.)	0.20
Tin	9.0–11.0	Iron (max.)	0.06
Zinc	1.0– 3.0		

Gun metal castings have an ultimate tensile strength of 30,000 lbs./sq. in., a yield point of 15,000 lbs./sq. in., and an elongation of 14%. It should not be used where the temperature will exceed 500° F. When used for bearings, it should not be annealed, or the hard delta eutectoid will be removed.

Phosphor Bronze. Phosphor bronze can be obtained in the following forms: rod, bar, sheet, strip, plate, and spring wire. It is used for the manufacture of bolts, valve disks, electric contacts, and small springs.

CHEMICAL COMPOSITION

Copper (min.)	94.0	Lead (max.)	0.20
Tin (min.)	3.5	Iron (max.)	0.10
Phosphorus	.05–.50		

Physical Properties

	U. T. S. lbs./sq. in.	YIELD POINT lbs./sq. in.	ELONGA- TION %
Rods and Bars			
Up to ½ in.	80,000	60,000	12
Over ½ to 1 in.	60,000	40,000	20
Over 1 to 3 in.	55,000	30,000	25
Over 3 in.	50,000	25,000	25
Sheet and Strip			
Spring temper, 0–8 in. wide	90,000	45,000	1
" " 8–12 in. wide	80,000	40,000	1
Half-hard, all sizes	50,000	25,000	25
Spring Wire			
Up to .025 in.	150,000		
Over .025 to .0625 in.	135,000		1.5
Over .0625 to .125 in.	130,000		2
Over .125 to .250 in.	125,000		3.5
Over .250 to .375 in.	120,000		5
Over .375 to .500 in.	105,000		9

Phosphor Bronze Casting Alloy. This casting alloy is sometimes called a leaded phosphor bronze or leaded gun metal. It machines more easily than gun metal. It is used for bearings, bushings, gears, and other applications requiring good strength and resistance to salt water corrosion.

Chemical Composition

Copper	86–89	Phosphorus (max.)	.05
Tin	7.5–11.0	Iron (max.)	.10
Zinc	1.5–4.5	Nickel (max.)	.75
Lead	0–0.3		

This alloy has an ultimate tensile strength of 40,000 lbs./sq. in. and an elongation of 20%.

Aluminum Bronze. Aluminum bronze possesses greater resistance to corrosion than manganese bronze, and hence may be used where greater strength and corrosion resistance is required. It has good bearing qualities as well as great strength. It may be readily forged. It is available commercially in the form of bars, rods, shapes, plates, and sheets.

Chemical Composition

Copper	88.0–95.0	Iron (max.)	4.0
Aluminum	4.5–10.0	Impurities (max.)	.25

PHYSICAL PROPERTIES

	U. T. S. lbs./sq. in.	YIELD POINT lbs./sq. in.	ELONGA- TION %
RODS AND BARS			
Up to ½ in....................	80,000	40,000	20
Over ½ to 1 in................	75,000	37,500	25
Over 1 in....................	72,000	35,000	30
SHAPES (all sizes)................	75,000	30,000	20
PLATES, SHEETS, STRIPS			
Up to ½ in., under 30 in. wide...	60,000	24,000	25
Up to ½ in., over 30 in. wide....	55,000	22,000	25
Over ½ in., all widths...........	50,000	20,000	30

Aluminum Bronze Casting Alloy. This alloy is as hard as manganese bronze, and has great strength and resistance to corrosion, shock, and fatigue. It is used for worm gears, valve seats, and bearings.

CHEMICAL COMPOSITION

	GRADE A	GRADE B
Copper............................	85.0–89.0	89.5–90.5
Aluminum.........................	7.0–9.0	9.5–10.5
Iron..............................	2.5–4.0	1.0 (max.)
Tin...............................	0.50 (max.)	0.20 (max.)
Other elements (max.)..............	1.0	0.50

Grade A alloy has an ultimate tensile strength of 65,000 lbs./sq. in. and an elongation of 20%.

Grade B alloy, which is always furnished heat treated, has an ultimate tensile strength of 80,000 lbs./sq. in. and an elongation of 5%. Grade B alloy is heat treatable because it contains over 9% aluminum.

Bronze Cable. Extra-flexible bronze cable, 7 by 19 strands, is manufactured for aircraft use. The weight and breaking strength for each size of cable is as follows:

DIAMETER Inch	WEIGHT PER 100 FT. Pounds	BREAKING STRENGTH Pounds
5/8	72.0	14,000
9/16	60.4	11,350
1/2	48.8	8,900
7/16	38.4	6,800
3/8	29.9	5,100
5/16	20.0	3,500
1/4	13.5	2,500
7/32	10.7	2,000
3/16	7.3	1,500
5/32	5.0	1,000
1/8	3.3	700

Season Cracking

Many of the brasses and bronzes are subject to a phenomenon called season cracking. These metals crack spontaneously after being in service for a period of time. It is believed this cracking is due to internal stresses left in the metal by cold working. A low temperature anneal is usually sufficient to relieve these stresses and avoid season cracking.

Specifications generally require the following test for material subject to season cracking: the sample is thoroughly cleaned with nitric acid and then dipped into a mercurous nitrate solution for 15 minutes. This solution consists of 100 grams of mercurous nitrate and 13 cubic centimeters of nitric acid (specific gravity 1.42) dissolved in a liter of water. After removal from the solution, the sample is washed with water and then alcohol. The sample will crack visibly within 24 hours after this treatment if the material is subject to season cracking. This treatment is sometimes called a *strain test*.

CHAPTER XI

WROUGHT ALUMINUM ALLOYS

At the present time aluminum alloys are used almost exclusively in the construction of aircraft. Aside from fittings carrying high concentrated loads, or parts subject to severe wear, or special forms of corrosion—for which special steel alloys are used —the general structure of the airplane as built today is aluminum alloy. The ascendancy of this material is due to its light weight, high strength, ease of fabrication, and its availability in all standard forms. It is about ⅓ as heavy as steel and can be obtained with a minimum ultimate tensile strength as high as 65,000 lbs. per sq. in. It is available in many tempers and forms, so that just the proper material may be selected for any particular application. These applications vary from formed cowling requiring a very ductile material to highly stressed wing beams requiring great strength.

Aluminum is found in most clays, soils, and rocks; but the principal commercial source is the ore, *bauxite*. Bauxite is largely aluminum oxide mixed with impurities. These impurities are removed by a chemical process leaving the pure aluminum oxide, *alumina*. An electrolytic process is used to obtain aluminum from the oxide. It was not until 1886 that a practical process was discovered to effect this separation on a commercial scale. In that year, Charles M. Hall in this country and P. L. T. Heroult in France, working independently, each discovered a practical process. The industrial development of aluminum began shortly after these discoveries.

The metallic aluminum obtained by the electrolytic process is cast into pig form. These pigs are later remelted to form the commercial ingots used in rolling, forging, extruding, and other fabricating processes. By the addition of other constituents during the remelting operations, many alloys of aluminum are obtained with varying properties. A great many structural shapes are wrought from the ingots by rolling, drawing, extruding, or

FIGURE 28. GRUMMAN NAVY FIGHTER
Aluminum Alloy Construction

forging. The common shapes used in aircraft construction are: sheet, tubing, wire, bar, angles, channels, Z-section, U-section, and so on. A number of the aluminum alloys are especially adapted for casting. Castings are regularly made in sand molds, permanent molds, or dies. As with other materials, castings do not have so great a strength as wrought material, but find numerous applications in aircraft.

Nomenclature

In order to identify the various aluminum alloys, they are designated by a number. If this number is followed by the letter "S" it indicates a wrought alloy. Casting alloys are designated by a number without the "S." Thus—

3S, 14S, 17S, 24S, 25S, 52S, 61S

are all wrought alloys, differing from each other in chemical composition and physical properties. Commonly used casting alloys are:

43, 142, 195

In a few cases a letter precedes the alloy number, as A17S. This letter indicates that this alloy has a slightly different chemical composition from the normal 17S alloy.

The wrought alloys can be manufactured in a number of different tempers. To distinguish these tempers another letter or symbol is added to the "S." Hence the temper of a wrought alloy that is strain-hardened by cold work is designated by ¼H, ½H, ¾H, H; "H" stands for "hard" and the fractions indicate the relative hardness. When the material is in the soft, annealed state, the letter "O" is appended to the "S." For instance, 3S material is available in five tempers which bear the following designations:

3SO, 3S¼H, 3S½H, 3S¾H, 3SH

Wrought alloys that are hardened by heat treatment are indicated by the addition of a "T" after the "S." Thus we have:

17ST, 24ST, 25ST, 53ST

These heat treatable alloys in the soft, annealed state are designated by the letter "O" following the "S" as:

17SO, 24SO, 25SO, 53SO

Alloys in the heat treated temper may be strain-hardened to improve their physical properties. When this is done the alloy is designated by the insertion of an "R" between the S and T, as in 17SRT, 24SRT. Some of the heat treatable alloys are subject to an intermediate heat treatment, and do not develop their full strength until given a second heat treatment called a "precipitation heat treatment." After this latter heat treatment, they are identified by the letter "T" following the "S" as described above. When only subjected to the intermediate heat treatment, these alloys are identified by adding a "W" after the "S." Thus we have:

$$25SW, 53SW, 61SW$$

In some instances an alloy may be heat treated in more than one way to obtain special physical properties. If a modified heat treatment is used the alloy is identified by a number after the normal heat treated designation. Thus we have:

$$53ST \text{ and } 53S\text{-}T5, 61ST \text{ and } 61S\text{-}T8$$

Some casting alloys require a heat treatment in order to develop their best properties. These alloys are denoted by their number, followed by a symbol designating the heat treatment. We have, therefore, 195-T4, "T4" indicating the heat treatment. This particular alloy is very generally used in aircraft construction.

CLASSIFICATION OF WROUGHT ALLOYS

As indicated above under Nomenclature, the wrought aluminum alloys may be broadly classified under one of two groups as either *strain-hardened alloys* or *heat-treatable alloys*. In the first group the physical properties are improved solely by cold working, whereas in the heat-treatable group the properties are improved by heat treatment. Further improvement of the heat-treated group is obtainable by cold working slightly after heat treatment. The strain-hardened alloys do not respond to any heat treatment other than a softening, annealing treatment.

The two extreme tempers in which all strain-hardened alloys can be obtained are the soft, annealed temper and the full, hard temper. The latter temper is produced by cold working the metal the maximum amount that is commercially practical. The intermediate tempers such as ¼H, ½H, and ¾H are produced by varying the amounts of cold work after annealing. In the manufacture of sheet, tubing, or wire the cast alloy ingot is broken down while hot into slabs, tube blooms, or rods. The amount of reduction in area of these sections by cold working can be closely

FIGURE 29. GRUMMAN MONOCOQUE FUSELAGE

24ST Aluminum Alloy

controlled by the setting of the rolls, or by the mandrel and die sizes selected. To obtain the intermediate tempers, it is only necessary to anneal the material at the proper size from which the remaining cold-finishing operations will give the desired temper.

The heat-treatable alloys can be obtained in the soft, annealed condition, the heat-treated condition, or the heat-treated and cold-worked condition. A few of the alloys also have an

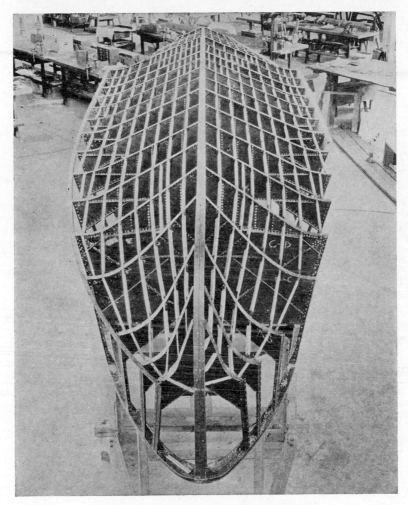

FIGURE 30. SIKORSKY S-41 HULL SKELETON
Aluminum Alloy

intermediate heat-treated condition. Greater strength is obtainable in the heat-treatable alloys than in the strain-hardened alloys. Consequently, they are used for structural purposes in aircraft in preference to the strain-hardened alloys.

CORROSION

Pure aluminum is very resistant to atmospheric corrosion but when alloying elements are added, the corrosion resistance is decreased. One strain-hardened alloy (52S) and one heat treatable alloy (53S) are as corrosion-resistant as commercially pure aluminum, but all the other alloys are somewhat inferior. It is customary in Naval aircraft work to protect all aluminum alloys with a protective coating of paint. A good protective coating is particularly important when the airplane will be subjected to severe corrosive conditions, as in the case of a seaplane.

One type of corrosion of aluminum alloys is the pitting of the surface, which is analogous to the rusting of iron. This eating away of the surface is accelerated in the presence of moisture, particularly salt water. If a dissimilar metal or impurities are also present, an electrical action is set up that eats away the aluminum alloy. All other metals used in aircraft except magnesium are above aluminum in the galvanic series, so that in any action set up the aluminum is the anode and will be attacked. Experience has shown that this type of corrosion occurs most often in parts of the structure that are poorly ventilated, and in inaccessible corners of internal joints.

Intercrystalline corrosion is a much more serious type of corrosion, since it greatly reduces the strength and destroys the ductility of the metal. This type of corrosion is apparently limited to aluminum alloys containing copper, such as 17S and 24S. The resistance of these materials to this type corrosion is lowered by incorrect heat treatment or by slow or delayed quenching. It is imperative that all quenching be done immediately in cold water to avoid intercrystalline corrosion. This type of corrosion gives practically no surface indication, but spreads through the interior of the metal along the grain boundaries. All types of corrosion must be guarded against in aircraft construction due to the light gage of material used.

ALCLAD * ALUMINUM ALLOYS

"Alclad" is the name given to standard alloys, such as 17S and 24S, when they have been coated with a thin layer of high

* "Alclad" is a registered trade mark of the Aluminum Company of America.

purity aluminum. Due to the fact that pure aluminum is highly resistant to corrosion, it protects the alloy sandwiched in between the two surface layers. The aluminum covering is electropositive to the underlying alloy and, consequently, also protects it by means of electrolytic action. This fact is important, because the soft aluminum covering is easily scratched and the edges of the sheet are not coated with aluminum, so that corrosion might occur in these places if it were not for the electro-positive aluminum coating. No painting of Alclad is necessary to protect it from corrosion unless it is subject to very severe service conditions such as under-water or bilge locations in seaplane float construction. In such cases it is desirable to anodically treat the alloy before painting in order to provide a good bond for the paint.

At the present time only sheet and wire are obtainable as Alclad materials. The aluminum coating is put on the alloy by a rolling process which makes it an integral part of the metal. In the case of wire, which is more likely than sheet to be subject to abrasion, an aluminum alloy coating is used in place of the soft, pure aluminum. This alloy coating is also electro-positive to the underlying alloy and protects it from corrosion. Efforts are being made to make other structural shapes available in the Alclad form.

In aircraft work the following Alclads are often used: Alclad 17ST, Alclad 17SRT, Alclad 24ST, Alclad 24SRT. A given thickness of Alclad will not be so strong as the same thickness of the standard alloy. This reduction in strength is of the order of about 8 to 10%. The exact strengths of Alclads and standard alloys are tabulated later in this chapter. Alclad has one great advantage, however, as regards strength, and that is the fact that after years of service it still retains most of its original strength. The standard alloys, even though protected by paint, may lose a great deal of their strength and nearly all of their ductility due to corrosion. Corrosion in modern airplanes is usually localized to poorly drained spots but may have serious effects on the strength of the airplane. This retention of strength is particularly important in the thin sections used in aircraft construction.

As explained later under Heat Treatment, it is important that Alclad be held only the minimum time at the soaking temperature. These precautions are necessary to prevent the aluminum coating from merging with the alloy.

EXTRUSIONS

In aircraft construction channels, angles, T-sections, Z-sections, and many other special structural shapes are required. These shapes are all obtainable in aluminum alloy by an extruding process. In this process a cylinder of aluminum alloy is heated between 750 to 850° F. and is then forced by a hydraulic ram through an aperture in a die. The aperture is the shape

FIGURE 31. EDO SEAPLANE FLOAT—ALCLAD

desired for the cross section of the finished extrusion. The extrusion is then straightened by stretching it under tension. Extruded material has performed satisfactorily but it does not have so fine a grain, nor is it so homogeneous as rolled or forged material.

Extruded shapes may be purchased in 17ST, 24ST, 53ST and 61ST material for aircraft purposes. The manufacturers have on hand a great many dies covering most of the commonly used sections. When a designer desires to use a new section, the manufacturer will make a new die for a very moderate cost and produce the necessary section. An extrusion pool has been established by a number of aircraft manufacturers and members are free to use any extrusion die in the pool.

Forgings

Aluminum alloys may be forged to close limits to provide light, strong fittings, or other structural parts. These forgings have a uniform structure and are free from blowholes, hardspots, or cavities. Only a few thousandths of an inch need be allowed for finish machining. In forging, the metal is heated to the proper forging temperature for the part in question and

FIGURE 32. WING BOX BEAM

then hammered, pressed or drop forged to shape. Pressed forgings have a fine finish and can be held to close tolerances. At present pressed forgings are available in circular shapes up to 6½ inches in diameter. At the temperatures used, the metal is not hot enough to flow easily, so tremendous power is required to form it. A higher temperature cannot be used because the metal becomes hot short and crumbly, and is ruined for future heat treatment. The power needed exceeds that used in forging steel. In laying out forgings a draft of 7° should be provided. The shrinkage allowance varies. The manufacturer should be advised of the finished dimensions desired. It is also important in forging design to avoid abrupt changes in section and to specify liberal fillets.

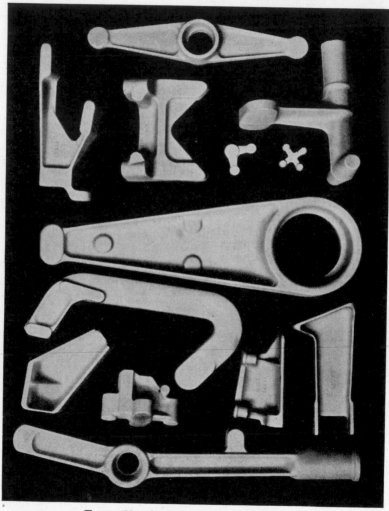

FIGURE 33.   ALUMINUM ALLOY FORGINGS

The aluminum alloys commonly used for aircraft forgings are 14ST, 17ST, 25ST, A51ST and 53ST. The most easily worked and the cheapest is A51ST but it has the lowest mechanical properties, and is used mostly for complicated engine forgings. 53ST has low mechanical properties but is very corrosion-resistant. 25ST works fairly easily and has properties similar to 17ST, which is hard to work but has somewhat better corrosion qualities. Forgings made from 25ST are used for aluminum alloy propeller blades. The highest mechanical properties are found in 14ST, and it is rapidly making a place for itself in aircraft construction in applications where high strength is required.

Because of their superior resistance to corrosion 14ST and 17ST are used in airplane structures. For engine parts A51ST and 25ST are used because the sections are heavy and frequently oily. Propellers made from 25ST have performed satisfactorily in service for years. 53ST press forgings are ideal for tank flanges which are welded in place.

Spot Welding Aluminum Alloys

Electric spot and seam welding of aluminum alloys has been generally adopted for joining non-structural and semi-structural parts. Spot welding is expected to displace riveting in many applications due to its speed, lower cost, and the elimination of projecting rivet heads. It has already been used successfully in welding fuel tanks. Another common use is the attachment of stiffeners to cowling, and in the assembly of brackets and shelves. Because of insufficient basic data on which to base strength calculations, spot welding has not yet been generally used in the fabrication of primary structural parts of airplanes.

Spot welding machines must have very accurate current, time, and pressure control. Machines in service at the present time have an amperage output of between 30,000 to 40,000 amperes and are capable of welding two $\frac{1}{8}$ inch sheets. The throat of the machine may be as great as 72 inches. All four surfaces of the material to be welded must be absolutely clean. A wire brush hooked up to an air drill is one satisfactory method of cleaning such surfaces. The brush must not be so stiff, however, that it will remove the aluminum coating from Alclad. A fine grade of abrasive cloth, or fine steel wool may also be used. A hydrofluoric acid etching solution can also be prepared for this purpose.

Alclad 17ST, Alclad 24ST, and 52S material are most satisfactory for spot welding. When resistance to corrosion is important and an extruded shape must be used, 53ST material should be selected if its physical properties are satisfactory. Anodically-treated material cannot be spot welded. For this reason 17ST and 24ST material must be spot welded first and the assembly anodically treated. Adequate protection against corrosion cannot be obtained on the faying services if this is done. For this reason Alclad material is preferred. More reliable welds are also obtained with Alclad materials.

It is possible to spot weld through wet zinc chromate primer. When maximum corrosion resistance is necessary of the faying surfaces of 17ST or 24ST they should be coated with zinc chromate primer just prior to spot welding.

Spot welds should be put in shear only, since they are relatively weak in tension. They are usually spaced apart about 8 times the minimum sheet thickness and 4 times this thickness from the edge of the sheet. For maximum efficiency three rows of welds are necessary. With this arrangement it is believed an efficiency of 70% is obtainable with Alclad sheet and 100% with 52S material. In either the soft or $\frac{1}{2}$ hard temper 52S has been used for fuel tanks.

HEAT TREATMENT

There are two types of heat treatment applicable to aluminum alloys. One is called "Solution Heat Treatment," and the other is known as "Precipitation Heat Treatment." Some alloys, such as 17S and 24S, develop their full properties as a result of Solution Heat Treatment followed by about 4 days aging at room temperature. Other alloys, such as 25S, 53S, and 61S, require both heat treatments.

Solution Heat Treatment is so named because during this treatment the alloying constituents enter into solid solution in the aluminum. It has been found that these alloying elements which increase the strength and hardness are more soluble in solid aluminum at high temperatures. After the metal is held at a high temperature for a sufficient time to complete the solution, it is quenched rapidly in cold water to retain this condition.

Precipitation Heat Treatment consists of "aging" material previously subject to Solution Heat Treatment by holding it at an elevated temperature for quite a long period of time. During this treatment a portion of the alloying constituents in solid solution precipitate out. This precipitation occurs at ordinary room temperatures in the case of 17S and 24S material. The phenomenon is known as *aging*. The precipitate is in the form of extremely fine particles which, due to their "keying" action, greatly increase the strength. The "natural aging" of 17S and 24S material at room temperatures is 90% to 98% complete after 24 hours, and fully complete after four days. 24S develops

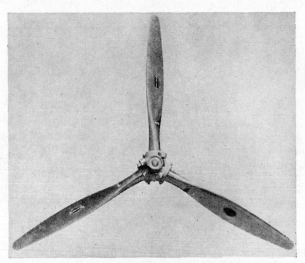

FIGURE 34. CONTROLLABLE PITCH PROPELLER
25ST Aluminum Alloy Blades

greater strength than 17S immediately after quenching, ages more rapidly, and is considerably less workable.

It has been found advisable to form aluminum alloys within one hour after Solution Heat Treatment before the aging has progressed too far. During this period the metal may be worked with ease and without danger of cracking. It has been found that the aging of 17S or 24S material may be retarded for as much as 24 hours if it is kept at or below a temperature of 32° F. Aging can be retarded for longer periods if a lower temperature is maintained. In practice, an icebox containing dry ice or a refrigerating unit is used to hold rivets or small pieces of sheet until the shop is ready to work them.

In the Solution Heat Treatment of aluminum alloys it is extremely important to hold the temperature within narrow limits. These limits are usually about 20° F. as in the case of 17S material when the heat treatment range is 930-950° F. The heat treatment range of 24S material is 910-930° F. Exceeding the upper temperature limit may cause incipient melting of the eutectic and result in serious blistering. If the temperature is too low, complete solution will not take place, and the full properties of the material may not be developed. Solution Heat Treatment is usually done in a salt bath heated by gas,

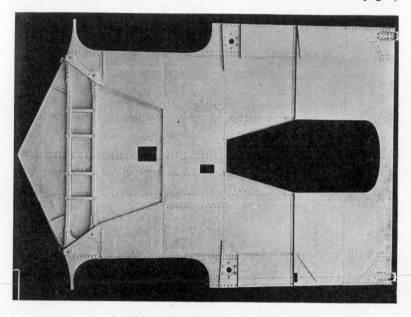

FIGURE 35. HULL BULKHEAD

oil, or electricity, or in an electric air furnace. The salt bath is composed of fused sodium nitrate, or a mixture of 50% sodium nitrate and 50% potassium nitrate. The 50-50 solution must be used if the bath is also going to be used for annealing. The most important point in connection with the furnace selected is that it must maintain an even temperature throughout its interior. All parts of the work being treated must be subjected to the same temperature. It is common practice to raise and lower the load, always keeping it submerged in the salt bath, to obtain circulation of the liquid and assure a uniform temperature. In the electric air furnace provision should be incorporated for circulating the air.

The length of time that material must be soaked at the proper temperature depends upon the nature of the material, the prior heat treatment of the material, the thickness of the material, and the type of heat treating equipment. Heavier material requires a longer soaking period. When various thicknesses are treated at one time, the soaking time necessary for the heaviest material should be used. The lighter material will not be injured by a moderately long soaking. This is not true of Alclad material which must be heated as rapidly as possible and soaked for the shortest possible time. If this is not done, the alloying elements of the base material will diffuse through the pure aluminum coating and destroy the corrosion resistance. For this reason Alclad should not be reheat treated in thicknesses up to .049 inch, and not more than twice in thicknesses up to 1/8 inch. The standard alloys can be reheat treated any number of times without affecting them.

The following tabulation gives the recommended time of soaking 17S and 24S material, but these may vary slightly for different heating equipment. Soaking time begins when the temperature of the bath or furnace has reached the minimum heat treatment temperature after inserting the load.

SALT BATH

THICKNESS OF MATERIAL	PREVIOUS CONDITION OF MATERIAL			
	17SO	17ST	24SO	24ST
Up to 1/16	15 min.	5	30	10
Over 1/16–1/8	20	5	30	15
Over 1/8–1/4	30	10	45	20
Over 1/4–1/2	45	10	60	30
Over 1/2	60	20	60	30

AIR FURNACE

Up to 1/32	20	10	30	15
Over 1/32–1/16	25	10	40	15
Over 1/16–1/8	30	15	45	20
Over 1/8–1/4	45	20	60	30
Over 1/4–1/2	60	30	90	45
Over 1/2	90	45	120	45

After soaking, the work is removed from the bath or furnace and quickly quenched in cold water. It is extremely important that not more than a few seconds elapse before quenching the hot material, or the corrosion resistance will be seriously affected. In many plants a hood is placed over the work while transferring it from the furnace to the quenching bath to prevent cooling. It is also important that the quenching bath be at a temperature below 85° F. when the hot work is immersed. The bath must be large enough to prevent the water temperature from rising above 100° F. while the work is cooling. If these conditions are met in the quenching bath, the corrosion resistance of the material will not be destroyed. It is advisable in the design of the quenching bath to provide for continuous running water and draining. This will aid in keeping the temperature of the bath low and will prevent the salting up of the bath caused by quenching material heat treated in a salt bath.

Material heat treated in salt baths must be rinsed after quenching to insure the removal of all the salt. Warm water is used for rinsing, but it must not exceed 150° F. The use of hot water for rinsing adversely affects the corrosion resistance and accelerates aging of the material. This latter point is particularly important when it is desired to work and form material immediately after heat treatment. In cases where severe forming must be done, it might be advisable to do it right after quenching, and then rinse the material later. By this means it would be possible to work the material in the period before age-hardening sets in.

Precipitation heat treatment of aluminum alloys consists in heating the material for from 12 to 18 hours at a temperature around 300° F. In practice an oven heated by steam coils or an electric furnace is used for heating.

The heat treatments required to develop the full physical properties of various types of aluminum alloys used in aircraft construction are summarized in Table 6.

TABLE 6
HEAT TREATMENT OF ALUMINUM ALLOYS

ALLOY	SOLUTION HEAT TREATMENT			PRECIPITATION HEAT TREATMENT		
	TEMPERA-TURE	QUENCH	TEMPER	TEMPERA-TURE	AGING TIME	TEMPER
17S	930–950° F.	Cold water		Room	4 days	17ST
24S	910–930° F.	Cold water		Room	4 days	24ST
25S	960–980° F.	Cold water	25SW	285–295° F.	12 hours	25ST
A51S	960–980° F.	Cold water	A51SW	315–325° F.	18 hours	A51ST
*53S	960–980° F.	Cold water	53SW	315–325° F.	18 hours	53ST
*61S	960–980° F.	Cold water	61SW	315–325° F.	18 hours	61ST

* Precipitation temperature may be 345–355° F. for 8 hours.

Heat Treatment of Aluminum Alloy Rivets. Rivets made from 17S material are very commonly used in aircraft construction. These high strength rivets may be identified by a small tit left on the head of the rivet. This identification is necessary to prevent substitution of weaker rivets made from 2S or 3S material. From the strength viewpoint it is necessary that the 17S rivets develop the full strength of the material in the 17ST temper. It is difficult in diameters over ⅛ inch to drive a 17ST rivet without cracking the head due to the hardness of the metal in this temper. But it has been found practical to heat treat 17ST rivets and then drive them within one hour before they have age-hardened. 24ST rivets age harden within 20 minutes. It is necessary either to heat treat small batches of rivets at frequent intervals to stay within the time limitation, or to keep the rivets in an icebox to retard the aging. This latter method will keep the rivets soft for 48 hours and is very generally employed in the aircraft industry.

FIGURE 36. FIN AND RUDDER
17ST Aluminum Alloy

All rivets should be anodized prior to heat treatment to prevent intergranular oxidation.

The actual heat treatment operation for rivets is similar to that described above for structural material, but the technique employed is quite different because of the small size of rivets and the large quantities that must be treated. It is customary to use a steel tube (from 1 to 2 inches in diameter) with a closed bottom and a loose fitting cap. A quantity of rivets is placed in this tube, the cap is placed on it, and the tube is immersed vertically in a salt bath. There it is held soaking at the heat treating temperature for 40 minutes. The top layer of rivets should be at least 4 inches below the surface of the salt bath, and the cap should be tight enough to exclude the entrance of cold air. The cap must be removed while the tube is still submerged and the rivets poured into the quenching bath without delay. The rivets are poured into a wire basket in the quenching bath to facilitate their removal. No rinsing of the rivets is necessary since the steel tube container protected them from contact with the salt bath. As stated above, the heat-treated rivets must be used within one hour of quenching or placed in an icebox to retard aging. Rivets may be reheat treated not more than 15 times.

In order to check the heat treatment and aging of the rivets, it is customary to check the hardness of a few rivets from each batch after they have aged for 24 hours. When subjected to a Rockwell test, using a $\frac{1}{16}$ inch ball and a 60 kilogram load, the shank of the rivet must show the following minimum hardness:

RIVET DIAMETER	ROCKWELL HARDNESS
3/32″	73
1/8″	75
5/32″	78
3/16″	82
1/4″	83

As explained in Chapter 2 under Hardness Testing this test should not be considered too reliable.

Annealing. The heat-treatable alloys may be annealed to remove the strain-hardening effects of cold working or to soften heat treated material that must be severely formed. Oftentimes the forming is too severe or will take too long to permit its being done within one hour after heat treatment, and in these cases the material must be annealed, formed, and then heat treated. Annealing of heat-treatable alloys must be carried out with great care as regards the temperature and the rate of cooling. If the temperature is too high, the material will be partially heat treated and will not attain its full softness. Under these conditions it is important to cool the material slowly to destroy as much of the heat treating effect as possible.

To anneal material which was originally in the soft state and was strain-hardened by cold working, it is only necessary to heat it to a temperature of 640 to 670° F. and cool it slowly in air. This operation would be necessary in a case where so much forming had to be done that the material would strain-harden and prevent further working before the job was done.

To anneal material in the heat-treated temper when maximum softness is not required, the method described in the previous paragraph may be used. This treatment will not remove all the effects of heat treatment, but it is usually satisfactory where only a moderate amount of forming is to be done.

To fully soften heat-treated material and remove all effects of the prior heat treatment, the material must be heated to a temperature of 790-810° F. and soaked at this temperature for two hours. It must then be cooled at a slow rate (not exceeding 50° F. per hour) until it has reached 450° F., after which it may be air-cooled. The rate of cooling is adjusted by leaving the material in the furnace and allowing the furnace to cool slowly. It is apparent that this method of annealing is costly due to the long soaking period and the tying-up of the furnace while the material is cooling. It is only necessary when severe forming is to be done. One such case is the flattening of the end of a tube. If

FIGURE 37. FUEL TANK
3S½H Aluminum Alloy

the tube is flattened so that both faces touch each other and no radius exists at the flattened edges, it is likely that these edges will crack unless the tube has been given the full annealing treatment.

17S and 24S are never installed in the airplane in the annealed condition because of their poor corrosion resistance and strength in this condition. After forming they must always be heat-treated.

It is sometimes necessary to anneal strain-hardened alloys, such as 3S and 52S, in order to complete forming operations. The method of doing this is described later in this chapter under the description of Strain-Hardened Alloys.

STRAIN-HARDENED ALLOYS

The strain-hardened alloys which are commercially available are 2S, 3S, and 52S. All of these alloys are commonly used in aircraft construction, but they are not used for primary structural purposes because their strength is not so high as other available materials. However, they are readily bent, formed, and welded and, for these reasons, are used for tanks, cowling, and fairings. In tubular form these materials are used for electrical conduit and for fuel and oil lines.

Chemical Composition

	2S	3S	52S
Aluminum (min.)	99.0%	97.0%	96.0%
Manganese		1.0–1.5	
Magnesium			2.2–2.8
Chromium			.15–.35
Copper (max.)		0.2	.07

Small amounts of impurities, particularly iron and silicon, are also present. Commercially pure aluminum (2S) has up to 1% of these impurities.

Physical Properties

	2S	3S	52S
Density (lbs./cu. in.)	.098	.099	.096
Elect. conductivity (% of copper)	58	41	40
Modulus of elasticity	10,300,000 lbs. per sq. in.		

It will be noted from Table 7 that the tensile strength, yield strength, and fatigue strength increase with the temper or hardness of the material. There is also a distinct gradation of strength between the three materials. In selecting a material it is usually preferable to choose one that will give the required strength in the softest temper. When this is done, the material that can be most easily worked is obtained.

Annealing. The strain-hardened alloys cannot be heat treated to improve their properties. Higher strengths are obtainable only by cold working. In the fabrication or forming of these materials, they will harden too much if worked severely and it is then necessary to soften them before further working. They can be softened by a simple annealing treatment which consists in heating the material to permit recrystallization. Softening due to recrystallization is practically instantaneous if the material is heated to a high enough temperature. For 2S and 52S material this temperature is 650° F., while for 3S material it is 750° F. The metal should not be heated too much above this temperature. Annealing may also be done by heating the metal for a longer period of time at a lower temperature. In either case the rate of cooling is not important, provided it is not so rapid as to cause warpage.

TABLE 7

STRAIN-HARDENED ALLOYS

TYPICAL MECHANICAL PROPERTIES

ALLOY AND TEMPER	U. T. S. lbs./sq.in.	YIELD STRENGTH lbs./sq. in.	*ELONGA-TION % in 2 in.	HARDNESS BRINELL 500 kg.–10 mm.	SHEARING STRENGTH lbs./sq. in.	FATIGUE† STRENGTH lbs./sq. in.
2SO	13,000	5,000	35	23	9,500	5,000
2S¼H	15,000	13,000	12	28	10,000	6,000
2S½H	17,000	14,000	9	32	11,000	7,000
2S¾H	20,000	17,000	6	38	12,000	8,000
2SH	24,000	21,000	5	44	13,000	8,500
3SO	16,000	6,000	30	28	11,000	7,000
3S¼H	18,000	15,000	10	35	12,000	8,000
3S½H	21,000	18,000	8	40	14,000	9,000
3S¾H	25,000	21,000	5	47	15,000	9,500
3SH	29,000	25,000	4	55	16,000	10,000
52SO	29,000	14,000	25	45	18,000	17,000
52S¼H	34,000	26,000	12	62	20,000	18,000
52S½H	37,000	29,000	10	67	21,000	19,000
52S¾H	39,000	34,000	8	74	23,000	20,000
52SH	41,000	36,000	7	85	24,000	20,500

* Elongation values are for 1/16 inch sheet. Thinner sheets have less elongation.
† Based on 500,000,000 cycles of reversed stress using R. R. Moore type of machine and specimen.

It is common shop practice to anneal strain-hardened alloys locally when they become too hard by playing a welding torch on the part to bring it up to heat and then allowing it to cool. Care must be taken not to overheat or burn the metal.

Working Properties. When the proper temper is selected, all the strain-hardened alloys can be satisfactorily worked to the desired form for their aircraft use. The easiest to form by drawing, spinning, or stamping is 2S material. Only slightly more difficult to form is 3S material, and it has better physical properties. For this reason it has superseded 2S material almost entirely in aircraft work. For spinning ring cowls 3SO or 52SO material is used. The material strain-hardens during the spinning and becomes equivalent to about 3S½H or 52S½H temper. 52S¼H is generally used for engine cowling because of its ease of forming and greater tensile and fatigue strength. Wherever its forming properties are satisfactory for the purpose 52S is rapidly displacing the other strain-hardened alloys. The high fatigue strength of this material is particularly important in reducing cowling cracks.

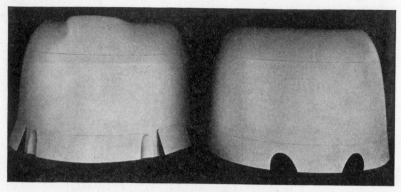

FIGURE 38. ENGINE RING COWL
Aluminum Alloy

The following table gives the bending qualities of the strain-hardened alloys. These bend radii will vary somewhat with the tools used, the particular operation, and the technique employed.

APPROXIMATE RADII FOR 90° COLD BEND

ALLOY	APPROXIMATE THICKNESS (t)				
	0.016	0.032	0.064	0.128	0.189
2SO	0	0	0	0	0
2S¼H	0	0	0	0	0–1t
2S½H	0	0	0	0	0–1t
2S¾H	0	0	0–1t	½t–1½t	1t–2t
2SH	0–1t	½t–1½t	1t–2t	1½t–3t	2t–4t
3SO	0	0	0	0	0
3S¼H	0	0	0	0	0–1t
3S½H	0	0	0	0–1t	0–1t
3S¾H	0–1t	0–1t	½t–1½t	1t–2t	1½t–3t
3SH	½t–1½t	1t–2t	1½t–3t	2t–4t	3t–5t
52SO	0	0	0	0	0
52S¼H	0	0	0	0–1t	0–1t
52S½H	0	0	0–1t	½t–1½t	1t–2t
52S¾H	0–1t	½t–1½t	1t–2t	1½t–3t	2t–4t
52SH	½t–1½t	1t–2t	1½t–3t	2t–3t	3t–5t

It is difficult to predict in advance just which material and temper will work best in a new application. It is recommended that several possible samples be obtained and worked under the actual shop conditions before a final selection is made. It must

FIGURE 39. COWLING AND FAIRING
3S½H Aluminum Alloy

be borne in mind that it is always difficult for a sheet metal worker to get the most out of a new, unfamiliar material.

Welding. The strain-hardened alloys are normally joined by gas welding in aircraft work. Electric arc welding is faster and causes less distortion, but the material must be at least $\frac{1}{16}$ inch thick. This type welding is seldom used in aircraft construction. Welding is done by either the oxyacetylene or the oxyhydrogen flame. Skilled aircraft welders can successfully weld 0.020 inch aluminum alloy with an oxyacetylene flame.

Most of the welding on strain-hardened aluminum alloys is done in the fabrication of fuel and oil tanks. These tanks are often subjected to a 15-hour vibration test after fabrication to check the design, the welds, and the quality of the material. Leaks caused by failure of welds or cracked material are cause for rejection. Seams to be welded are not butted directly together but are flanged slightly, the faces of the flanges butted together, and then the entire flange burnt down to the level of the sheet proper in the welding operation. By this method a continuous, sound, thorough weld is obtained.

A welding rod of pure aluminum, or of the same composition as the metal being welded, may be used. In aircraft welding a rod containing about 95% aluminum and 5% silicon is found to be best. Due to the formation of an oxide film on the surface, it is necessary to use a flux in welding aluminum alloys. It is sometimes necessary to weld two or more of the strain-hardened alloys together. This can be done satisfactorily if the 5% silicon welding rod is used.

After welding, the material on either side of the weld is in the annealed condition and the weld itself is a cast structure. The strength in the region of the weld is the same as the material in the soft temper. Unless the welds are ground down, they will develop greater strength than the adjoining metal. Welds can be hammered to flatten them without reducing their strength. In fact, the working should improve it somewhat.

Corrosion. 2S aluminum is highly resistant to atmospheric corrosion. The addition of various elements to aluminum to form the alloys changes the corrosion resistance characteristics.

3S is somewhat inferior to 2S material in resisting atmospheric corrosion.

52S material will resist corrosion even better than 2S. It will retain its mechanical properties better, as well as its surface appearance.

In aircraft work it is considered good practice to protect all aluminum alloys with paints. It is essential that the material be given a surface treatment first. This treatment forms an oxide on the surface, which aids in protecting the surface, and also provides an excellent base for the paint. Painting usually consists of one coat of a good primer, followed by two coats of lacquer or enamel.

When tanks are fabricated by welding, it is essential to remove all traces of the flux which is corrosive towards aluminum alloys. This flux should be removed as soon as possible after completion of the welding. It may be removed by immersing the work in a tank containing a warm 5% solution of sulphuric acid, followed by a thorough rinsing in clear, warm water, and then drying. All accessible welds should be scrubbed with a stiff bristle brush before or during the water rinse. In the case of tanks, the rinsing water should be agitated in order to clean the interior welds that are not accessible for scrubbing.

Available Shapes. From time to time as the demand arises, the aluminum alloys are made available in new forms. At present it is possible to obtain the strain-hardened aluminum alloys in the following forms:

STANDARD SHAPES—STRAIN-HARDENED ALLOYS

Shape	2S	3S	52S
Sheet	*	*	*
Plate	*	*	*
Rod and bar	*	*	*
Wire	*	*	*
Extrusions	*	*	
Tubing	*	*	*
Rivets	*	*	

Sheet is .250 inch or less in thickness; plate is over .250 inch. Sheet can only be obtained up to .162 inch thick in the ¾H temper and up to .128 inch thick in the full H temper.

Bar stock is similar to plate, but is only obtainable up to 10 inches in width.

Cold-finished rod is obtainable from ⅜ to 1½ inches in diameter. Rolled rod is obtainable up to 8 inches in diameter.

Wire can be obtained drawn anywhere from 36 gage up to ⅜ inch diameter.

Tubing can be obtained in practically all diameters and wall thicknesses.

Uses. As stated previously, strain-hardened alloys are commonly used in aircraft construction for cowling, fairings, tanks, electrical conduits, and fuel and oil lines. No one alloy excels the others for all purposes, but must be considered in connection with the particular application. The following alloys and tempers have been successfully used for the purposes described:

3S½H for welded fuel tanks, and for general engine cowling
52SO and 52S½H for cowling and fairings subject to severe vibration in service including ring cowl spinnings
2S½H tubing for electrical conduit
52SO tubing for fuel and oil lines
3SO for ring cowls and other parts that are formed by spinning

HEAT-TREATABLE ALLOYS

There are many types of heat-treatable aluminum alloys available commercially but not all of them have found an application in aircraft construction. The two most common of these alloys used in aircraft work are 17S and 24S. In addition to these 14S, 25S, and 53S are sometimes used. Alclad 17S and alclad 24S, which are special corrosion-resistant forms of 17S and 24S, are being very generally used in aircraft construction. The heat-treatable alloys are used for structural purposes because of their relatively high strength. They are available in many structural shapes and may be formed, worked, or machined readily.

Chemical Composition

	14S	17S	24S	25S
Aluminum (min.)	92.0%	92.0%	92.0%	92.0%
Manganese	.4–1.2	.4–1.0	.3–.90	.4–1.2
Magnesium	.2–.75	.2–.75	1.25–1.75	.02 max.
Chromium				
Copper (max.)	3.9–5.0	3.5–4.5	3.6–4.7	3.9–5.0
Silicon	.5–1.2			.5–1.2

	A51S	53S	61S	A17S
Aluminum (min.)	96.5%	96.0%	98.0%	
Manganese	.2 max.			
Magnesium	.45–.8	1.1–1.4	.8–1.2	.3
Chromium	.15–.35	.2–.3	.35 max.	
Copper (max.)	.3 max.	.05 max.		2.5
Silicon	.6–1,2	.5–.9	.4–.8	

Small amounts of iron, zinc and other impurities are also present.

Physical Properties

	14S	17S	24S	25S
Weight (lbs./cu. in.)	.101	.101	.100	.101

	A51S	53S	61S	A17S
Weight (lbs./cu. in.)	.097	.097	.098	.099

Modulus of elasticity—10,300,000 lbs. per sq. in.

Table 8 lists the mechanical properties of the heat-treatable alloys used in aircraft construction. It is recommended that this table be used only for reference purposes and ANC-5 or the manufacture of the material be consulted when a design must be based on the allowable strength. Manufacturers of materials will always furnish a minimum guaranteed strength for material in the form it is to be used.

TABLE 8

HEAT-TREATABLE ALLOYS

TYPICAL MECHANICAL PROPERTIES

ALLOY AND TEMPER	U. T. S. lbs./sq.in.	YIELD STRENGTH lbs./sq.in.	ELONGA-TION % in 2in.	HARDNESS BRINELL 500 kg.– 10 mm.	SHEARING STRENGTH lbs./sq.in.	FATIGUE STRENGTH
14ST........	65,000	50,000	10	130	45,000	16,000
17SO........	26,000	10,000	20	45	18,000	11,000
17ST........	62,000	40,000	20	100	36,000	15,000
17SRT......	62,000	46,000	13	110	36,000	
Alclad 17ST.	56,000	33,000	18	...	32,000	
Alclad 17SRT	57,000	40,000	11	...	32,000	
24SO........	26,000	10,000	20	42	18,000	12,000
24ST........	68,000	45,000	20	105	41,000	18,000
24SRT......	70,000	55,000	13	116	42,000	
Alclad 24ST.	62,000	41,000	18	...	40,000	
Alclad 24SRT	66,000	50,000	11	...	41,000	
25SO........	26,000	10,000	20	45	18,000	9,000
25SW.......	48,000	25,000	18	80	30,000	14,500
25ST.......	58,000	35,000	20	100	35,000	15,000
A51ST......	43,000	34,000	12	90		
53SO........	16,000	7,000	25	26	11,000	7,500
53SW.......	33,000	20,000	22	65	20,000	10,000
53ST........	39,000	33,000	14	80	24,000	11,000
61SO.......	18,000	8,000	22	30	12,500	8,000
61SW.......	35,000	21,000	22	65	24,000	12,500
61ST.......	45,000	39,000	12	95	30,000	12,500
61S-T8.....	50,000	47,000	10	98	32,000	.....

Heat Treatment. As the name implies, the heat-treatable alloys can be heat treated to improve their physical properties.

In aircraft work they are used only in the fully heat-treated state. As explained earlier in this chapter, the material is sometimes annealed to improve its forming qualities, but it is always heat treated after forming.

The structure of many airplanes built nowadays consists of both 17S and 24S material. In heat treating these materials it is advisable that they be done separately since their heat-treating

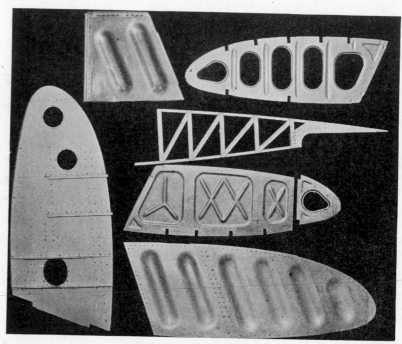

FIGURE 40. WING RIBS

temperatures are different. The temperature for 17S material is 930-950° F.; for 24S material it is 910-930° F. It is possible to heat treat 17ST as low as 900° F. without decreasing the tensile or yield strength more than 5-6%. Government specifications do not permit heat treatment of 17S below 930° F., however. If 24S material was treated above 930° F., it would blister because of overheating. The fabricating shop should definitely identify the type of aluminum alloy when it is sent to the heat-treating shop so that no costly errors are made.

Working Properties. These alloys can be formed to any structural shape used in aircraft construction, or they can be bent, drawn, or rolled as necessary provided the proper temper is selected. For severe forming operations requiring over 20 minutes for completion, it is necessary to use the material in the "SO" temper. If the forming operation can be completed quickly, it is customary to heat treat the work and form it within one hour before it has aged. The first 20 minutes of this hour is by far the best time to form the material. By this method heat treatment of the completed work is avoided. When work has been formed in the annealed state and then heat treated, it will distort badly. It must be straightened out before it can be used. The distortion is caused by the severe cold water quench.

Heat treatable alloys 17S or 24S, either in their standard or Alclad forms, are most commonly used in aircraft construction. The latter, 24S, is slightly more difficult to form than 17S, but it is rapidly superseding 17S because of its higher yield point. The following table gives the bend radii for various thicknesses and tempers of aluminum alloys and is a good criterion for relative forming properties.

APPROXIMATE RADII FOR 90° COLD BEND

APPROXIMATE THICKNESS (t)

Alloy	0.016	0.032	0.064	0.128	0.189
17SO......	0	0	0	0	0–1t
17ST......	1t–2t	1½t–3t	2t–4t	3t–5t	4t–6t
17SRT....	1½t–3t	2t–4t	3t–5t	4t–6t	4t–6t
24SO......	0	0	0	0	0 1t
24ST......	1½t–3t	2t–4t	3t–5t	4t–6t	4t–6t
24SRT....	2t 4t	3t–5t	3t–5t	4t–6t	5t–7t
53SO......	0	0	0	0	0
53SW.....	0–1t	¼t–1¼t	1t–2t	1¼t–3t	2t–4t
53ST......	½t–1¼t	1t–2t	1¼t–3t	2t–4t	3t–5t
61SO......	0	0	0	0	0–1t
61SW.....	0–1t	0–1t	½t–1½t	1t–2t	1½t–3t
61ST......	0–1t	½t–1½t	1t–2t	1½t–3t	2t–4t

Alclad 17S and Alclad 24S can be bent over slightly smaller radii than the corresponding tempers of the standard alloy.

Radii given for 17ST and 24ST are for the fully aged condition. Much smaller radii can be used if formed immediately after quenching.

The heat-treatable alloys machine beautifully.

Welding. The heat-treatable alloys cannot be welded with the oxyacetylene torch without destroying their mechanical properties. Even if subsequently heat treated after welding, the original mechanical properties cannot be restored. These alloys are difficult to weld in any event and are generally considered unweldable for aircraft purposes.

FIGURE 41. WING TIP FLOAT AND BRACING
17ST Aluminum Alloy—Sheet and Tubing

Prior to the introduction of electric spot welding these alloys were joined only by riveting or bolting. As described earlier in this chapter, electric spot welding is rapidly displacing riveting for nonstructural parts and will be extended to structural parts when more basic data on strength and performance is available.

Riveting. Aluminum alloy rivets for structural parts may be grouped in two classifications: those requiring heat treatment just before driving, and those that can be driven as received. Heat treatment is required by 17S and 24S rivets, whereas A17ST, 53SO, 53SW, and 53ST rivets can be driven as received.

On extremely important work where every pound of rivet strength is necessary 17S and 24S rivets are used. Because of their better heading qualities 17S rivets are used more often even in 24S structural assemblies. While 17S rivets can be driven within one hour of heat treatment, 24S rivets must be driven within 20 minutes of treatment. The aging of both these types of rivets can be retarded by storing in an icebox. The 17S rivets are identified by a small raised tit in the center of the head; 24S rivets have two small radial dashes at the ends of a diameter on the periphery of the head.

A17ST rivets do not have so good strength as 17S or 24S rivets, but are very generally used even in structural assemblies, such as metal covered wings and fuselages. They are particularly good for field repairs since no heat treatment is necessary. The A17ST rivets have a small dimple at the center of the head. From an appearance standpoint 53S rivets of the appropriate temper are best for riveting 52S or Alclad material. Electrolytic corrosion will not attack these metals adjacent to 53S rivet heads even when unpainted.

The strength properties of these various rivets are as follows:

	17ST	24ST	A17ST	53S	53SW	53ST
U. T. S. (lbs./sq. in.)	55,000	62,000	38,000	18,000	25,000	35,000
Yield Str. "	30,000	40,000	18,000	15,000	14,000	28,000
Shear Str. "	30,000	35,000	25,000	12,000	18,000	22,000
Bearing Str. "	75,000	90,000	60,000	30,000	48,000	60,000

Corrosion. Alclad material should be used whenever severe corrosion conditions must be met in service. 53S material has excellent corrosion resistance being comparable to pure aluminum, but its mechanical properties are not so high as the other heat-treatable alloys. Consequently it is not practical to use 53S if great strength is a primary requisite. 61S material also has excellent corrosion resistance and is considerably stronger than 53S. The other heat-treatable alloys have about equal corrosion resistance, except 25S which is somewhat inferior. The heat-treatable alloys do not have so good corrosion resistance as the strain-hardened alloys.

It is standard practice in aircraft designed to operate under severe corrosive conditions to anodically treat aluminum alloys and then to apply one coat of primer and two coats of paint. Oftentimes joints and fittings, subject to corrosive conditions, are also coated with hot beeswax or paralketone as an added protection.

17ST and 24ST are much more corrosion resistant than 17SO and 24SO. If these alloys are heated above the boiling point of

water their corrosion resistance is also lowered. Heating has
the same effect on the alloys that require precipitation heat
treatment, and for this reason these alloys in the ST temper are
inferior to the SW temper. However, 53ST is only slightly inferior to 53SW. Baked enamel finishes are not recommended for
aluminum alloys, because it is questionable whether the added
paint protection is equivalent to the basic corrosion resistance
that is lost due to the baking temperature.

53S and 61S material have good corrosion resistance in all
tempers.

FIGURE 42. WING ASSEMBLY

Available Shapes. The alloys most often used in aircraft
construction, 17S and 24S, may be obtained in practically all
standard forms. As explained in the paragraph on Extrusions,
the designer may even specify the shape he wants and the
manufacturer will supply it. Some of the other alloys are only
available as forgings. The following summarizes the standard
commercial forms:

STANDARD SHAPES—HEAT-TREATABLE ALLOYS

Shape	14S	17S	Alclad 17S	24S	Alclad 24S	25S	A51S	53S	61S	A17S
Sheet.......		*	*	*	*			*	*	
Plate.......		*	*	*	*			*	*	
Rod and bar.		*		*				*		
Wire........		*	*	*	*			*		
Extrusions...		*		*				*	*	
Tubing......		*		*				*	*	
Rivets......		*		*				*		*
Forgings....	*	*				*	*	*		
Rolled shapes		*						*		

Sheet used in aircraft work usually falls between .014 and .120 inch in thickness. It is usually purchased in seven basic standard sizes as follows: 0.020″ × 36″ × 144″, 0.025″ × 36″ × 144″, 0.032″ × 36″ × 144″, 0.032″ × 48″ × 144″, 0.040″ × 48″ × 144″, 0.051″ × 48″ × 144″, 0.064″ × 48″ × 144″.

Annealed temper coiled strip is available at a considerable price saving compared to flat sheet.

Plate is purchased in much smaller pieces, usually 1 × 2 feet, since it is used for fabricating small fittings.

Rod can be obtained up to 8 inches diameter.

Bar can be rolled to a maximum cross-sectional size of 3 × 10 inches. Bar 10 inches wide is often used in place of plate for fittings.

Tubing is available in many round and streamline sizes. A table of standard tubing sizes used in aircraft construction is given in the Appendix.

Square tubing is also available and is often used.

Uses. The heat-treatable alloys are used for practically all structural purposes in aircraft. They are used only in the heat-treated temper but they are often formed in the annealed temper and then heat treated.

17ST in sheet form is used for covering monocoque fuselages and metal covered wings. It is also used for fabricating bulkheads, ribs, gussets, and brackets. 17ST plate is used for block fittings which are often used in conjunction with monocoque construction. 17ST extrusions are used for stringers, bulkhead reinforcements, and similar strength members. 17ST tubing is used for brace struts, control operating mechanism, and reinforcements. 17ST rivets are standard.

24ST is rapidly displacing 17ST because of its greater strength. It is somewhat more difficult to work, however, and for this reason there may be some applications where 17ST will be retained. 24ST is particularly good for wing beams where its high yield strength is important. 24ST extrusions, therefore, are also very popular. 24ST is also used for engine cowl panels. These panels are sometimes found in the SO state and then heat-treated.

Alclad 17ST and Alclad 24ST are often substituted for 17ST or 24ST sheet when corrosion is important. This is particularly true in covering seaplane floats and hulls. Alclad 17SRT or Alclad 24SRT can be used to advantage when no forming is necessary.

25ST forgings are used for propeller blades.

A51ST forgings are used for complicated engine parts and for aircraft fittings where the mechanical properties of this alloy are adequate for the purpose.

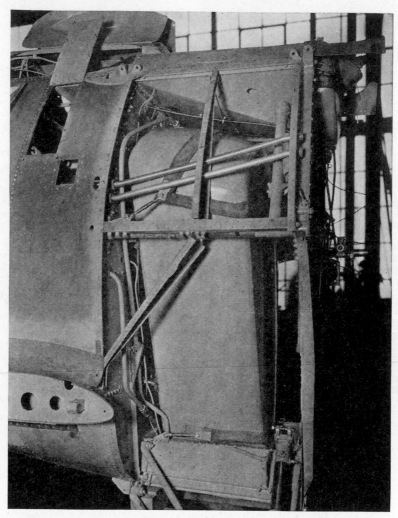

FIGURE 43.   FORWARD END OF MONOCOQUE FUSELAGE SHOWING TANK INSTALLATION—ALUMINUM ALLOY

14ST is finding a place in aircraft construction due to its excessively high yield point.   When long lengths are required they can be hand forged.

TABLE 9

ALUMINUM ALLOY SPECIFICATIONS—WROUGHT

Alloy Designation	Shape	Navy Specification	Army Specification	Federal Specification
2S..........	Bar	46A3	QQ–A–411	QQ–A–411
	Sheet	47A2	57–151–1	QQ–A–561
	Tubing	44T19	WW–T–783	WW–T–783
3S..........	Bar	46A6	QQ–A–356	QQ–A–356
	Sheet	47A4	QQ–A–359	QQ–A–359
	Tubing	44T20	WW–T–788	WW–T–788
14S........	Forgings	46A7	QQ–A–367	QQ–A–367
17S........	Bar	46A4	QQ–A–351	QQ–A–351
	Sheet	47A3	QQ–A–353	QQ–A–353
	Tubing—ropnd	44T21	WW–T–786	WW–T–786
	Tubing—streamline	44T22	57–187–2	....
	Forgings	46A7	QQ–A–367	QQ–A–367
Alclad 17S...	Sheet	47A6	57–152–2	QQ–A–361
24S........	Bar	46A9	QQ–A–354	QQ–A–354
	Sheet	47A10	QQ–A–355	QQ–A–355
	Tubing—round	44T28	10235	....
	Tubing—streamline	44T31	57–187–2	....
Alclad 24S...	Sheet	47A8	11067	QQ–A–362
25S........	Forgings	46A7	QQ–A–367	QQ–A–367
A51S.......	Forgings	46A7	QQ–A–367	QQ–A–367
52S........	Bar	46A11	....	....
	Sheet	47A11	QQ–A–318	QQ A–318
	Tubing	44T32	57–187–3	....
53S........	Bar	46A10	QQ–A–331	QQ–A–331
	Sheet	47A12	QQ–A–334	QQ–A–334
	Tubing	44T30	....	WW–T–790
61S........	Sheet	......	....	QQ–A–327
	Tubing	......	....	WW T–789

53S material is used when corrosion resistance is of primary importance.

61S is a relatively new material with good strength and excellent forming characteristics. It is rapidly finding favor for stamped and pressed sheet metal parts. It should be fabricated in the ST condition wherever possible to avoid the necessity for artificially aging the material from the SW temper.

CHAPTER XII

ALUMINUM ALLOY CASTINGS

Aluminum alloy castings are frequently used in aircraft construction. As is the case with all castings their mechanical properties, shock resistance, and ductility are inferior to those obtainable with wrought alloys. When used in aircraft, it is a general rule that the casting must have a 100% margin of strength. It is also necessary to break down one typical casting of a given design under load to establish its strength. It is common practice in the aircraft industry to furnish the foundry with drawings that show the intensity, direction, and point of application of the principal loads on the casting. The casting technique is then adjusted to obtain the optimum strength. In the production of important castings it is customary to have the manufacturer X-ray sufficient castings to ascertain if there are any interior flaws. With these precautions, plus intelligent design, it is possible to use castings for many aircraft applications. Castings are particularly useful when the part is so complicated that an excessive amount of machining would be necessary to fashion it from bar stock. Another important application occurs on experimental planes when only a limited number of parts are required. In production these parts can be redesigned to obtain the greater strength and ductility of a forging. For limited production a casting is much cheaper than a forging.

There are a large number of casting alloys with varying properties available for use. In selecting the alloy to be used, it is necessary to bear in mind the primary service requirement which may be any one of the following: strength and ductility, strength at elevated temperatures, pressure tightness, corrosion resistance, ease of casting due to complicated shape, low cost.

There are three ways of casting aluminum alloys: (1) sand casting, (2) permanent mold casting, and (3) die casting. *Sand casting* is the most common and is used for complicated shapes or where only a few parts are required. *Permanent mold casting* is similar to sand casting, but a metal mold is used which permits the making of many parts with better accuracy than sand casting. *Die casting* is used when many small parts must be made and held to close tolerances.

The chemical composition of the aluminum alloy casting materials that have found applications in aircraft construction are given below:

ALLOY	COPPER	IRON	SILICON	MAGNESIUM	NICKEL	ZINC
13			12.0			
43			5.0			
85	4.0		5.0			
122	10.0	1.2		0.2		
A132	0.8	0.8	12.0	1.0	2.5	
142	4.0			1.2	2.0	
195	4.0					
B195	4.5		2.8			
214				3.75		
A214				3.75		2.0
220				10.0		
355	1.25		5.0	0.5		
356			7.0	0.3		

Per cent of alloying elements is given in above table. Aluminum and impurities constitute remainder.

Some of the above alloys are used both for sand and permanent mold casting. Others are used for only one type of casting, being developed especially for that purpose. Each type of casting will be described in detail and the physical properties obtainable with the different alloys tabulated. These values will vary with the type of casting even though the same alloy is used.

Heat-Treated Castings. Casting alloys have been developed which when heat-treated possess superior mechanical properties as compared to castings which are not susceptible to heat treatment. Both types of castings are included in the preceding tabulation. For some purposes the common unheat-treated castings are more suitable than the higher strength heat-treated castings.

There are several patented heat treatments applicable to heat-treatable castings. Starting with the same basic material the mechanical properties are altered in different ways by the various heat treatments. The resulting product is denoted by adding a "T" and a number which designates the particular treatment to which it was subjected. Thus, 195-T4 and 195-T6 have quite different physical properties. Alloy No. 195 was given a "T4" heat treatment in one case and a "T6" heat treatment in the other.

Alloy No. 195-T4 heat treatment consists of soaking in an electric air furnace for 12 hours at 941-977° F. A constant temperature of 970° F. is desirable. The part is then quenched in water above 125° F. If the casting is intricate or has abrupt changes in section the quenching water should be between 200-212° F. The final operation is the aging of the quenched casting for 2 hours in boiling water.

SAND CASTING

Sand casting of aluminum alloys is the method most frequently resorted to in obtaining castings for aircraft construction. The quantity of castings required is usually fairly small and would not warrant the manufacture of a permanent metal mold or die. The wooden patterns used for sand casting will stand up under the manufacture of several hundred castings unless they are abused or the casting is of unusual shape. Patterns made of white metal are sometimes substituted for wood. If more than several hundred castings are to be made, the unit cost of making a second pattern will be very small.

FIGURE 44. SAND CAST CYLINDER HEAD
Aluminum Alloy

It is advisable to let the casting manufacturer also make the pattern from the designer's blueprint. When this is done there can be no question about obtaining the proper shrinkage and machining allowance. The shrinkage allowance for aluminum alloy sand castings is ⁵⁄₃₂ inch per foot. If a machine finish is desired, ¹⁄₁₆ inch should be allowed for machining, particularly on the upper surface of the casting where the impurities collect.

Aluminum alloy sand castings cannot be manufactured with a wall thickness of less than ⅛ inch. There is practically no limit to the size or core complexity of castings made by this method.

The following table gives the mechanical properties of sand cast aluminum alloys used in aircraft construction:

SAND CAST ALUMINUM ALLOYS

ALLOY	U. T. S. lbs./sq. in.	ELONGATION %	HARDNESS BRINELL	DENSITY lbs./cu. in.
43	19,000	4.0	40	0.096
195–T4 *	31,000	8.0	65	0.100
195–T6	36,000	4.0	80	0.100
214	25,000	9.0	50	0.095
220–T4*	45,000	14.0	75	0.092
355–T6	35,000	3.5	80	0.097
356–T4*	28,000	6.0	55	0.095

* Alloy No. T4 will very nearly attain the properties of T6 if allowed to age at normal temperatures for six months.

Applications. Alloy No. 43 remains fluid down almost to the solidification point and for this reason can be used for complicated castings and thin-walled castings. It also makes a dense, leak-proof casting with good corrosion resistance. It has been used for carburetors, hot air scoops, fuel line fittings, and fuel and oil tank flanges. In this latter application it can be readily welded to the sheet metal of the tank.

Alloy No. 105-T4 is largely used for structural aircraft castings. It has good strength and maximum shock resistance. It does not cast as well as No. 43 nor have as good corrosion resistance but it machines much better and has considerably greater strength.

Alloy No. 195-T6 is somewhat stronger than 195-T4 but has less elongation and shock resistance.

Alloy No. 214 has maximum corrosion resistance. It is difficult to cast into intricate, leak-proof castings.

Alloy No. 220-T4 has high tensile and yield strength as well as good impact and elongation values. It has good corrosion resistance and machines well. It is not pressure tight, requires special foundry technique, and uniform sections at least ¼-inch thick are desirable because of high solidification shrinkage.

Alloy No. 355-T6 has excellent casting qualities and retains its strength well at temperatures up to 400° F. Its leak-proof and heat-resisting qualities have been utilized in the manufacture of water-cooled cylinder heads for engines.

Alloy No. 356-T4 can be substituted for 195-T4 when the casting is complicated. To some extent aging alone will improve the properties of this alloy without heat treatment. This fact is utilized in intricate castings that cannot withstand quenching stresses.

PERMANENT MOLD CASTINGS

Permanent mold casting is similar to sand casting except for the use of a metal mold. The manufacture of this mold is relatively expensive and is only justified when a large number of castings are required. Castings with complicated cores cannot be manufactured in metal molds. Sometimes cores are fabricated of sand in the metal mold. This process is called semi-permanent mold casting. It utilizes the advantages of both sand and mold casting.

In mold casting the molten metal is fed into the mold by gravity. The mold is hot but chills the molten metal as it comes in contact with it. Chilling results in more rapid solidification and a finer grain. This finer grain makes permanent mold castings more susceptible to heat treatment, and improves their corrosion resistance and physical properties.

Due to the metal mold a fairly smooth finish is obtained on the casting. If a machined finish is desired, it is only necessary to allow about $\frac{1}{32}$ inch for machining. Permanent mold castings can be produced with a wall thickness of $\frac{3}{32}$ inch. It is possible to hold overall dimensions to a tolerance of ± 0.01 inch.

The mechanical properties of several commonly used permanent mold casting alloys are as follows:

PERMANENT MOLD CAST ALUMINUM ALLOYS

ALLOY	U. T. S. lbs./sq. in.	ELONGATION %	HARDNESS BRINELL	DENSITY lbs./cu. in.
43	21,000	2.5	45–55	0.097
122–T65	40,000	...	125–150	0.104
A132–T4	34,000	1.0	90–120	0.097
142–T61	40,000	...	100–130	0.100
B195–T4	33,000	4.5	70–90	0.101
A214	21,000	2.5	50–65	0.096
355–T6	37,000	1.5	90	0.097
356–T4	28,000	5.0	60	0.095

There are also several other heat treatments which give different properties than those listed for Alloys Nos. 122, A132, 142, B195, 355 and 356.

Applications. Alloy No. 43 when cast in a permanent mold will have a better finish and can be held to closer dimensional tolerances than when sand cast. The cost of machining can thus be saved for some applications.

Alloys Nos. 122, A132, and 142 have been used for engine pistons. A132, in particular, has a very low coefficient of expansion and the lowest weight, both of which are important considerations for this use. These alloys have also been used for brake shoes and bearing caps. 142 is also used for cylinder heads of aircraft engines.

Alloy No. A214 has the same nontarnishing property as the sand casting alloy 214.

It should be noted that the permanent mold alloys have slightly higher strengths than the equivalent sand casting alloy. Due to the difficulties involved in permanent mold casting, it is advisable to consult with the manufacturer before definitely selecting an alloy.

Die Casting

Die casting consists in forcing molten metal under pressure into water-cooled dies. The pressure imposed and the chilling of the molten metal results in a homogeneous, fine-grained casting. The castings have an excellent finish and may be held to very accurate dimensions. A section tolerance of ± 0.0025 inch can be held. It is also possible to produce sections as thin as 0.030 to 0.040 inch but $\frac{1}{16}$ inch is preferred. Because of the dimensional accuracy and fine finish little machining is necessary. Even holes are cored to size ready for reaming or tapping.

Only small parts required in large quantities are die cast due to the high cost of the dies. There are many limitations to the process, so that it is almost mandatory to discuss the problem with the die caster before laying out the job or selecting the alloy. The casting properties of the alloy are sometimes more important than the mechanical properties. Two of the most commonly used die casting alloys are Nos. 13 and 85.

Die Casting Aluminum Alloys

ALLOY	U. T. S. lbs./sq. in.	ELONGATION %	HARDNESS BRINELL	DENSITY lbs./cu. in.
13	33,000	1.8	80	0.095
85	35,000	3.0	70	0.100

These alloys are used extensively for aircraft accessories. Alloy No. 13 has good corrosion resistance and excellent casting properties. Alloy No. 85 presents the best combination of strength and ductility.

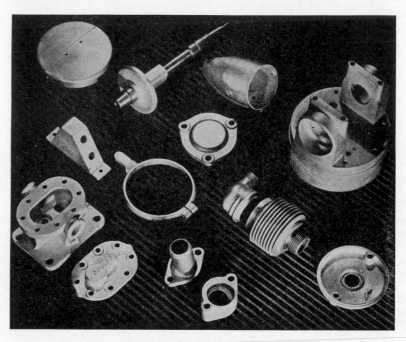

FIGURE 45.　ALUMINUM ALLOY DIE CASTINGS

DESIGN OF CASTINGS

The following precautions should be taken in the design of all castings:

　1. High stress concentrations should be avoided.
　2. Reëntrant angles between surfaces with pockets and corners where porosity or cracks may develop due to shrinkage and air bubbles should be avoided.
　3. Slender cantilever lugs, sharp corners, and abrupt changes in section should be avoided. Generous filleting is very important.
　4. Eccentricities should be avoided.
　5. Allow a reasonable margin between the design stress and the elastic limit of the casting. A 100% margin on the ultimate tensile strength is a good method of obtaining this margin.

Castings should not be used for the following purposes:

1. Main structural fittings whose failure would endanger the airplane.

2. Lugs attached to struts and wires exposed to the air stream, or to parts subject to vibration, such as the engine mount.

3. Castings should not be used to take moderately high bending stresses.

4. Castings should not be used with lugs which may be subject to accidental bending stresses during assembly, disassembly, alignment, or ground handling. Many casting failures have occurred due to cracks started by careless mechanics performing one of these operations and imposing bending on lugs designed to take tension.

5. Castings should not be used for fittings subject to reversal of loads of high magnitude.

TABLE 10

ALUMINUM ALLOY SPECIFICATIONS—CASTINGS

ALLOY DESIGNATION	DESCRIPTION	AN AERO SPECIFICATION
	Alum. alloy; castings, general................	AN–QQ–A–364
43	" " (5% Si); sand castings............	AN–QQ–A–405
195	" " (Al–195); sand castings..........	AN–QQ–A–390
B195	" " (Al–B195); permanent mold castings	AN–QQ–A–383
220	" " (Al–220); sand castings.........	AN–QQ–A–392
355	" " (Al–355); permanent mold and sand castings.....................	AN–QQ–A–376
356	" " (Al–356); sand castings..........	AN–QQ–A–394
	" " (4% Cu–3% Si); sand castings.....	AN–QQ–A–397
	" " (Cu Ni Mg); permanent mold and sand castings...................	AN–QQ–A–379
	" " (8% Cu–1% Si); sand castings.....	AN–QQ–A–399
	" " (4% Mg.); sand castings..........	AN–QQ–A–402
	" " (Si–Ni–Cu–Mg); permanent mold castings......................	AN–QQ–A–386

CHAPTER XIII

MAGNESIUM ALLOYS

GENERAL CHARACTERISTICS

Magnesium is the lightest of the structural metals available for aircraft construction. Pure magnesium weighs only 65% as much as aluminum. In the pure state magnesium is relatively soft and does not have the strength or other properties to make it fit for structural use. Fortunately it alloys readily with aluminum, manganese, zinc, tin, copper, and cadmium to form a variety of structural alloys. These alloys weigh approximately two-thirds as much as the aluminum alloys. They can be sand or die cast, and are available in the form of rods, bars, plate, tubing, sheet, extrusions, and structural shapes.

Magnesium alloys have an excellent strength/weight ratio, machine easily, weld readily, and can be manufactured from brine and ores found in abundance in this country. These alloys have poor corrosion resistance in salty atmospheres, and can be bent, bumped, and formed only with difficulty. They can be cast, forged, and extruded in many shapes, however.

Magnesium alloy castings are used for aircraft engine parts, for landing wheels, and miscellaneous other uses. Forged propeller blades of magnesium alloy have also been manufactured. At the present time these alloys are only being used for secondary purposes in aircraft construction—for seats, shelves, flooring, boxes, bracket, and so on. When designers and shop personnel become more accustomed to handling them, it is believed they will be used more generally. Service reports on magnesium alloy parts now installed in airplanes will determine to what extent they will be adopted for general structural use.

Magnesium is obtained by the electrolysis of molten magnesium chloride. The pure magnesium collects at the cathode. This process has been perfected so that large quantities of magnesium are available at reasonable prices.

Many of the magnesium alloys manufactured in this country are produced by the Dow Chemical Company and have been given the trade name of Dowmetal alloys. To distinguish between the alloys each is assigned a letter. Thus we have—Dowmetal J, Dowmetal M, and so forth. There are a number of Dowmetal alloys suitable for aircraft work. Another large manufacturer of magnesium alloys is the American Magnesium Corporation which is a subsidiary of the Aluminum Company of America. The magnesium alloys manufactured by this company are designated in the same manner as aluminum alloys. Thus we have 265 which represents a casting alloy, and 3S, 57S, etc., which represent wrought alloys.

Chemical Composition. The chemical composition of the magnesium alloys that are used in aircraft construction are given in Table 11.

TABLE 11

MAGNESIUM ALLOYS—CHEMICAL COMPOSITION

ALLOY			ALU-MINUM	MAN-GANESE	ZINC	SILI-CON	IRON	NICKEL	MAG-NESIUM
No.	Amer. Mg.	Dow Chem.							
4	265	H	6.0	0.2	3.0				
8	57S	J–1	6.5	0.2	0.7		0.005max.	0.005max.	Remainder
9	58S	O.1	8.5	0.2	0.5		0.005max.	0.005max.	
11	3S	M		1.5					
12	230	K	10.0	0.1		0.5			
13	263	R	9.0	0.2	0.6				
15	74S	X–1	3.0	0.2	3.0		0.005max.	0.005max.	
17	260	C	9.0	0.1	2.0				

Nickel, iron, copper, silicon, and impurities are held to small maximum percentages in nearly all of these alloys.

Physical Properties. The mechanical properties of magnesium alloy castings and wrought material are given in Table 12. The properties listed in the table are for the most part conservative. Most of the alloys can be obtained with tensile and yield strength several thousand pounds above those listed. It is recommended that manufacturers be consulted as to the values they will guarantee before proceeding too far with design work. In this way the designer can take advantage of the latest developments.

TABLE 12

MAGNESIUM ALLOYS—PHYSICAL PROPERTIES

Form	Navy Spec	Navy No.	Army Grade	Army Spec	Amer. Mg.	Dow Chem.	U.T.S.	Yield	Shear Str.	Fatigue*	Condition	General Use
Castings	M-112	4		57-74-1C	265	H	24,000	10,000	17,000	10,000	As cast	General casting use, particularly stressed parts
							30,000	10,000	18,000	10,000	Solution ht-tr.	
	M-112	17			260	C	32,000	16,000	19,000	9,000	Solution ht-tr., aged	Pressure tight castings
							20,000	10,000	18,000	10,000	As cast	
	M-112	11	2	57-74-1C	403	M	30,000	10,000	20,000	10,000	Solution ht-tr., aged	Weldable and resistant to salt water
							32,000	18,000	22,000	10,000	As cast	
							12,000	4,000	11,000		As cast	
Die castings	M-369	12	1	11,319	230	K	30,000	22,000			As cast	Thin section die castings
	M-369	13	1	11,319	263	R	33,000	20,000			As cast	General die castings
Extruded bars and rods	M-314	8	1	11,320	57S	J-1	40,000	26,000	20,000	17,000	As extruded	High strength extrusions
	M-314	8	1	11,320	57S	J-1	40,000	26,000		15,000	Extruded, stretched	
	M-314	11	2	11,320	3S	M	32,000	20,000		10,000	As extruded	Good salt water resistance, weldable
	M-314	15	1	11,320	74S	X-1	39,000	26,000		18,000	As extruded	Heat-treatable bar
	M-314	15a	1	11,320	74S	X-1	41,000	30,000		17,000	" " , aged	
Extruded shapes	M-314	8	1	11,320	57S	J-1	38,000	23,000			As extruded	High strength extrusions
	M-314	11	2	11,320	3S	M	32,000	17,000			" "	Good salt water resistance, weldable
	M-314	15	1	11,320	74S	X-1	39,000	22,000			" "	Heat-treatable shapes
	M-314	15a	1	11,320	74S	X-1	40,000	25,000			" " , aged	
Extruded tubing	M-366	8	1	11,318	57S	J-1	36,000	17,000			As extruded	Moderate strength parts, weldable, corrosion-resistant
	M-366	11	2	11,318	3S	M	32,000	17,000			" "	Lightly stressed parts, weldable, corrosion-resistant
	M-366	15	1	11,318	74S	X-1	36,000	17,000			" "	Heat-treatable tubing; good strength, thin-walled tubing
	M-366	15a			74S	X-1	37,000	19,000			" " , aged	
Press forgings	M-126	8		11,321	57S	J-1	38,000	22,000	21,000	15,000	As forged	Moderate strength press-forgings. Simple forgings, high strength
	M-126	9			58S	O-1	42,000	24,000	22,000	16,000	" "	Welded forgings. Can be hammer-forged
	M-126	11			3S	M	29,000	12,000			" "	
	M-126	15			74S	X-1	38,000	20,000		12,000	" "	Heat-treatable. Press-forges nicely.
	M-126	15a			74S	X-1	38,000	22,000		12,000	" " , aged	
Sheet	M-111	11	1	11,317	3SH	Mh	32,000	24,000	12,000	8,000	Hard rolled	Moderate strength, weldable, resistant to salt water corrosion.
	M-111	11	1	11,317	3SO	Ma	35,000 max.				Annealed	

The fatigue endurance limits listed in the tables may be compared directly with those for aluminum alloys given in the chapters on Wrought Aluminum Alloys and Aluminum Alloy Castings. Both sets of values were obtained on the R. R. Moore type of machine based on 500,000,000 cycles of completely reversed stress.

Physical properties of the magnesium alloys are:

Weight (lb./cu. in.) —0.064 to 0.066
Modulus of elasticity—6,250,000 to 6,500,000 lb./sq. in.
Melting Point   —1100° F. to 1200° F.

Pure magnesium has the following properties:

	EXTRUSIONS	AS ROLLED
Ultimate tensile strength (lb./sq. in.).......	28,000	25,000
Elongation (%).........................	8	4
Brinell hardness........................	35	40
Specific gravity........................	1.74	1.74

Heat Treatment. Magnesium alloy castings respond to heat treatment but wrought material reacts only slightly. Wrought material is fabricated hot and develops mechanical properties which can be only slightly improved by heat treatment. Wrought alloys can be heated to facilitate working without destroying the physical properties.

The heat treatment of magnesium alloys is similar to the treatment of aluminum alloys. There are two types of heat treatment—*solution heat treatment* and *precipitation* (aging) *heat treatment.* The natural aging of magnesium alloys at room temperature produces a negligible change in the properties of the metal. Artificial aging by precipitation heat treatment is necessary to develop the full properties.

Solution heat treatment consists of heating the work at 630° F. for 4 to 5 hours followed by heating at 715° F. for a period of 12 to 14 hours. Both the furnace and the material must be at the required temperature for this period. This treatment increases the tensile strength, ductility, and toughness of the castings but does not change the yield strength or hardness.

The precipitation heat treatment or "aging" consists of heating the previously solution heat-treated material for 16 to 18 hours at 350° F. This raises the yield strength and hardness but reduces the ductility and toughness.

Castings may be purchased as cast or in either of the two heat-treated conditions. The airplane manufacturer does not have to concern himself about heat treating these alloys at his plant.

WORKING PROPERTIES

The technique of working magnesium alloys is being continually improved. They machine excellently with the proper tools, but there is a slight fire hazard that must be guarded against. Bending, forming, and spinning are more difficult than with other metals because these alloys work harden very rapidly when cold. A method of heating the material to be worked has been successfully developed. When heated the magnesium alloys can be worked with ease. Certain of the alloys can be forged with good results. Press forging is better than hammer forging. In general, magnesium alloys are adaptable to all the operations commonly used in the fabrication of aircraft parts but require somewhat different treatment than steel or aluminum alloys. The development of the proper technique should not be difficult for aircraft mechanics and should not delay adoption of this material in applications for which it is suitable.

Machining. Magnesium alloys machine better than any other metal used in aircraft construction. A fine smooth finish is obtainable without any tendency to drag or tear. Heavy cuts and feeds can be used at high cutting speeds without overloading the machine or overheating the work. Cutting tools designed for use with other metals can be successfully used on magnesium alloys, but they must have a sharp cutting edge and good clearance. The basic principle in all cutting tools for magnesium alloys is to limit the friction between work, tool, and chips to avoid the generation of heat and possible fire hazard.

Turning, shaping, and planing tools should be similar to those used for brass. Coarse tooth milling cutters should be used, because the heavier cut obtained causes less frictional heat and consequent distortion. Ordinary twist drills, and spiral reamers with about 6° relief behind the cutting edge give satisfactory results. Threading by means of taps, dies, or lathe turning is readily done. Roll threading is not satisfactory because it involves excessive cold working of the metal. Tapped holes should be 2 to 3 times the diameter of the stud. Magnesium alloy threaded parts will not seize when mated with other common metals or even with the same composition alloy. Band or circular saws for cutting magnesium alloys should have from 4 to 7

Courtesy of Dow Chemical Company

FIGURE 16. STRATOSPHERE GONDOLA

Magnesium Alloy Sheet

teeth per inch and must be very sharp. Hand hack saw blades should have 14 teeth per inch. Single cut files are preferable for use with magnesium alloys. No lubricant is usually necessary in machining these alloys. When excessive heat is generated by the machining operations a lubricant such as kerosene or a mixture of kerosene and lard oil should be used.

Precautions must be taken to reduce the fire hazard when machining magnesium alloys. Cutting tools must be sharp, and machines and floor must be kept clean. Scrap should be kept in covered metal containers. Lubricants should be used for automatic machine work or when fine cuts are being made at high cutting speeds to minimize the frictional heat. There is no serious danger from fire if care is exercised by the operator.

Forming. Due to their rapid work hardening magnesium alloys can be formed cold only to a very limited extent. The permissible bend radii for cold bending for sheet stock is as follows:

Dowmetal M, AM3SO   Soft sheet (heat treated).................. 3t
Dowmetal M, AM3SH   Hard sheet (heat treated and rolled)....... 5t

Under general shop conditions it may be advisable to increase these radii by one to two thicknesses. Before bending, all sharp corners and burrs should be removed from the edges of the sheet near the bend line. A soft pencil should be used to mark the bend line instead of a scribe in order to avoid scratching the metal. Scratching or prick punching the surface may result in fatigue cracks after a period of service.

In hot bending of magnesium alloys a radius of twice the sheet thickness can be used for all alloys and tempers. The work must be bent slowly and must be evenly heated to obtain the best results. Hot working of these alloys is best done between 500° F. and 750° F. Work is heated to the required temperature by means of a blow torch, by submerging in a heated oil bath of 600W, or by preheating in a furnace. The use of heated dies and reheating by means of the blow torch during the forming operations is advisable. The temperature can be checked by using a two-point contact pyrometer, or by marking with blue carpenter's chalk which loses its color at 600° F. The metal must not be heated above 800° F. since it become hot short above this temperature. The heating of hard-rolled sheet decreases its strength and hardness and increases its elongation. The heating of annealed sheet does not change its properties.

Long parts of uniform section, such as angles or channels, may be made by rolling or drawing the strip metal through forming dies. When corner radii are small, it is necessary to preheat the strip. There should be only gradual changes in contour between adjacent rolls or dies. Rolls and dies, which are made of steel or cast iron, must be exceptionally smooth to prevent scratching the softer magnesium alloy.

Magnesium alloys can be moderately drawn or pressed. Shallow draws with larger corner radii are advisable. Heating the work and aluminum alloy pressing dies will give the best results. For hand forming, the use of a wooden mallet and a leather backing pillow loosely filled with sand is recommended.

The beading of magnesium alloy sheet requires the preheating of the area to be beaded by means of a blow torch. Shallow beads, such as used in aircraft tank design, may possibly be done cold if all other conditions are perfect.

The spinning of magnesium alloy sheet is difficult, but it can be accomplished if the work is heated while mounted in the spinning lathe. This can be done with a blow torch. Laundry soap is used for lubrication during the spinning operation. The soap film turns a dark brown glossy color at the proper spinning temperature. Spinning is effected at a speed of between 300 to 450 r.p.m.

Dowmetal M, AM3S sheet has good forming characteristics and corrosion resistance and is used where these properties are desired.

Extrusions. Sections, such as bars, rods, angles, channels, beams and tubing, are extruded in the alloys listed in Table 12. Magnesium alloy extruded sections develop their maximum strength without heat treatment. They can also be heated to 500° F. to 700° F. for hot forming without loss of strength or injury to the metal. Larger corner fillets are used on magnesium alloy extrusions. Dies designed for aluminum alloy extrusions can be employed but it is preferable to use specially designed dies.

Forgings. Magnesium alloy forgings can be successfully made if heating is controlled accurately, the billets are handled rapidly, and preheated dies are used. The forging range for these alloys falls between 600° F. and 825° F., but some alloys must be kept within narrower limits. The working temperature range for Dowmetal J, AM57S is only 650° F. to 775° F. Forgings should always be made from extruded stock instead of cast billets so as to take advantage of the greater latitude in forging temperature and forging speed permitted. Press forging is preferable to hammer forging because of the greater time available for metal flow. Magnesium alloy forgings develop their maximum strength during forging and do not require annealing or heat treatment.

JOINING METHODS

Magnesium alloys may be joined together by riveting or by welding. Magnesium alloy rivets are not commercially available because of their unsatisfactory heading due to their excessive hardening when cold worked. When certain precautions are taken aluminum alloy rivets can be used successfully. Magnesium alloys can be welded by practically all commercial methods. Gas welding and electric resistance welding are most generally used.

Riveting. For lightly stressed joints 53S anodized aluminum alloy rivets may be used, but for more heavily stressed joints A17S, 17S or AM55S aluminum alloy rivets should be used. The latter alloy is preferable because it contains 5% magnesium and reduces the electrolytic action between rivet and sheet. AM55S rivets have a tensile strength of 41,000 lb./sq. in. and a shear strength of 32,000 lb./sq. in. This type rivet is made from annealed wire and does not require heat treatment of any kind. The bearing strength of magnesium alloy sheets may be taken as 1½ times their tensile strengths for purposes of designing riveted joints.

All rivet holes in magnesium alloys should be drilled rather than punched. If parts are drilled jointly they should be disassembled and all shavings removed from the joint. Holes should be $\frac{1}{64}$ to $\frac{1}{32}$ inch over the shank diameter of the rivet to prevent local over-stressing of the surrounding metal due to the lateral pressure developed when the rivet is headed. Care must also be taken in riveting not to mar the adjacent sheet, otherwise fatigue cracks will develop in service.

Welding. The welding of magnesium alloys is similar to the welding of aluminum alloys. The weld material is equivalent to good cast material and has about 75% of the strength of the parent metal. Because of the corrosive action of the flux required for welding, all welds must be made in accessible locations in order to permit thorough cleaning. Only butt, or flange welds can be used for this reason. Lap welds would have flux inclusions that could not be washed out and must, therefore, not be used. This regulation also applies to "T" welds where the edge of one sheet is welded to the surface of another sheet. In this case an extruded T is used, and sheets are welded to the edge of each leg thus giving three butt welds. Fortunately, this type of weld seldom occurs in aircraft construction. Welded members with closed hollow cross sections must have a hole drilled adjacent to the weld to permit thorough cleaning and flux removal.

Gas welding of magnesium alloys may be done with either an oxyacetylene or oxyhydrogen flame. The oxyhydrogen flame is preferable for thin sheet but, as in the case of aluminum, a good welder can do equally well with an oxyacetylene flame. A neutral or slightly reducing flame should be used, and it should be held at a flat angle to the work to avoid burning through. A welding rod of the same composition as the material being welded should be used. Dowmetal M, AM3S is the only wrought magnesium alloy commonly gas welded. Dowmetal M, AM3S rod may be used for welding all cast aluminum alloys. To prevent oxidation during welding, the welding rod and both sides of the seam should be covered with flux. After welding all traces of flux must be removed by scrubbing with hot water and a wire brush. The part should then be immersed in a chrome-pickle solution, as described in the chapter on Corrosion. If desired, welds in magnesium alloy sheet may be hammered to increase their strength and ductility. Hammered welds can be bent and formed to the same extent as the original sheet. Hammering should be done after cleaning and treatment to prevent the inclusion of any flux in the welded seam.

Resistance welding of magnesium alloys is fast and economical, and is free from corrosion possibilities since no flux is used. As with steel and aluminum, good spot welding depends upon accurate control of the current, time, and pressure. The surfaces must be thoroughly clean. The current time varies from a fraction of a second up to 3 seconds. Water-cooled copper electrodes are used to minimize the amalgamation of the copper with the magnesium alloy. After welding the spots should be scrubbed with hot water to remove any copper deposits. The different magnesium sheet and extruded alloys may be spot welded to each other successfully.

Electric seam welding may be done on magnesium alloy sheet to obtain pressure tight joints as required in tanks. Flat sheets cannot be welded by this method without excessive buckling unless done under water. A similar buckling occurs in gas welding flat sheets. The surface adjacent to the seam should be beaded before welding to absorb expansion and reduce the

Courtesy of Dow Chemical Company

FIGURE 47. DOWMETAL SAND CAST AIRPLANE LANDING WHEELS

buckling. The linear expansion of magnesium is approximately 10% greater than aluminum.

No strength values have been given for electric resistance welding because the data available indicates a wide variation between operators and machines. Good strength is obtainable by this method of welding but design values should be established by each airplane manufacturer for his own use.

Small defects in castings may be welded up if it will not affect strength, use, or machinability. Castings must be preheated to 600-700° F. in a furnace if they are at all complicated to prevent cracking when the welding torch is applied. Simple castings can be preheated with the welding torch. Care must be taken to see that no welding flux is trapped in the weld metal. Thorough cleaning is, of course, necessary after completion of the weld.

CORROSION RESISTANCE

Magnesium alloys are quite resistant to normal atmospheric corrosion even when unprotected. When given a chrome-pickle treatment and properly painted, these alloys will resist the corrosive effects of salt air. They should not be used for parts in continuous contact with salt water. Magnesium alloys suffer only visible surface corrosion and are not subject to intercrystalline corrosion. Unpainted engine castings that are oily or greasy most of the time do not suffer corrosion. Powdering or roughening of the surface indicates corrosion.

Magnesium alloys must be insulated from contact with other metals to avoid electrolytic corrosion. Pure aluminum (2S) has very little effect and may be used as an insulator.

Corrosion protection treatments for magnesium alloy parts are described in the chapter on Corrosion.

AVAILABLE SHAPES

Magnesium alloys may be sand cast, die cast, permanent mold cast, forged, rolled, and extruded in all standard structural shapes. Different alloys are adaptable to different forming operations. No one alloy can be obtained in all the forms mentioned.

Sand Casting. Patterns used for aluminum alloy castings can be used for magnesium alloy castings, but, when possible, it is desirable to increase the size of fillets and bosses. Changes may also be necessary to improve the gating and pouring of the magnesium alloys. A shrinkage of $\frac{3}{16}$ inch per foot is obtained with unrestrained shrinkage, and $\frac{5}{32}$ inch per foot when free shrinkage is prevented by bosses or cores. This shrinkage is almost exactly the same as aluminum alloys.

The selection of a casting alloy depends upon the intended use and the properties desired. Three different alloys commonly used for aircraft and engine parts are listed in Table 12. These alloys may be purchased as cast or heat treated, depending upon the combination of properties desired.

Die Casting. Small castings with good dimensional accuracy, uniformity, and excellent surface finish requiring a minimum of machining can be obtained by die casting. High pressure die casting is used for best results with magnesium alloys. The present equipment and technique appears to be the only limit on the size of this type casting. The maximum permissible wall thickness is 0.375 inch and the minimum is 0.060 inch (small castings only).

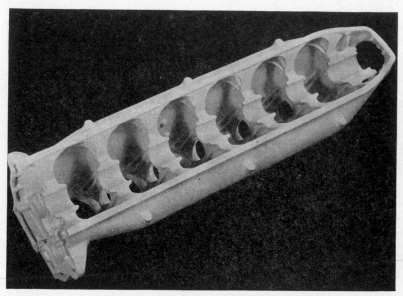

Courtesy of Dow Chemical Company

FIGURE 48. CRANKCASE

Magnesium Alloy Casting

A length tolerance of 0.0015 inch per inch of length can be met with die castings. Holes as small as 0.062 inch diameter can be cast. The draft of side walls or cores must be 0.010 inch per inch of length.

Dowmetal K, AM230 or Dowmetal R, AM263 are most generally used because they possess good casting qualities as well as mechanical properties. The properties of these alloys are given in Table 12.

Permanent Mold Castings. When the quantity of parts justifies the cost of the mold, this type of casting is preferable to sand casting. A smoother surface, finer grain, and closer dimensional accuracy is obtained. Improved mechanical properties are also obtained.

Rolled Sheet and Plate. By definition, *plate* is rolled metal having a thickness of ¼ inch and over. Sheet can be obtained in most gages up to 48 inches wide and 20 feet long. Sheet is obtainable in 6 inch increments of width from 12 to 30 inches, and in 2 inch increments from 30 to 48 inches.

Dowmetal M, AM3S material is the alloy used in the fabrication of sheet and plate. The various tempers, along with

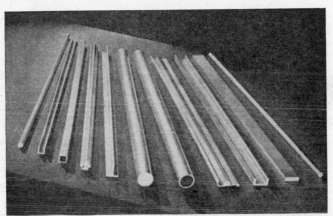

Courtesy of Dow Chemical Company

FIGURE 49. A VARIETY OF DOWMETAL EXTRUDED SHAPES

mechanical properties, in which this alloy may be procured are listed in Table 12. The annealed temper is more corrosion resistant than the hard-rolled temper.

Forgings. Hammer forgings or small die forgings can be made by using dies designed for aluminum alloy forgings. Forgings made from the magnesium alloys listed in Table 12 develop their full properties without subsequent heat treatment.

Extrusions. Practically all the magnesium alloys can be extruded successfully. They are stretched after extrusion to straighten them and to increase the mechanical properties by the cold work involved. Bars and rods are also extruded in all standard sizes as well as angles, channels, beam sections, and tubing. Figure 49 shows a variety of extruded shapes.

Extruded tubing is available in outside diameters from $\frac{3}{8}$ inch up to 4 inches. The minimum wall thickness is $\frac{1}{16}$ inch in the smaller sizes of tubing and more than that in the larger diameters. Accurate dimensions can be obtained by subsequently drawing the extruded tubing.

Dowmetal J, AM57S extrudes well and has good mechanical properties. Dowmetal M, AM3S is the most resistant to salt water corrosion but has lower mechanical properties. Extrusions develop their full strength without subsequent heat treatment.

Uses

Each of the magnesium alloys described in the preceding pages is best adapted for certain definite applications. In some cases more than one alloy will satisfy all the service requirements, in which case the cheapest one should be selected. In general, wrought material should be used in the manufacture of aircraft parts whenever possible to take advantage of its higher fatigue strength.

Most sand castings are made from Dowmetal H, AM265. This alloy has good strength characteristics and good corrosion resistance. In the heat-treated state this alloy is used for aircraft landing wheels, aircraft engine crankcases, and other motor parts.

Dowmetal M, AM403 castings have excellent corrosion resistance, are weldable but do not have good mechanical properties.

Dowmetal M, AM3S alloy is obtainable as sheet or extrusions. It is noted for its good forming and welding characteristics and its superior corrosion resistance. The corrosion resistance is slightly better when the alloy is in the heat-treated condition. Its properties in this condition are practically the same as obtainable by a simple annealing treatment. This material in the soft condition is suitable for the construction of fuel and oil tanks. In the hard-rolled condition it is used for cowling and semi-structural applications.

Dowmetal J, AM57S alloy can be pressed forged. It has very good mechanical properties and notable resistance to shock and fatigue. It also forges fairly well.

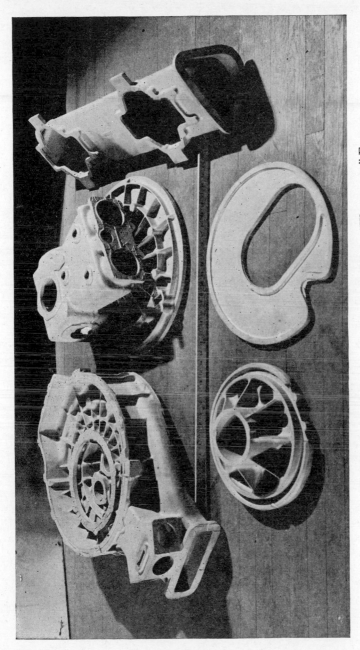

FIGURE 50. MISCELLANEOUS ENGINE CASTINGS FOR WRIGHT "WHIRLWIND" ENGINE
DOWMETAL "G" ALLOY HEAT TREATED

Dowmetal O, AM58S is a press forging alloy with the highest mechanical properties of any of the forging alloys. It is somewhat more difficult to forge than Dowmetal J, AM57S. It is used for forgings of comparatively simple design, such as airplane propeller blades.

CHAPTER XIV

WELDING—BRAZING—SOLDERING

Metals may be joined by mechanical means (such as bolting or riveting) or by welding, brazing, or soldering. All of these methods are used in aircraft construction. There are three general types of welding: gas, electric arc, and electric resistance welding. All three are used in aircraft construction but gas welding is most common. Soldering is divided into hard or soft soldering, depending upon the type of solder used. Soft soldering is never used on aircraft structural parts because of its lack of strength. Brazing is really a soldering operation, using a copper base solder, and it is intermediate in strength between welding and hard soldering. All of these operations require heating the base metal and forming some type of fusion joint. A good job is dependent upon the skill of the workman, the equipment used, and the proper preparation of the parts to be joined.

GAS WELDING

Aircraft fittings fabricated from chrome-molybdenum or mild carbon steel are often gas welded. Engine mounts, landing gears, and entire fuselages constructed of steel tubing are also welded by this means. Aluminum alloy parts made from strain-hardened alloys are also gas welded. Such parts as fuel and oil tanks, air scoops, and cowling are in this category. There are two types of gas welding: oxyacetylene, and oxyhydrogen. Nearly all gas welding in aircraft construction is done with an oxyacetylene flame, although some manufacturers prefer an oxyhydrogen flame for welding aluminum alloys. The oxyacetylene flame is much hotter, but can be controlled by a skillful welder to give an excellent weld on aluminum sheet as thin as 0.020 inch.

The oxyacetylene flame is produced by the combustion of acetylene gas with oxygen. A heat of 6700° F. is produced at the tip of the torch. Acetylene is a hydrocarbon gas produced by the reaction of water on calcium carbide. The carbon in the carbide combines with the hydrogen of the water to form acetylene gas.

There are three types of flame possible with the oxyacetylene torch. The first is a *neutral flame* in which the amount of acetylene and oxygen are just suited to each other with no excess of either. This type of flame can be identified by the clear, well-defined, white cone at the tip of the torch. This flame is generally used for welding and gives a thoroughly fused weld, free from burned metal or hard spots. The second type of flame is called a *carbonizing* or *reducing flame*. It is produced when an excess of acetylene is burned and can be identified by a feathery edge on the white cone. This flame introduces carbon into the weld. Due to the difficulty of holding a perfect neutral flame, a slightly reducing flame is often used in welding corrosion-resisting steel to insure against having an oxidizing flame at any time. The *oxidizing flame* is the third type of flame. As the name implies, it is produced by an excess of oxygen. It is identified by its small pointed white cone and shorter envelop of flame. An oxidizing flame will oxidize or burn the metal and result in a porous weld. It is only used in welding brass and bronze.

The oxyhydrogen flame may also be neutral, reducing, or oxidizing depending upon whether the hydrogen supply is just right, in excess, or deficient. The neutral flame has a well-defined cone in the center of the large flame. The reducing flame is long and ragged and has no well-defined cone at the center. The oxidizing flame is small and has a very short cone at the tip of the torch. A neutral flame should be used to obtain a clean, sound weld.

In gas welding steel, no flux is necessary but a filler rod must be used. There are two types of welding rods generally used. A low carbon rod containing a maximum of 0.06% carbon, 0.25% manganese (max.), and not over 0.04% of sulphur or phosphorus is used on parts that are not going to be heat treated after welding. In welding chrome-molybdenum steel bar, sheet, or tubing that is going to be heat treated after welding a higher carbon welding rod is used. This rod has from 0.10 to 0.20% carbon, 1.00 to 1.20% manganese, and a maximum of 0.04% sulphur or phosphorus. These rods are obtainable in the following sizes: $\frac{1}{16}$, $\frac{3}{32}$, $\frac{1}{8}$, $\frac{5}{32}$, $\frac{3}{16}$, $\frac{1}{4}$, $\frac{5}{16}$, and $\frac{3}{8}$ inch. A rod diameter of the approximate thickness of the material being

welded should be used. A normalized piece of chrome-molybdenum tubing (95,000 lbs./sq. in. ultimate tensile strength) when
butt welded with low carbon welding rod will show a minimum
strength of 80,000 lbs./sq. in. without heat treatment. Based on
this fact, welded steel tubes in tension are usually figured for
80% of their unwelded strength. In many cases chrome-molybdenum tubing butt welded with high carbon welding rod and heat
treated will break outside the weld, or at a strength equal to
unwelded tubing given the same heat treatment. In other words,
a welded joint after heat treatment can develop the strength of
the unwelded material. This, of course, is partly due to the
extra area of the weld metal. In structural analysis, however, it
is customary to figure welded parts in tension for 80% of the
heat treatment strength.

Corrosion resisting steel is welded by using a very slightly
reducing flame to avoid any possibility of oxidizing the weld. A
flux composed largely of borax is mixed with sodium silicate and
water to obtain the desired consistency, and is painted on the
rod and on both sides of the seam to be welded. This flux protects the metal against oxidation and floats impurities in the weld
to the surface. A welding rod containing columbium or molybdenum is generally recommended for use with this metal. One
such rod that has been found satisfactory has the following chemical composition: carbon, 0.07 max.; manganese, 0.20 to 0.70;
nickel, 8.0 min.; chromium, 18.0 min.; columbium, 0.80 min.;
silicon, 0.50 to 1.00; phosphorus and sulphur, 0.04 max. each.
The diameter of the rod used should be approximately equal to
the thickness of the metal being welded. Diameters of rods most
often used are: $\frac{1}{16}$, $\frac{3}{32}$, and $\frac{1}{8}$ inch. As explained in Chapter
VIII on Corrosion-Resisting Steels, it is usually necessary to
stabilize this material after welding in order to protect it against
intercrystalline corrosion. If properly welded, this material can
be bent flat along the axis of the seam of a butt weld without
cracking. Butt-welded joints in sheet will develop at least 80%
of the strength of the unwelded sheet.

In welding aluminum or aluminum alloys a flux is always used
to remove the oxide film on the work to be welded. The flux is
applied either to the seam or the welding rod prior to welding.
An acceptable flux for aluminum welding is composed of sodium
chloride, potassium chloride, lithium chloride, and sodium fluoride.

Either of two types of rod may be used in welding aluminum alloys.

2S wire (pure aluminum) should be used for welding 2S or 3S material.

43S wire (5% silicon and remainder aluminum and impurities) should be used for welding 52S alloy or heat-treatable alloys 51S or 53S which are also weldable.

43S wire should be used whenever parts are held tightly in jigs because its lower solidification shrinkage, and melting point will dissipate contraction strains. It should also be used in other locations, such as when welding fittings on tanks or in repairing welds, where it is advisable to reduce the strain on the weld when cooling.

On the other hand, 2S wire gives a somewhat more ductile weld and is better adapted for butt and edge welds which are not subjected to severe cooling strains. In many shops 43S welding wire is used exclusively with good results.

As with other materials the diameter of the welding rod should approximate the thickness of the metal being welded. Standard rod sizes are $\frac{1}{16}$, $\frac{1}{8}$, $\frac{3}{16}$, and $\frac{1}{4}$ inch diameter. All flux must be removed from the weld shortly after it has cooled to prevent corrosion. The method of doing this is described in Chapter XIV on Corrosion. The strength of welds in aluminum alloys is always greater than the strength of the annealed material just outboard of the weld. Calculations should, therefore, be based on annealed material.

Other metals beside the foregoing can also be welded with an oxyacetylene flame. Among these are Inconel, K Monel, and Monel for which the process has been described in Chapter IX on Nickel Alloys. Brass, bronze, copper, nickel, iron, and cast iron can also be welded, but these metals have no welded application in aircraft construction.

ELECTRIC ARC WELDING

This process is based upon the heat generated in an electric arc. There are two types of arc welding—*carbon arc* and *metallic arc,* depending upon whether carbon or metal is used for one electrode. In either case the work to be welded is the other electrode. The carbon arc will develop a temperature of about 7000° F., and the metallic arc about 6000° F. In the carbon arc method the filler rod is fused into the seam. In the metallic arc method the filler rod is the metallic electrode and fuses into the seam. The actual application of carbon arc welding is similar to welding with an oxyacetylene flame and can be used in many instances interchangeably with that process.

In arc welding there is less buckling and warping of the work than in gas welding. The temper of the sheet is also less affected due to the concentration of the heat and the quicker welding. The localization of heat in electric arc welding is advantageous in welding up cracks in crowded places, such as in an engine mount installed on an airplane. Metallic arc welding is also applicable to corrosion-resisting steel, but to secure the best results the material must be at least $\frac{1}{16}$ inch thick. For this reason it has not been generally used in aircraft construction. A similar condition exists in the case of aluminum welding by means of the metallic arc. A material thickness of at least $\frac{1}{16}$ inch is necessary. Carbon arc welding is applicable to aluminum for thicknesses from $\frac{1}{32}$ to $\frac{1}{16}$ inch when a butt or simple lap weld is made. Electric arc welding is used extensively in aircraft work in welding chrome-molybdenum steel $\frac{3}{32}$-inch or greater in thickness.

Electric Resistance Welding

Electric resistance welding is based on the principle that heat is generated by the resistance offered by a conductor. The heat increases with an increase in resistance. Current is admitted to the work through large, low resistance copper electrodes. The low voltage, high amperage current meets much greater resistance when it enters the work to be welded, and intense heat is generated. Three commonly used types of electric resistance welding are *butt*, *spot*, and *seam welding*.

Butt Welding. Butt welding is very generally used commercially to weld together long sheets, bars, tubes, rods, or wires. It applies only to duplicate or production work because the welding machine is only designed to handle one particular type of joint. Butt welding is applicable to almost all metals, among them being steel and aluminum. As yet it has no special place in aircraft construction.

In butt welding the work to be welded is clamped in large

copper jaws, which are also electrodes. One of the jaws is movable. At the proper time pressure is applied to the movable jaw to bring the work in contact. This pressure amounts to approximately 2000 lbs./sq. in. in the case of aluminum. The intense heat developed at the joint, due to the resistance it offers to the current, combined with a high pressure, results in a union of the two pieces. The heating of the joint starts at the center and works outward to the surface, so that a perfect weld is obtainable with complete fusion and contact along the entire seam.

Spot Welding. Spot welding is frequently used in aircraft construction. It is used almost exclusively for joining structural corrosion-resistant steel. This process is described in detail in Chapter VIII. The spot welding of aluminum alloys has been very generally adopted. At the present time it is very generally approved for Alclad materials and 52S alloy, because these alloys are very corrosion resistant. Anodically treated surfaces cannot be spot welded and, consequently, the faying surfaces of a spot welded seam must be left unprotected either by anodic treatment or paint. For this reason there is some doubt about the advisability of spot welding other aluminum alloys than those mentioned if subject to severe corrosion. It is possible to spot weld through wet zinc chromate primer placed in the faying surfaces, and then to apply a surface treatment to the assembled parts. For secondary work, such as cowling stiffeners, 3S aluminum alloy is used and spot welded in place. Corrosion of the faying surfaces should not be particularly serious in such locations.

In spot welding aluminum alloys there must be accurate control of the time, pressure, and current as in all spot welding. Using a 60 cycle alternating current, a time of 3 cycles for 0.020 inch material, varying to 12 cycles for 0.120 material, is generally satisfactory. A constant time of 10 cycles can be used successfully for all thicknesses of material if it is desired to eliminate this variable. The pressure required varies from 300 pounds for 0.020 inch material to 1200 pounds for 0.120 material. For the same extremes of thickness the current varies approximately from 18,000 amperes to 35,000 amperes. All of the foregoing figures vary somewhat with the apparatus used, the technique of the welder, and the material being spot welded. When unequal thicknesses are welded together, the time and pressure are determined by the thinner material. The amperage, however, varies with different combinations.

The exact strength of spot welds in aluminum alloys is still an uncertain quantity. Each manufacturer should run a series of tests to establish his own design values. A shear strength per spot of 250 pounds when using 0.020 inch material can be expected. This strength will increase to about 1250 pounds per spot with 0.080 inch material. Spot welds are quite weak in tension and should not be used to take this type of stress. They appear to stand up exceptionally well under vibration stresses, as proven by their service record in engine cowlings.

Seam Welding. Seam welding is identical with spot welding, except for the use of power-driven rollers as electrodes. A continuous air-tight weld can be obtained by this method. It is possible to seam weld from 2 to 6 feet per minute when welding aluminum alloys.

WELDING CONSIDERATIONS

There are a number of general considerations that all designers should be familiar with in connection with the design of welded joints. The following comments on these points apply particularly to oxyacetylene welding or arc welding.

1. Straight tension welds should be avoided because of their weakening effect. When a weld must be in tension, a fish-mouth joint or finger patch should be used to increase the length of weld and to put part of it in shear.

2. A weld should never be made all around a tube in the same plane. A fish-mouth weld should be made. This situation arises frequently when attaching an end fitting to a strut.

3. Two welds should not be placed close together in thin material. Cracks will result because of the lack of metal to absorb shrinkage stresses.

4. Welds should not be made on both sides of a thin sheet.

5. Welds should not be made along bends, or cracks will develop in service.

6. Welded reinforcements should never end abruptly. The sudden change of section will result in failures by cracking when in service.

7. Aircraft bolts are made of 2330 nickel steel. They should never be welded in place because they cannot be satisfactorily

welded to chrome-molybdenum steel. If such design is necessary, bolts should be machined from chrome-molybdenum steel and welded in place. It is possible to weld standard aircraft nuts in place, because they are made from 1025 carbon steel. Tack welding in three places is all that is usually necessary to position them. Complete welding weakens the material and distorts the nut.

8. All welded parts should be normalized or heat treated after completion to refine the grain and relieve internal stresses caused by shrinkage. If welded parts are not normalized they will develop cracks in service, particularly if subject to vibrational stresses. This is due to the fact that weld material is cast metal which does not have the strength, ductility, or shock resistance of wrought metal. The internal stresses are also seeking to adjust themselves. Sharp bends or corners, or rapid change of section in the vicinity of welds are especially liable to cracking.

BRAZING

Brazing as applied to aircraft is the process of uniting metal parts by means of a molten brass spelter. Brazing is really a soldering operation in which a spelter that melts at a very high temperature is used. The brass spelter when molten at high temperature has a surface alloying action with steel and other metals and forms a very strong bond. In the past, aircraft fittings were very commonly brazed. An allowable shear stress of 10,000 pounds per square inch was used in figuring the strength of brazed parts. Welding has largely superseded brazing in recent years. Welding is easier and more reliable, as well as being free from the possibility of corrosion because of dissimilar metals being in contact.

The brazing spelter used for aircraft work is a brass composed of 80% copper and 20% zinc. This spelter starts melting at 1750° F. and is completely molten above 1830° F. The brazing operation is usually performed between 1830° F. and 1870° F. It is customary to heat treat alloy steel parts after brazing if the required heat-treatment temperature is not above 1650° F. Above this temperature the brazing spelter begins to soften and causes a weakening of the joint. The heat treatment of brazed parts corrects the large grain structure caused by heating the material in the vicinity of 1850° F. for brazing.

A flux is necessary in brazing to clean the steel of oxide scale. The recommended flux consists of 2 parts of borax to 1 part of boric acid. But before brazing the parts must be thoroughly cleaned of all oil, grease, or paint by means of benzol or a hot caustic soda solution. Heavy scale should be removed by pickling, followed by a caustic dip to neutralize the acid.

Parts to be brazed must be securely fastened together to prevent any relative movement. This fastening can be done by riveting, electric spot welding, or tack welding with oxyacetylene. Tack welding causes scale formation, which requires another pickling operation for removal, and, thus, is not considered as satisfactory as the other methods. The strongest brazed joint is one in which the molten spelter is drawn in by capillary action and, therefore, a close fit is advisable. The molten spelter will penetrate into any joint no matter how tight.

In flame brazing, the parts are preheated slowly by means of a bunsen burner or blow torch to the brazing temperature. An oxyacetylene flame is not mild enough for this operation. The joint should be liberally coated with flux during the heating operation. When the brazing temperature is reached, brass should be applied to the joint in the form of granules or wire. The brass will melt in contact with the hot steel and run into the joint by capillary action. When the brass comes out the opposite side of the joint, enough has been applied. The parts should then be cooled slowly as described below.

In dip brazing, the parts are heated to 1000° F. in a furnace and soaked at this temperature for at least 20 minutes. They are then lowered slowly into a flux bath, maintained at about 1300° F., and left in it for five minutes. After this they are immersed in a second flux bath, maintained at about 1600° F., and left in this bath for five minutes. The parts are then transferred to the dip-brazing pot. The dip-brazing pot contains molten brass at a temperature of 1830° F. to 1870° F. The molten brass is covered with a 2 inch thick layer of flux. The parts must be lowered very slowly into the brazing pot to avoid a rapid change of temperature with its attendant cracks. The parts should be left immersed for 2 to 3 minutes and should then be raised and lowered two or three times through the flux layer, after which they should be submerged for another minute or two.

After removal from the brazing pot or upon the completion

of flame brazing, the parts must be cooled very slowly. They can either be buried in lime (or a similar insulating powder) or be placed in a cooling chamber maintained at 1000° F. After cooling to blackness, they can be cooled in air at room temperature. During the cooling operation the parts are protected by the flux coating from surface oxidation. After cooling this flux is removed from the parts by immersing them for 30 minutes in a lye solution. This lye solution, which consists of one pound of lye per gallon of water, is maintained at 212° F.

The brass coating is removed from all surfaces except the joints by an electrolytic stripping operation. The joints are protected from the stripping action by coating them with paraffin. A solution containing 12 ounces of sodium nitrate to the gallon of water is used as the electrolyte. The brazed fittings are suspended from the positive bus bar of a 6 volt generator. The steel tank or steel electrodes are used as the negative bus bar. The brass can be removed in from 10 to 30 minutes by this method without appreciably affecting the steel fitting.

HARD SOLDERING

Hard soldering, like brazing and soft soldering, is based on the fact that practically any metal will surface-alloy with another metal that has a higher melting temperature. This latter metal must have a chemically clean surface and be heated to the melting temperature of the solder. There are a number of hard solders, but in aircraft work this term refers almost exclusively to silver solders. These solders all contain some silver and melt around 1200° F. They can be used to solder metals that fuse at 1400° F. or above, such as copper, brass, bronze, iron, steel, corrosion-resistant steel, Inconel, Monel, nickel, and silver. This solder will make a strong joint. Its temperature range is intermediate between soft solder and brazing, and it should be used where strength without excessive heating is desired.

Before soldering all surfaces must be thoroughly cleaned. A flux coating is then applied to the entire joint and to the solder to protect against oxidation and to aid the flow of the solder. Powdered borax mixed with water to form a thick paste is a good flux. For corrosion-resisting steels and other metals that form oxides hard to remove, a flux composed of borax, boracic acid, and zinc chloride solution is best. Silver soldering fluxes are readily soluble in hot water and can be removed by dipping or scrubbing.

A silver soldering or silver brazing alloy, as it is sometimes called, that is particularly suitable for use with steel, corrosion-resisting steel, Inconel, and Monel has the following chemical composition: silver, 50%; copper, 15%; zinc, 16%; cadmium, 18%. This solder melts at 1175° F. and is yellow-white in color.

Another soldering alloy especially suitable for copper, brass, and other nonferrous alloys has the following chemical composition: copper, 80%; silver, 15%; phosphorus, 5%. This alloy has a melting point around 1300° F. It has a shearing strength of approximately 30,000 lbs./sq. in. at 200° F. Its strength is about one half this amount at 700° F.

The application of silver solder is similar to brazing. A gentle flame must be used to preheat the work to the required temperature before applying the solder. When the solder is brought under the flame of the torch, it melts and flows rapidly along the joint.

SOFT SOLDERING

Soft soldering is never used in aircraft work for joints requiring strength. It is used for making electrical connections, and to solder the wrapped or spliced ends of flexible aircraft control cables.

The standard soldering flux used for soft soldering is a paste composed of 75% mineral grease (petrolatum), wax, and resins, combined with 25% zinc chloride. This flux can be used generally except for the soldering of aluminum, which it will corrode seriously. It will also corrode other metals and must be removed as completely as possible after soldering.

Common soft-soldering alloys are composed of tin and lead. A good grade generally used is composed of 50% tin and 50% lead. This alloy has a melting point of 370° F. Solders containing more lead are cheaper, have higher melting points, and are not as strong. A "fine" solder containing two parts of tin to one part of lead is best for soldering steel, iron, copper, and brass. This alloy has a melting point of 340° F.

Another solder universally used in aircraft work is composed of 5 to 6% silver and the remainder lead. This solder has a melting point between 580° F. and 700° F. It will develop a shearing strength of 1500 lbs./sq. in. at 350° F. When applying this solder to hard drawn brass or copper, the temperature should not exceed 850° F.

There are numerous aluminum solders on the market but they have little practical application in aircraft construction. If the heat-treatable alloys are soldered, the heat destroys their properties. One acceptable solder for use on aluminum alloy is composed of 75-79% tin, and 25-21% zinc. This material may be used for non-structural applications such as attaching strainer screens to fuel and oil line fittings, and filling in abraded areas of cowling and other aluminum sheet assemblies.

Chapter XV

CORROSION AND ITS PREVENTION

All metals are affected to some extent by the atmosphere. This effect which is called corrosion is especially important in aircraft due to the loss of strength it causes. Corrosion reduces the strength and ductility of metals to an alarming extent if not restrained. In the relatively thin sections used in aircraft construction even a small amount of corrosion is unsafe. For these reasons extensive study has been devoted to the protection of metals against corrosion. Metals have also been developed that are corrosion-resistant in themselves, and they are very generally used when their other properties are suitable to the intended application. Such metals as Inconel, K monel, Alclad, and corrosion-resisting steels are in this category. In general these metals are only given a protective coating of paint when it is desired to carry out some particular color scheme.

It has been generally established that corrosion is caused by the moisture in the air. A dry piece of metal in dry air will not corrode. This point is vividly brought out by the fact that sandblasted steel surfaces will oxidize in a few hours on Long Island if not painted; whereas in Wichita, Kansas, they can stand for days without painting. With this in mind it is obvious that all traps should be eliminated and plenty of drain holes provided in aircraft to drain off water or condensed moisture. In order to minimize the amount of condensation, it is necessary to adequately vent all the nooks and crannies. This is particularly true of inaccessible locations in seaplane hulls. Provision should be made for the inspection of all parts of an airplane when in service. Timely and thorough inspection will detect corrosion in its initial stages when it can be easily arrested before becoming dangerous.

There are two distinct types of corrosion to which metals used in aircraft construction are subject. The first type is the eating away or pitting of the surface as in the rusting of steel and iron. Practically all metals are subject to this type of corrosion when they oxidize in the presence of air. This type of corrosion is visible and can be prevented or retarded by protecting the surface with a plating or paint. The second type of corrosion is one that is not visible on the surface and is, therefore, very dangerous. It is called intergranular or intercrystalline corrosion, because it eats its way internally through the metal around the grain or crystal boundaries. This type of corrosion is found in some aluminum alloys and some corrosion-resisting steels. It has been described in detail in the chapters devoted to those metals. The resistance of materials to this type corrosion is lowered by improper treatment of the metal and can be prevented by proper technique. Protective coatings have little or no influence on this type of corrosion.

CORROSION OF DISSIMILAR METALS

The corrosion of dissimilar metals in contact deserves special treatment. It has been found through sad experience, especially in naval airplanes, that when two dissimilar metals are in contact one of them will eat the other away. The fact that this phenomena is more common in seaplanes indicates that the presence of moisture is a necessary condition. Every metal has an inherent electric potential. When set side by side with a metal of different potential, and an electrolyte is present, such as moisture, an electric action is set up. It is found that this electric action causes pitting of the metal with the higher potential. When two metals of different potentials are compared, the one with the higher potential is said to be anodic to the other. The anodic metal is then the one that is destroyed by electrolytic corrosion, as it is called. When two metals have practically the same potential, there is very little interaction. The following tabulation lists the commonly used metals in the order of their potential magnitude. The anodic metals are on top. The metals grouped together do not have a strong tendency to corrode each other because of the slight differences in their electric potential.

Corroded End (Anodic)
Magnesium
Aluminum

Zinc
Cadmium
Chromium
Iron
Chromium-iron (active)
Chromium-nickel-iron (active)

Solder
Tin
Lead

Nickel
Brass
Bronze
K Monel
Monel
Copper

Inconel
Chromium-iron (passive)
Chromium-nickel-iron (passive)

Silver solder
Protected End (Cathodic)

Before really serious electrolytic or galvanic action can set in between any two of the above metals, it is necessary for the electrolyte present to be a solution in which one of the metals is susceptible to corrosion. Insofar as aircraft materials are concerned, namely aluminum and steel, moisture (more particularly sea water or spray) fulfills this condition.

Figure 51 shows graphically the action that takes place when two metals of different potentials are placed side by side. Current flows from the anodic metal to the cathodic metal of lower potential. The surface of the anodic metal is pitted by this action.

To avoid electrolytic corrosion, joints between dissimilar metals should be avoided when-

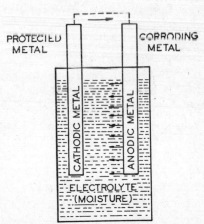

FIGURE 51. GALVANIC CELL ACTION

ever possible. In aircraft work aluminum alloys in particular should be kept away from steel, stainless steel, and copper bearing alloys because of the great difference in potential. When joints must be made between two dissimilar metals the following precautions should be taken to prevent corrosion:

Steel and Aluminum Alloy Joint. The steel surface should be cadmium plated or metallized with aluminum spray and then given two coats of primer before assembly. After anodic treatment the aluminum faying surface should also be given two coats of primer. All coats of primer should dry thoroughly before assembly. The faying surfaces should be insulated from each other by canton flannel or fabric impregnated with bituminous paint, soya bean oil compound, or marine glue. An alternative insulator for non-watertight joints is a pure aluminum sheet that has been anodically treated and primed. Aluminum foil and cellophane tape are two other insulators that have been used successfully. The insulator should extend beyond the edge of the faying surfaces at least $\frac{3}{16}$ inch. This protruding insulator does not look very neat, but if trimmed close to the edge of the faying surfaces it will not do its job of insulating. This point should be impressed on shop personnel.

Stainless Steel and Aluminum Alloy Joint. The stainless steel need not be plated, but in all other respects the joint should be the same as for steel. Stainless steel has a much greater affinity for aluminum alloys than steel; so even greater care should be taken in insulating it.

Copper, Brass, Bronze, and Aluminum Alloy Joints. The copper bearing alloys should be cadmium plated and given the same treatment as a steel joint.

Threaded connections and pressed fit bushings are of necessity excluded from the above recommendations.

CORROSION PROTECTION

Aircraft metal parts are almost always given special treatments to improve their resistance to corrosion. These treatments usually consist of a cleaning treatment, such as sandblasting or pickling, which is followed by a plating process, such as cadmium plating, chromium plating, galvanizing, and so on, and finally a paint job. Steel parts are subject to this whole sequence of operations. Aluminum alloy parts are usually cleaned, anodically treated, and painted. Alclad parts, corrosion-resisting steel, Inconel, K Monel, Monel, and other corrosion-resistant materials are frequently left in their natural state without plating or paint unless it is desirable to match a color scheme.

The finishing operations will be described in detail in the order normally followed for steel parts. The anodic oxidation treatment of aluminum alloys will be described under the plating operations. There are many plating operations described but cadmium plating is generally used. There is a wide choice in paints and varnishes, but they all require an adequately prepared surface for satisfactory adherence.

CLEANING OPERATIONS

Sandblasting. Sandblasting is a general name applied to the process of cleaning parts by blowing abrasive particles against the surface. Sand, steel grit, and other abrasives are sometimes used. Steel parts that have been welded or heat treated are normally sandblasted to remove the scale. This also applies to corrosion-resisting steel exhaust collectors which are subjected to both welding and heat-treatment operations. Aluminum alloy parts are seldom sandblasted because of their softness, thinness, and loss of ductility after blasting. Occasionally aluminum alloy surfaces are sandblasted in the manner described below when it is necessary to remove abraded or corroded areas.

The sand used for blasting should pass through a No. 24 sieve and not through a No. 40 sieve. It should be at least 98% silica and free of salts, silt, dust, or other foreign matter. Steel grit used for blasting is called No. 50. It must be uniform and have sharp edges.

The actual blasting operation consists of blowing the grit through a nozzle by means of air pressure. The distance the nozzle is held from the surface, its angle relative to the surface, and the air pressure used are all dependent upon the type of work. In the case of thin aluminum alloy the nozzle must be held from 18 to 24 inches away from the work, and must not make an angle greater than 45° to the surface. Sand is used for blasting under an air pressure of 70 pounds per square inch or less. For heavier aluminum alloy parts, such as castings, the blasting operation may be made more severe.

Sandblast parts should not be handled with dirty or greasy hands, and they should be given a protective coating of paint as soon as possible. Sandblast parts will rust very quickly if allowed to stand in that condition for any length of time. This is particularly true of damp locations—along the seaboard, for instance.

After sandblasting, parts must be cleaned by means of an air blast or by brushing to remove excess abrasive. If steel parts are to be electroplated after sandblasting, all imbedded particles must be removed by immersing the part in a dilute solution of hydrofluoric acid consisting of ½ pint of acid per gallon of solution. This treatment should not be used for aluminum alloy parts.

Care must be taken in sandblasting not to eat away the metal and thus seriously reduce the strength. Sandblasting of a part should be limited to the minimum amount necessary to clean the surface. This applies particularly to parts of thin section or subject to high stresses in service. Parts requiring a ground or polished surface should not be sandblasted. These parts are usually heat treated in a liquid bath to avoid scaling and do not require cleaning by blasting. Aluminum alloy sheet should not be sandblasted unless absolutely necessary because of the loss of ductility resulting from even a light sandblast.

Pickling Steel. Steel parts are pickled to remove scale, rust, and so on, particularly before plating them. The pickling solution may be either a sulphuric acid solution (5% to 10% of concentrated sulphuric acid, by weight) or a hydrochloric (muriatic) acid solution (15% to 25% of concentrated muriatic acid, by weight). The pickling solution, which is kept in a stoneware tank, is heated to 140° F. to 150° F. by means of a steam coil.

Paint, oil, grease, and so forth, are removed from the part before pickling by immersing it in a hot solution of lye. After rinsing in running water, it is immersed in the pickling solution for the minimum length of time necessary to remove the scale or rust. This period varies from 5 to 15 minutes. If the scale is especially heavy, it is advisable to loosen it up by scrubbing with a wire brush to reduce the pickling time. All acids must be drained from the part, after which it should be thoroughly rinsed in cold running water. Parts to be electroplated should be transferred immediately to that bath after rinsing. All other parts should be immersed in a lime bath for 5 minutes to insure neutralization of any acid left on the part from the pickling solution. The lime bath is made by dissolving 20 pounds of quicklime in 100 gallons of water. After removal from the lime bath, the part should be drained, rinsed in clean hot water, and allowed to dry.

The pickling bath must be renewed occasionally, particularly if it turns brown. The lime bath will eventually become acid and must then be renewed. It should be tested periodically with a piece of blue litmus paper, which will turn red when the bath is too acid.

Pickling Aluminum Alloy. Aluminum alloy parts that have been welded, such as fuel and oil tanks, are given a pickling treatment to remove all traces of the welding flux. The complete and prompt removal of welding flux is necessary to prevent serious corrosive attack. A 10% sulphuric acid bath at room temperature is used for this treatment. The solution is held in a wooden tank lined with lead or painted with asphalt paint. After removing as much flux from the part as possible by washing with water, it is immersed in the acid bath long enough to remove all traces of the flux. This may take up to one hour. It is necessary to renew the acid bath as soon as it loses its effectiveness. After removal from the acid, the part should be washed in fresh running water for ½ hour. This is best done by means of a rinsing tank with a continuous supply of fresh water and an overflow.

In preparing a sulphuric acid solution, the acid should be poured slowly into the water while stirring with a wooden paddle. The water should never be poured into the acid.

Pickling Corrosion-Resisting Steel. Several methods and solutions for pickling corrosion-resisting steel are given in Chapter VIII.

PLATING OPERATIONS

Cadmium Plating. Cadmium plating is used more generally on aircraft parts than any other plating method. It is a general practice to cadmium plate all steel parts small enough to fit in the bath, prior to painting. Welded tubular fuselages, engine mounts, and landing gears are not cadmium plated because it is impractical. Steel parts are cadmium plated to increase their corrosion resistance. Cadmium plating does not improve the paint adherence to the surface but resists corrosion itself. In fact, it is sometimes difficult to make paint stick to cadmium plated surfaces unless they are kept exceptionally clean.

Parts made from copper or its alloys are frequently cadmium plated in order to reduce the electric potential between these parts and adjacent steel or aluminum parts. Cadmium lies between steel and aluminum in the galvanic series, which, in turn, are far removed from copper.

Aluminum can also be cadmium plated but it is seldom done because there is a better treatment available, known as the *anodic oxidation process* (which is discussed in the next section).

Cadmium plating is an electrical process carried out at a low voltage not exceeding 12 volts. The cadmium is deposited directly on the surface without the necessity of a preliminary coating of another metal. The cadmium deposit must be adherent, and without blisters, porosity, or other defects. A coating 0.0005 inch thick is usually specified except on threads where a minimum coating 0.0002 inch thick is required. Parts plated in this manner will withstand a 250-hour salt spray test without showing evidence of corrosion of the base metal. It is customary to select cadmium plated samples at random and submit them to a salt spray test periodically to check the quality of the plating that is obtained in production.

Before putting parts in the cadmium plating bath, they must be thoroughly cleaned by pickling or sandblasting. Pickling is preferable. Parts with more than 0.60% carbon should not be sandblasted. It is also essential to remove all particles of sand by immersing the part in a dilute solution of hydrofluoric acid. Copper, brass, and bronze parts must be pickled in a sulphuric acid solution prior to plating. All parts should be immersed for at least 30 seconds in a 2 oz./gal. solution of sodium cyanide immediately before plating.

The plating solution consists of sodium cyanide, cadmium oxide, and caustic soda dissolved in water at room temperatures. If a bright plating is desired, a brightener, such as hide glue or molasses, is added to the bath. The work to be plated is suspended by hooks or racks from the cathode bus bar and is completely immersed in the solution. Cadmium anodes are used. A voltage between 4 and 6 volts is required for this method of cadmium plating. Another method called the "barrel plating" method requires 8 to 12 volts. In this method the work to be plated is placed in a perforated barrel which revolves during the plating operation.

The thickness of the cadmium plating deposit is dependent upon the time and the current density. As expected, increasing either the time or current will increase the thickness of the coating obtained. The physical character of the coating is also determined by the rate of formation as controlled by the current density. A coarse, soft deposit is obtained with a low current, while a stronger current produces a fine-grained, hard deposit. A high current results in a "burnt" deposit. The ideal time and current density for any particular set of conditions must be established to obtain the desired hardness and appearance. For a cadmium deposit of 0.0005 inch the following combinations of time and amperage may be used to obtain satisfactory results. The amperage given is per square foot of surface to be plated.

TIME IN MINUTES	AMPERES PER SQ. FT.
10	29.5
20	14.8
30	9.8
40	7.4

It should be noted that the current is inversely proportional to the time.

After completion of the plating operation the work should be removed from the bath and rinsed with clean, warm water. It should then be immersed for one to two minutes in a 3% to 5% solution of chromic acid and given a final rinse in warm or hot water. The chromic acid solution removes all traces of alkali remaining on the plated surfaces and also passivates the cadmium. This treatment improves adhesion of paint to cadmium plating.

Springs and other parts less than ¼ inch in thickness and containing more that 0.40% carbon must be given a strain-relief treatment after electroplating or after pickling if no subsequent electroplating is done. Internal stresses are set up in thin material of high carbon content by the pickling process. The strain-relief treatment consists in baking the part at 350-400° F. for three hours after plating.

In shop practice the thickness of the cadmium coating is

determined by measuring the part, before and after coating, with a good micrometer. The thickness of the coating can also be determined by applying either of the following methods to test specimens:

1. The specimen is first cleaned with alcohol and wiped dry with a clean cloth. It is then immersed in a stripping solution which removes the cadmium plating. This solution consists of the following ingredients:

Hydrochloric acid (37%)............... 73 c.c.
Water............................... 27 c.c.
Antimony triocide.................... 2 grams

When immersed in this stripping solution the part gasses until the cadmium is all removed. The length of time that gassing continues depends upon the thickness of the cadmium coating. For each 0.0001 inch thickness of cadmium, gassing will continue for 20 seconds from the time the part is immersed. Thus, 60 seconds of gassing indicates an average plating thickness of 0.0003 inch.

2. The second method depends upon accurately weighing a specimen of known area when plated and after removal of the plating. Cadmium plating weighs 0.072 ounce per square foot for 0.0001 inch thickness of plating. A 0.0003 inch thick coating weighs 0.216 ounce per square foot of surface. To remove the cadmium plating, the antimony trioxide solution described above may be used, or a solution consisting of one pound of ammonium nitrate per gallon of water. This latter solution will remove the cadmium coating in two to three minutes. Both solutions should be used at room temperature.

If the cadmium plating on a part is defective or soiled it can readily be removed by means of one of the above solutions and the part replated. All brazing and welding of parts should be done before cadmium plating or the plating will be destroyed. It is very important that plated parts be painted as soon after plating as possible to minimize the amount of dirt or grease that will settle on the plated surface if allowed to stand. The parts should be handled as little as possible between plating and priming. For example, it was found that in one shop paint would not adhere satisfactorily to cadmium plated surfaces until the handling of the parts was cut in half by having inspection done in the paint shop itself. The chromic acid dip was also an aid in improving the paint adherence.

Galvanizing (Zinc Plating). Steel sheets are frequently galvanized for commercial work but seldom for aircraft. Before cadmium plating became common, it was the general practice to galvanize all steel aircraft fittings before painting. Galvanizing is not so effective in resisting corrosion as cadmium plating. Parts are galvanized by dipping them in molten zinc maintained at a temperature between 800-925° F. The parts remain in the zinc bath only a short time and are then removed and hung up until cool. Before dipping the parts in the bath, it is necessary to have them perfectly clean—an important requirement for all plating operations.

A zinc film can also be deposited on metal parts by an electroplating process similar to that described for cadmium plating. A solution of zinc sulphate and cyanide is used as the electrolyte and metallic zinc as the anode. A somewhat thicker plating is used than for cadmium plating to obtain equivalent corrosion resistance.

Sherardizing. Parts are sherardized by heating them in an atmosphere of zinc oxide. The zinc combines with the surface of the metal part increasing its hardness, durability, and corrosion resistance. The process is carried out by heating the parts in a closed, rotating chamber containing zinc oxide, at a temperature of about 700° F. Sherardizing is not considered to be as effective as zinc or cadmium plating.

Parkerizing. Parkerizing consists in heating the parts to be treated in a bath of dilute iron phosphate. The bath is kept at about 190° F. by steam coils. When the work is immersed in the bath, a rapid stream of bubbles passes off for a period of 30 to 45 minutes. When the bubbles stop, the coating process is complete. The coating left on the treated part is a mixture of ferrous and ferric phosphate and black iron oxide. The surface is dull gray in color and of smooth texture. It furnishes an excellent base for painting. This process has the added advantage of coating the inside of tubular members which cannot be done by any electroplating process. This property is particularly important for seaplanes where moisture is frequently trapped in crevices or inside tubular members.

Bonderizing. Bonderizing is the same as parkerizing, except for the addition of reagents to the bath which speed up the reaction. The process is completed in from 3 to 5 minutes by this method. After treatment the parts are removed from the bath and hot rinsed and dried. Bonderizing has the same characteristics as parkerizing with reference to paint adherence and penetration in crevices. Neither of these coatings is very corrosion-resistant in itself but are quite satisfactory when painted. These and similar processes are frequently referred to as compound phosphate rust-proofing.

Coslettizing. Coslettizing is almost identical with parkerizing, except for the fact that the solution used consists of iron filings and phosphoric acid and is more dilute. This treatment gives a black, non-rusting surface. It is used to some extent for engine parts.

Granodizing. Granodizing is an electroplating process by which zinc phosphate is deposited on the surfaces treated. The work to be coated is suspended from the cathode bar which is insulated from the tank containing the granodizing solution. The tank itself is the anode. An effort is made to coat the interior surfaces of tubing and remote corners by running anode mandrels inside them if possible. A current density of 36 amperes per square foot of surface is required for this treatment. A plating thickness of 0.005 inch is obtained in a period of about 3 minutes. The work is removed from the granodizing bath and immediately rinsed in cold water and dried. The coating is dull gray-black in color and is soft and velvety to the touch. It provides an excellent base for paint.

Metal Spraying. Metal spraying or metallizing, as it is sometimes called, is the surface application of molten metal on any solid base material. It is possible by this process to spray aluminum, cadmium, copper, nickel, steel or any one of a dozen metals onto metal, wood, or any solid base. In aircraft work the process is used chiefly to spray a coat of pure aluminum on steel parts to improve their corrosion resistance and paint adherence. Another very useful application is the spraying of seams and crevices in fittings which might trap moisture and then corrode. Metallizing seals these crevices and prevents the entrance of moisture.

The sprayed metal relies purely on the roughness of the surface of the base material for its adherence. The base material must be sandblasted to obtain a rough surface, as well as a perfectly clean surface. The sandblasting of aluminum alloy parts should be done with caution to avoid eating away too much of the metal. In order to prevent soiling of the surface by handling or oxidation, metal spraying should be done as soon after sandblasting as possible.

Metal spraying equipment consists of a supply of oxygen and acetylene piped to the spray gun and ending in a nozzle, at which point they can be ignited as in a welding torch. A supply of compressed air is also piped to the spray gun. This compressed air operates a feeding mechanism that draws the wire through the spray gun, and it also impels the molten wire onto the surface thus treated. The appropriate wire is led from a revolving reel through the rear of the spray gun, through the automatic feeding mechanism, and out through the nozzle. The wire is melted by the hot oxyacetylene flame and thrown against the surface by the compressed air. When the molten metal strikes the surface, it solidifies and cools fairly rapidly. If the surface is properly prepared, a perfect bond is formed between the metallized coating and the base material.

The spray gun is held from 4 to 6 inches away from the surface and as nearly perpendicular to the surface as possible. The nozzle must not be held at an angle less than 45° to the surface otherwise the metal particles will glide off and not adhere. In metallizing aluminum alloys, the base metal must not be permitted to become hot or its resistance to intercrystalline corrosion will be lowered. The surface is gradually covered by passing the gun back and forth with as much overlap as necessary to insure covering the entire surface evenly. The gun should be moved at such speed as required to obtain a satisfactory thickness of coating. The surface is slightly rough and forms a good base for paint.

In naval aircraft construction steel fittings in contact with aluminum alloy are metallized with pure aluminum and then painted. By this means corrosion due to dissimilar metals is eliminated. Whenever possible, steel structural parts which have been metallized with aluminum alloy should be boiled for 30 minutes in a 15% solution of potassium dichromate, rinsed in fresh water and dried. This treatment will increase the resistance to corrosion.

The following metals in wire form have been successfully passed through the spray gun and deposited on a surface: aluminum, babbitt, brass, bronze, cadmium, copper, high and low carbon steels, 18-8 corrosion-resisting steel, lead, monel, nickel, tin, zinc.

One of the major commercial uses of this operation is the building up of worn parts by spraying a thick coating of metal on the worn surface. In the case of steel shafts this is done by revolving the worn shaft slowly in a lathe and spraying it until it is about $\frac{1}{16}$ inch over the required size. It is then ground to size. A rough thread is cut in the worn surface before metallizing to provide a good bond for the sprayed metal. A metallized surface that is almost file hard can be obtained by using a high carbon steel wire.

Chromium Plating. Chromium plating is used particularly for its appearance, but it also resists corrosion. It makes a very hard surface which is exceptionally wear resistant—a property essential in the manufacture of chromium plated brake drums. Successful experiments have also been made on chromium plating worn shafts and wing hinge bolts, thus restoring them to their original dimension with a harder, more wear-resistant surface. The best results are obtained when the chromium is deposited in thick layers on the worn surfaces of fairly hard metal. In this process the chromium plating is deposited directly on the steel or other surfaces. When chromium plating for appearance, it is customary to copper or nickel plate the part first and then chromium plate.

Chromium plating is an electroplating process utilizing a bath consisting of 20% to 30% of chromic acid (CrO_3), a very small amount of sulphates in the form of sulphuric acid (1% of the chromic acid content), and the remainder water. This bath must be kept between 122° F. and 140° F. during the plating operation. A current density of 150 to 200 amperes per square foot of surface will produce a bright deposit over polished surfaces. Too high a current will produce a burned or satin finish, while too low a current will give a bluish plate or insufficient covering.

Parts to be plated must be thoroughly cleaned by immersing in an alkali bath, rinsing, immersing in a hydrochloric acid bath, rinsing, and finally placing in the chromium bath while still wet. If a polished chromium surface is desired, the part must be polished and buffed before cleaning and immersion in the plating bath. It is difficult to chromium plate in recesses due to the poor throwing power of the solution. If it is necessary to plate recesses, the anodes must be shaped in a similar manner to the recess and located as far in as possible.

Anodic Oxidation Process

This process, which is referred to as *anodizing,* is used exclusively for coating aluminum and aluminum alloy surfaces. An aluminum hydroxide surface is produced on the work which has good corrosion resistance and provides an excellent bond for paint. This treatment is *not* a plating process. The anodized surface is soft and easily scratched, which necessitates giving the treated surface a coating of primer before handling it to any extent.

Government agencies require the anodic treatment of all aluminum or aluminum alloy parts and the manufacturer recommends it for all alloys, except Alclad. If Alclad is to be left unpainted, no anodic treatment is necessary. If the Alclad is to be painted, however, it should be anodically treated to provide a bond for the paint. Aluminum alloys containing over 5% copper cannot be anodically treated without destroying the electrolyte in a chromic acid bath and must be anodized in a sulfuric acid bath. Castings are seldom anodically treated, because they already have an excellent rough surface for the adherence of paint. In addition castings usually have sufficient thickness of metal to minimize the danger from a little surface corrosion. Steel and copper parts cannot be treated by this process. All steel and copper parts must be left off assemblies to be anodically treated.

It is a general practice to anodically treat all parts prior to assembly. When subassemblies do not contain any dissimilar metals, fabric, or sealing compound, and are not subjected to contact with salt water, it is permissible to treat them as a unit. Such parts as wing ribs, built-up brackets and shelves are in this classification. The anodic film will penetrate about one inch inside the edge of a riveted joint, but will not coat the metal immediately adjacent to the rivet inside the joint. It is important to do all cutting, drilling, and forming possible prior to anodic treatment in order not to break up the film. The rupture of the film after treatment permits local corrosion. To avoid even slight abrasion of the anodic film, all work is primed after treatment before assembling. This coat of primer also improves the corrosion resistance of the material between faying surfaces. It is sometimes impractical to do all drilling prior to anodizing as in the construction of a monocoque fuselage or hull where it would be necessary to make a complete assembly, dismantle it, anodically treat the parts, and then reassemble permanently. In such cases it is permissible to drill holes on assembly after anodizing. The screws or rivets inserted in these holes must be coated with wet primer when inserted to protect the raw edge exposed by the drilling.

The standard electrolyte used in the anodic oxidation process is a solution of chromic acid (CrO_3) in water. The chromic acid content varies from 5% to 10% in different baths. The chromic acid must be at least 99.5% pure and is limited in its sulphate and chloride content. The tank is made of steel and is equipped with iron pipe coils for heating and cooling purposes, as well as equipment for agitating the electrolyte. A direct current generator permitting voltage control between 20 and 40 volts is used. In order to adequately rinse the plated parts and facilitate drying, a second tank containing water at 150° F. to 185° F. must be available.

Parts to be treated normally require no cleaning, but, if coated with grease, oil, or paint, they should be cleaned with thinner, solvent, or free-rinsing soap or cleaners. The parts to be treated are suspended in the electrolyte by means of wires, clamps, or perforated containers made of aluminum or aluminum alloy. These clamps or attachment parts must make a complete electrical contact to insure a free passage of electric current throughout the entire system. The parts are suspended from the anode connection; the steel tank is the cathode. If parts are too large to fit in the tank, they can be treated in sections by slightly overlapping adjacent films. During treatment the temperature of the electrolyte must be maintained between 91° F. and 99° F. The voltage is gradually built up to 40 volts and maintained at that figure as long as necessary. The length of time depends upon the percentage of chromic acid in the electrolyte. A minimum period of 30 minutes is required for a 10% chromic acid solution. A longer time is required with more dilute solutions. After treatment to accelerate drying the parts are washed in clean, fresh, hot water at a temperature between 150° F. and 185° F.

Because of the importance of a perfect anodic film all parts are inspected after treatment and before painting. Any discontinuity or damage to the film requires retreatment. If there is some doubt about an imperfection in the film, an indelible pencil or ethyl violet dye mark should be made on the spot and then rubbed off with a damp cloth. If the film is satisfactory, it will retain the indelible mark. This fact is made use of in stamping anodically treated surfaces. An inspection stamp is made on each part using indelible ink. This inspection stamp will remain on the part even after the removal of paint that has been subsequently applied. The anodic film will also bring out small cracks in the metal that were invisible before treatment. All bends are particularly examined after anodic treatment for cracks. When inspecting anodically treated parts care must be taken to avoid soiling the surface, which would destroy the paint adherence. If inadvertently soiled, the anodic surface should be cleaned with carbon tetrachloride before painting. All anodically treated parts should be given at least one coat of primer before issuing to the shop for assembly purposes.

The effectiveness of the anodic bath should be checked monthly by selecting random samples anodized with routine production work and submitting them to a salt spray test. The salt spray test consists of exposing the sample to a 20% sodium chloride solution for 30 days. Its appearance is compared before and after exposure to this test. Any evidence of corrosion is cause for rejection. The physical properties of the corroded specimens are also checked by means of tensile tests on three samples, and compared to the results obtained on two samples prior to the salt spray test. The maximum allowable decrease in strength is 5%, and decrease in elongation 10%, of the original physical properties as established by the two tests prior to the salt spray test.

Welded aluminum alloy tanks can be successfully anodically treated provided all the welding flux is removed by pickling, as previously described in this chapter. The anodic coating on the inside of the tank is inferior, however, unless an elaborate arrangement of cathodes is provided for the interior of the tank. Riveted tanks with a seam compound for sealing cannot be treated without destroying the seam compound. In this case the material should be treated before riveting. Rivets are anodically treated before heat treatment. Parts must not be heat treated in a salt bath after anodic treatment, otherwise the film will be destroyed. All parts except rivets are anodically treated after heat treatment and forming are complete. When rivets are heat treated in a tubular container, as described in the chapter on Wrought Aluminum Alloys, the anodic film is not injured.

There are several other solutions besides chromic acid for the anodic treatment of aluminum and its alloys. The most important of these is a sulphuric acid solution method which is patented in this country. It is used for aluminum alloy parts containing over 5% copper. It cannot be used for anodizing sub-assemblies, however, since any sulfuric acid not removed from crevices will cause corrosion. This sulfuric acid anodize is called the Alumilite treatment.

Potassium dichromate has been found to be an effective inhibitor of corrosion of aluminum alloys. When applied to anodized surfaces the dichromate is absorbed in the anodic coating and greatly improves its corrosion resistance. The interior of fuel tanks is protected by this means after anodizing. They are boiled in a 4% potassium dichromate solution for 30 minutes to seal the anodic coating. An alternate method is the location of small perforated cartridges filled with potassium dichromate at the lowest point of the fuel tank. This method is recommended for the protection of low points along the keel inside seaplane floats and hulls. Any moisture or salt water that collects at these points will leech out small quantities of potassium dichromate, which will inhibit corrosion. Potassium dichromate gives water a brownish color. When clear water is drained from a fuel tank it indicates the dichromate crystals are exhausted. In washing out the interior of hulls, it is believed the addition of a small amount of potassium dichromate to the rinsing water will prove beneficial. A mild solution of 0.5% by weight is generally recommended.

Alrok Process. This is a chemical dip process for the surface treatment of aluminum alloys which is almost as good as anodic treatment. It consists of oxidizing by immersion in a hot solution (212° F.) of sodium carbonate and potassium dichromate for about 30 minutes followed by a sealing treatment in a hot 5% potassium dichromate solution.

The Aluminum Company of America licenses the use of this process for a nominal sum. It is approved for use by the Army.

Treatments for Magnesium Alloy Parts

Chrome-Pickle Treatment. This treatment is designed exclusively for magnesium base alloy parts to improve their corrosion resistance and paint adherence. This treatment removes from .001 to .002 inch of metal surface. All magnesium alloy parts as obtained from the producer, except die castings, are given this treatment to protect them during shipment, storage, and machining. This treatment is applied primarily to electrical system parts requiring low electrical resistance. It is necessary to remove all oil, grease, oxide film, and welding flux from parts to be treated. Grease and oil may be removed by washing with carbon tetrachloride, gasoline, benzol, or other solvents that will not attack the metal. The oxide film may be removed by wire brushing, steel wool, light sandblasting, sanding, or by a sulphuric acid pickle. The pickle solution should contain from 1% to 10% sulphuric acid. After pickling, the parts should be quickly washed in cold running water, followed by a hot water rinse. To remove welding flux, the welds must be thoroughly scrubbed with hot water and a wire brush. Inaccessible welds should be washed with a high velocity stream of hot water.

The chrome-pickle solution is held in an earthenware, aluminum, or stainless steel tank. It is composed of 1½ pounds of sodium bichromate, 1½ pints of nitric acid (specific gravity 1.4), and enough water to make one gallon of solution. The solution must be maintained at a temperature between 70° F. and 90° F. All parts to be treated must be thoroughly clean and dry before immersion in the chrome-pickle solution. Unwelded parts are immersed in the solution for from ½ to 2 minutes. Welded parts should be thoroughly agitated in the solution for 2 to 3 minutes. Large parts that cannot be immersed in the solution should be preheated with steam or hot water and then brushed with plenty of the hot chrome-pickle solution. About 5 seconds after removal from the chrome-pickle bath the parts should be washed in cold, running water followed by hot water to accelerate drying. Paint should be applied to the treated surfaces as soon as they are dry.

Parts properly treated have an iridescent, brassy coating. When the bath is low in acid a loose, brown coating is formed. Acid must then be added in small quantities until the proper coating is obtained. When the sodium bichromate is low, a green foam collects on the solution and a pale green coating is obtained on the part. Nitric acid must be added more frequently than bichromate.

Modified Alkali-Chromate Treatment. The protection toward salt water afforded by this treatment is superior to that obtained by the chrome-pickle treatment. Furthermore this treatment will not affect the dimensions of the parts treated. It is the preferred treatment for all the alloys in their various forms with the exception of Alloy No. 11, AM3S, Dowmetal M. This alloy should be given the galvanic anodizing treatment described below.

Parts to be treated must be thoroughly cleaned as described under the chrome-pickle treatment. Any chrome-pickle coating remaining on parts will not impair the modified alkali-chromate treatment, and does not have to be removed.

This treatment consists of immersing parts for 5 minutes in a water solution containing 15 to 20% by weight of hydrofluoric acid at room temperature followed by a thorough wash in cold running water. The parts are then immersed for 45 minutes in a boiling solution containing:

Ammonium sulphate	4 oz./gal.
Sodium dichromate	4 oz./gal.
Ammonia	$\frac{1}{3}$ fl. oz./gal.
Water to make	1 gal.

They must then be washed thoroughly in cold running water followed by boiling for at least 5 minutes in a water solution containing 1% by weight of arsenous oxide. This is followed by rinsing in cold running water and a dip in hot water to facilitate drying.

Properly applied coatings will vary from dark gray to black.

Galvanic Anodizing Treatment. This treatment is preferred for Alloy No. 11, and is second choice for the other magnesium alloys. Any chrome-pickle coating remaining on parts will not impair the effectiveness of this treatment.

Parts to be treated should be cleaned and given the 5-minute hydrofluoric acid dip described above under the modified alkali-chromate treatment. The parts should then be immersed and galvanically anodized for 30 minutes at room temperature in the same ammonium sulphate, sodium dichromate, ammonia, water solution described above. The parts to be treated are electrically connected with the cathode and a current density of at least 2 amperes per square foot is maintained. Parts must be rinsed in cold running water and then be dipped in hot water to facilitate drying.

This treatment produces a uniform dark gray to black coating. The dimensions of parts are not affected by this treatment.

Sealed Chrome-Pickle Treatment. This treatment is identical with the chrome-pickle treatment described above except that after drying the chrome-pickled part is immersed in a bath containing 10-20% dichromate (potassium, sodium, or ammonium) by weight maintained at a boiling temperature. After remaining in this bath for 30 minutes the parts are rinsed in cold running water and then dipped in hot water to facilitate drying.

This treatment is applicable to all magnesium alloy tanks.

PAINTS

The final finish operation on aircraft materials is painting. The sole purpose of most of the plating operations is to improve the bond between the paint and the surface of the part. The added corrosion resistance contributed by the plating is, of course, welcome, but it is subordinate to a good paint job. A satisfactory paint must be resistant to corrosive mediums such as salt water, must resist abrasion, must be elastic to prevent cracking, must have good adhesive qualities, and must give a smooth finish and good appearance. There are any number of paints on the market that will meet these requirements to a reasonable degree.

Painting consists of the application of a priming coat, followed by finishing coats of varnish, enamel, or lacquer. All of these have given satisfactory service on airplanes. For special locations, such as the interior of seaplane hulls, a bituminous paint is used. In the vicinity of storage batteries an acid-resisting paint is used. The various types of paints used will be described in the following pages.

Paint. Paint is a mechanical mixture of a vehicle and a pigment. The vehicle is a liquid that cements the pigment together and strengthens it after drying. The pigment gives solidity, color, and hardness to the paint.

The pigment selected for paint must be corrosion inhibitive and inert in order to protect the underlying surface. Since the pigment also contributes color to the paint, a variety of pigments are used in different colored paints. Among the commonly used pigments are: iron oxide, zinc chromate, titanium oxide, iron blue, lead chromate, carbon black, and chrome green.

The vehicles used for paint may be divided into two general classes:

1. *Solidifying oils* which, on exposure, dry and become tough, leathery solids. The most common of these oils used in aircraft paints is known as China Wood oil, or Tung oil. This oil dries quickly and is tough, durable, and free from cracks. Another common solidifying oil is linseed oil. It is not so good as China Wood oil but does dry to a tough, elastic film. It can be obtained in the raw state, in which it is most effective, but it takes several days to dry. The addition of driers, such as lead or manganese oxides, will shorten the drying time appreciably by acting as catalysts and drawing oxygen from the air into the oil. Boiled linseed oil will also dry quickly but is not so effective as raw linseed oil.

2. *Volatile oils*, or spirits, which evaporate when exposed. These oils are used to dilute paint to the proper consistency and to dissolve varnish resins. The most common volatile vehicles are: alcohol, turpentine, benzine, benzole, toluene, ethyl acetate, and butyl acetate.

Ordinary paints, varnishes, and enamels are usually composed of a pigment and a mixture of both solidifying and volatile oils. Lacquer, which is noted for its rapid drying, is composed only of pigments, resins, and volatile oils.

Primer. A priming paint must have definite corrosion inhibitive qualities since it is in direct contact with the surface of the metal. It must also have good adherence on the bare metal or plated surfaces, as well as furnishing a good base for the top coats of paint. In aircraft work it is customary to assemble parts after priming and apply the finish coats after assembly. Under these conditions the primer must be tough and durable to resist abrasion and scratching. There are two primers that are generally used on aircraft; namely, *red iron oxide* primer, and *zinc chromate* primer. Zinc chromate primer has practically superseded red oxide primer.

Red iron oxide primer has a brownish-red color. Its pigment is iron oxide and a small amount of zinc chromate. The nonvolatile vehicle is made of a resin, China Wood oil, and some linseed oil. About one-third of the primer is composed of volatile mineral spirits and turpentine. This primer spreads and adheres well and is very durable. It will dry to touch in 1½ hours, and completely in 6 hours. This primer is satisfactory for use on metals as a protective primer coating under oil enamels, but not under nitrocellulose lacquers or enamels. It should not be used on wood.

Zinc chromate primer has become the universal choice for aircraft work because of its general all-around qualities. This primer is greenish-yellow when applied. When the color is too yellow, it indicates too thick a coat. Its pigment is practically all zinc chromate with some magnesium silicate. The vehicle consists of resins, drying oils, and hydrocarbon solvents. The exact selection of the vehicle is left to the discretion of the paint manufacturer. This primer dries to touch in 5 minutes, and completely in 6 hours. This rapid drying to touch is a great aid in speeding up shop operations. Zinc chromate primer is satisfactory for use under oil enamels or nitrocellulose lacquers. It is also an excellent dope-proof paint. It can be painted over enamels to protect them from subsequent doping operations as on fabric covering of wings or fuselages.

The application of zinc chromate primer should be done by spraying because of its rapid drying qualities. It is thinned with toluene to obtain a suitable working viscosity. It can be applied rapidly by brush but the operation is difficult and undependable. Parts can also be dipped in this primer but should be withdrawn slowly enough to permit excess primer to run off.

Zinc chromate primer will only adhere to cadmium plated

parts if they have been given a chromic acid dip and are perfectly clean. If cadmium plated parts are baked after priming, satisfactory adherence will also be obtained. One and one-half hours of baking at 160° F. is normally required.

The dope-proofing qualities of zinc chromate primer are excellent. For this purpose a heavy coating should be used as indicated by a full yellow color. This primer can also be used in a similar capacity to seal an oil enamel finish to which a lacquer coating must be applied. Six hours should be allowed for drying before application of the lacquer.

Aluminum powder is frequently added to zinc chromate primer for use as an interior finish coat. This material is excellent except in locations subject to usage or handling.

Zinc chromate pigment has better corrosion inhibiting properties than any other pigment. It is believed these properties are derived from the electrolytic depolarizing action of chromate ions which are liberated in the presence of water. This action makes zinc chromate primer very resistant to the starting or continuation of electrolytic corrosion.

Lacquer. A nitrocellulose lacquer is often used for the finishing coats on airplanes. These lacquers consist of cellulose nitrate, glycol sebacate, glycerol phthalate resin, volatile spirits such as toluene, butyl acetate, butyl alcohol, and ethyl acetate, and pigment as necessary to give the correct color. Lacquers can be obtained in practically any color desired. They are lighter in weight than other airplane finishes and can be touched up readily in service. Lacquer dries almost instantly when applied. It may be used on fabric or metal surfaces. Lacquer does not have as good corrosion-resisting qualities as aluminum pigmented varnish, but is wholly satisfactory for other than seaplane work.

Varnish. Varnish, unlike paint, is a solution and not a mixture. It consists of resins dissolved in oil or mineral spirits. Oil varnishes are those in which the oil dries and becomes part of the film after application.

Aircraft Spar Varnish is used for outside exposed surfaces of wood, metal, and doped fabric. It gives a clear, transparent protective coating. It is also used as a vehicle for aluminum pigment, aircraft enamels, and primers. This varnish is a phenol formaldehyde varnish. It consists of resin, China Wood oil, some linseed oil, driers, mineral spirits, turpentine, and dipentine. It can be brushed or sprayed successfully. It dries to touch in 1½ hours, and completely in 5 hours. This varnish is particularly good under conditions involving exposure to salt water as in seaplane hulls.

Glyceryl Phthalate Spar Varnish also gives a clear, transparent coating. It is used as a finishing coat on wood, metal, or primed surfaces, as well as a vehicle for aluminum pigment. The enamel formed by aluminum pigment and this varnish is very often used to finish airplanes. Glyceryl phthalate resin, modifying agents, and hydrocarbon solvents are the ingredients of this varnish. It can be brushed or sprayed. It dries to touch in 3 hours, and completely in 18 hours.

Enamel. Enamel is a mixture of a pigment and varnish. Varnish acts as the vehicle. Enamels are harder and more durable than paints. They are frequently used for the top coats in finishing airplanes. The color of enamels depends upon the pigment. Practically all aircraft enamels are made by mixing a pigment with spar varnish or glyceryl phthalate varnish, both of which are described just above.

Aluminum pigmented varnishes are being rapidly adopted for general use because of their protective qualities. The spar varnish mixture is believed to be somewhat better than the glyceryl phthalate varnish mixture as a protection against salt water corrosion. For general work, however, aluminum pigmented glyceryl phthalate varnish is more often used. The aluminum pigment is usually purchased in the form of a powder or paste and mixed with the varnish as needed. The aluminum pigment is made from commercially pure aluminum. An extra fine powder capable of passing through a No. 325 sieve is used for aircraft paints. This pigment mixes well with the varnishes described and gives a continuous, brilliant film. It is advisable to apply a final coat of clear varnish to fix the aluminum pigment which otherwise adheres to any object that touches it, especially clothing.

Acid-Resistant Paint. Acid-resistant paint is used to coat the inside of battery boxes and the vicinity of such boxes. An asphalt varnish that is resistant to mineral acids is used for this purpose. This varnish is jet black in color and has good brushing qualities. It dries to touch in 5 hours, and completely in

24 hours. It is resistant to sulphuric acid, nitric acid, or hydrochloric acid.

Bituminous Paint. Bituminous paint is manufactured from a coal tar derivative and suitable solvents. For aircraft purposes it is usually pigmented with aluminum powder. The unexposed parts of hulls, floats, wings, and tail surfaces on seaplanes are usually protected with two coats of aluminum bituminous paint. This paint will bleed through any other paint. Particular care must be taken when it is used under fabric covering to prevent it from staining the fabric. In this case all painted parts in contact with the fabric should be thoroughly covered with aluminum foil prior to covering. Generous lapping of the foil is necessary to protect the fabric.

Soya Bean Oil Compound. This compound is composed of non-volatile raw soya bean oil, ester gum, and China Wood oil combined with a small amount of volatile turpentine. It is used as a seam compound for making metal hulls and floats watertight. This compound weighs 7.85 pounds per gallon. When completely exposed it takes over six days to dry hard.

Marine Glue. Marine glue contains rosin, pine tar, denatured alcohol, and a drying oil, such as China Wood oil, rosin oil, or linseed oil. It is used as a seam compound on either wood or metal hulls for watertightness. It is very adhesive and remains tacky.

Rust Preventive Compound. Rust preventive compounds are applied to fittings, strut ends, and similar places over their regular protective finish to increase the corrosion protection. They are applied by brushing, dipping, or spraying at a temperature around 150° F. They are nondrying and form a continuous, adherent, protective coating. They can be removed with kerosene.

Beeswax and Grease. A mixture of beeswax and grease applied hot is often used in place of rust preventive compound. This mixture is very effective in resisting corrosion.

Paralketone. Paralketone is an all-purpose rust preventive compound for use on both ferrous and non-ferrous metals and for the lubrication and protection of cables. It has also been used to spray inaccessible parts of seaplanes over the normal paint finish. It has displaced beeswax and grease and other rust-preventive compounds to a large extent.

FINISH OF DETAIL PARTS

In this section the author will endeavor to recommend a satisfactory finish for each of the parts that makes up an airplane. The recommendations will apply particularly to seaplanes in which the most severe corrosion conditions are met. Many of the recommendations can be modified somewhat for less severe service conditions.

Control Cables. These cables should not be painted, but will be satisfactory if coated with a mixture of white lead and tallow, or graphite, or grease. The coating must be renewed periodically.

Oil Tanks. Oil tanks constructed of aluminum alloy should be anodized and painted with one coat of primer and two coats of varnish, enamel, or lacquer on the outside surface. The inside is left unpainted. If the oil tank is visible and readily accessible, the painting may be replaced by a coating of rust preventive compound.

Fuel Tanks. Fuel tanks should be anodized and painted the same as inaccessible oil tanks. To protect the inside of the fuel tank, it should be boiled, after anodic treatment, in a 4% potassium dichromate solution for 30 minutes.

Tank Supporting Straps. These straps should be given the regular finish of one coat of primer and two top coats. The padding for the tanks and straps should be immersed in castor oil until impregnated.

Storage Battery Boxes. The inside of battery boxes and surfaces within 12 inches of the battery, or other surfaces on which acid might be spilled, should be given the regular finish plus two coats of acid-proof paint followed by two coats of clear varnish.

Copper, Brass, Bronze. These parts do not require any treatment unless it is necessary to match a paint job, or for insulation between dissimilar metals such as steel or aluminum.

Magnesium Alloy Parts. These parts should be given a chrome-pickle treatment followed immediately by a coat of primer and three coats of the finish paint.

Faying Surfaces. Non-watertight faying surfaces should be given two coats of primer, or one coat of primer and one coat of finish paint. The first coat should be thoroughly dry before applying the second. Watertight faying surfaces should be given the same treatment and should be assembled with a strip of impregnated fabric or flannel between the joint. The fabric should be impregnated with a sealing compound, such as soya bean oil compound, marine glue, bituminous paint, or one of the patented compounds on the market.

Steel Tubular Members. The ends of these members should be sealed by welding to exclude the entrance of moisture. After completion of all fabrication operations, the inside of the tubing should be flushed with hot raw linseed oil or a rust preventive compound. Oil at a temperature over 160° F. is forced through a small hole in one end of the tube under pressure. When the assembly comprises more than one tube as in a welded fuselage, interconnecting holes are drilled between adjacent tubes. The presence of the hot oil in each tube must be checked by feeling it with the hand. The oil must remain in the tubes not less than two minutes after which it is drained. All holes opened to the outside should then be filled with cadmium plated self-tapping screws. These oil holes should be located in the region of lowest stress, and the drive screws should just fit the hole snugly without stretching, cracking, or splitting the surrounding metal. Serious failures have resulted from cracks started by driving self-tapping screws in highly stressed locations.

Aluminum Tubular Members. It is not practical to seal the ends of aluminum alloy members by welding; so they should be left wide open at the ends to permit drainage. The interior surfaces should be given the same finish as the outside surfaces. End fittings should be designed, so that they do not form pockets to trap moisture.

Welded Steel Structures. Structures such as fuselages, landing gears, and engine mounts should be oiled internally, sandblasted, and painted.

Hull Interiors. The interior of hulls and floats should be finished with two coats of aluminum bituminous paint.

Seaplane Finish. After being given their regular finish, all open end struts should be dipped in a hot rust preventive compound to a depth of 18 inches from the end. The strut should then be drained and wiped on the outside. All strut attachment fittings should be coated with rust preventive compound after assembly. All other parts subject to spray should also be coated with this compound. An alternative to rust preventive compound is a mixture of beeswax and grease which can be applied in the same way.

Aside from the special treatments just described, all parts of the airplane should be finished with one coat of primer and two or more top coats. Inaccessible parts subject to severe corrosion should be given three top coats or two coats of aluminum bituminous paint. All steel parts should be cadmium or zinc plated when possible prior to painting. Other steel parts should be sandblasted, parkerized, bonderized, or granodized. Aluminum alloy parts should be anodically treated prior to painting. Careful preparation and care in painting will pay dividends in freedom from corrosion troubles.

Chapter XVI

WOOD AND GLUE

General Uses of Wood

The use of wood in aircraft construction has been largely superseded by aluminum alloys and steel. It is still used extensively, however, in the construction of wing spars and ribs for small commercial airplanes. Wood propellers are still in common use and in some countries are preferred to metal propellers. Wood is also used with good effect for interior cabin trim and flooring. Due to its relative cheapness and the ease with which it can be worked to any desired shape, wood is ideal for the construction of the first experimental model of an airplane. The practice of using wood for this purpose will become more general, it is believed, when mass production of airplanes is a reality. Under these conditions the manufacture of jigs and dies will be too costly a gamble until a cheaply built experimental plane has been thoroughly test flown. In England and France it is common practice to construct entire airplanes of wood covered with plywood.

Wood has the advantage of large bulk for a given weight, combined with relatively great strength. The tensile strength of wood in particular is exceptionally good. These properties make wood ideal for the manufacture of lightly stressed wing spars, such as are found in small civil aircraft. The ease of working is also important when only small quantities of planes are being built. Wood has excellent elastic properties which permit stressing almost to the breaking point without excessive permanent deformation. It also has the ability to resist a greater load for a short period of time than it is capable of carrying for a long period. This ability is very valuable in aircraft construction in which peak loads are only imposed momentarily.

The nonhomogeneity of wood is its greatest disadvantage. The properties of wood vary even for two pieces taken from the same tree. The properties of a piece of wood are also dependent upon the moisture content. Then too the direction of the grain is of prime importance to the physical properties. Being the product of natural growth in the form of trees, wood is subjected to numerous experiences which leave their mark in the form of defects or flaws. A very careful inspection must be made of all wood before it can be accepted for aircraft use. This inspection limits the amount of wood available for aircraft and increases the cost. It is extremely difficult to obtain a long length of wood of moderate cross-sectional dimensions for use as a wing spar. Before designing a wooden spar it is advisable to locate a reliable source of supply that can furnish wood of acceptable quality and of the desired dimensions.

Naming Wood. In purchasing wood it is essential that the botanical as well as the common name be given. The same wood frequently has many different common names. One species of pine has as many as thirty local names. On the other hand, the common name of cedar is often applied to several unrelated species.

The botanical name of a plant or tree is made up of terms denoting the genus and species. For example, Picea is the generic name that includes all the species of spruce, while sitchensis, rubens, and canadensis apply to particular species of the genus spruce. Picea sitchensis, Picea rubens, and Picea canadensis are complete botanical names for what are commonly called Sitka spruce, red spruce, and white spruce, respectively.

Classification of Trees and Woods. Trees are divided into two general groups which are known as:

1. *conifers*—softwoods, needleleaf, evergreen
2. *hardwoods*—deciduous, broadleaf, dicotyledons, non-coniferous

Conifers is the most common name applied to the first group. The other names are not all applicable because some of the woods of this group are not soft, some do not have narrow leaves as indicated by "needleleaf," and others are not evergreens. Pines, firs, cedars, and spruces belong in this group. Coniferous trees cover large areas in parts of Canada and the United States. Their wood is comparatively light in weight, is easy to work, and is obtainable in large, straight pieces.

Hardwoods is the common name applied to the second group. This name, as well as the others applied to this group, are not wholly true. Some of the woods of this group are soft, others are not deciduous but retain their leaves. Ash, birch, mahogany, maple, oak, poplar, and walnut belong in this classification. Hardwood trees grow in many parts of the world in natural forests and under cultivation. They are relatively heavy in weight, difficult to work because of their complicated cell structure, and obtainable only in relatively small lengths.

There is also a third type of tree known as Monocotyledons. This group includes the palm and bamboo trees. They have little or no structural value.

STRUCTURE OF WOOD

A tree trunk is composed of four distinct parts—a soft central core called the *pith*, concentric rings immediately surrounding the pith called the *heartwood*, which in turn is surrounded by the *sapwood*, followed by the *bark*.

The pith or medulla, as it is technically called, is evident in the sections of young trees for which it serves as a food storage place. In mature trees the pith is nothing but a point or a small cavity.

Heartwood or duramen is a modified sapwood. Each year as a new annular ring is added to the sapwood the heartwood also increases. It is formed from the adjacent sapwood, which dies, and the infiltration of coloring matter and other substances into the cell walls and cavities. Heartwood is heavier, tougher, and darker than sapwood. In the living tree heartwood is subject to attack by fungi, but after cutting it is more resistant to insect attack, decay, stain, or mold than sapwood. The amount of heartwood present in a tree varies with the species from one half to over ninety per cent of the area.

Sapwood or alburnum is the younger, lighter colored, more porous wood located just under the bark of the tree. The cells of sapwood are alive and serve for the storage and translocation of food. Sapwood is more pliable than heartwood and is preferable when severe bending must be done. It is as strong as heartwood except in the case of very old trees, in which the sapwood is inferior.

Bark is the husk or outer cover that protects the tree. It does not serve any useful structural purpose.

Wood is composed of a great number of minute structural

units or cells. These cells vary considerably in size and shape within a piece of wood and between species. The thickness of the cell walls and their arrangement, together with associated materials such as water, determine the physical properties of the wood. Due to its cellular structure wood has good bending strength and stiffness for a given weight, but it has low hardness.

The specific gravity of the substances that comprise wood is practically the same for all woods. The differences in physical properties of various species of wood are due to the cell size and wall thickness. For any particular wood the strength is proportional to its specific gravity.

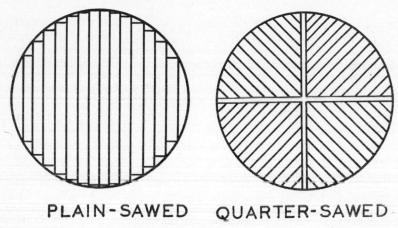

PLAIN-SAWED   QUARTER-SAWED

FIGURE 52. METHODS OF SAWING LOGS

Sawing Wood. All trees, except Monocotyledons, grow annually by the addition of a concentric layer of wood around the outside surface of the sapwood. An examination of any tree trunk or log will show these concentric layers which are called annual rings. In sawing logs into planks the wood can be sawed in either of two ways: along any of the radii of the annual rings, which will expose the radial or vertical-grain surface; or tangent to the annual rings. These two methods of sawing are shown in Figure 52. There would be too much waste involved in sawing only along the radii; hence a modification, called *quarter-sawing*, is actually used. Even quarter-sawing wastes considerable material and is therefore more expensive than tangential sawing. Quarter-sawed lumber shrinks and swells less, and develops fewer flaws in seasoning than tangential lumber. Tangentially cut lumber is commonly called *plain-sawed* or *flat-grain surface*.

Government specifications for aircraft wood usually specify that either vertical-grain (quarter-sawed) or flat-grain material is acceptable providing not more than 25% of any shipment is flat-grain material.

Grain. The grain of wood is determined by the direction of the fibres. It always runs along the length of a piece of lumber, but it is not always straight. The strength of a piece of wood without reasonably straight grain is greatly reduced. Aircraft wood specifications require that the grain shall not deviate more than one inch in twenty inches from a line parallel to the edge of the lumber. Even less deviation than this is desirable for the best strength properties. For parts whose failure will not endanger the airplane, a grain slope of one in fifteen is usually acceptable.

Spiral grain is a defect often found in lumber. Spiral grain occurs when the fibres take a spiral course in the tree trunk as if the tree had been twisted. In examining for spiral grain, the edge of the board farthest from the center should be used since the slope of the spiral grain is greater in this location than it is at the center. An artificial spiral grain is produced if straight-grained stock is not cut parallel with the fibres as seen on the tangential face. All spiral grain is objectionable because of its weakening effects, the rough surface produced by planing against the grain, and its tendency to twist in seasoning. The slope of spiral grain should not exceed 1 in 20 for important members and 1 in 15 for other parts used in aircraft construction.

Diagonal grain, which is also objectionable, is produced when the direction of sawing is not parallel to the bark. It occurs when timber is sawed parallel to the center, or in sawing crooked logs. This type of grain also weakens the wood and produces a rough surface when planed against the grain. The same slope of grain is permissible as with spiral grain for aircraft work.

Interlocked grain occurs when adjacent layers of wood are spirally inclined in opposite directions. This condition is found mostly in hardwood trees, such as mahogany and sycamore. This type of grain causes warping and makes planing difficult. Interlocked-grain lumber does not split so easily as straight-grained material. Mahogany used for aircraft propellers has interlocked grain, but does not warp seriously or offer much difficulty in planing.

Wavy and curly grain are the result of the wood fibres in a tree following a contorted course. The grain is always distorted when knots or wounds are grown over. These types of irregular grain weaken the wood and cause irregular shrinkage and rough surfacing when machined.

STRENGTH OF WOOD

The strength of wood depends upon a great many factors. The absence or limitation of defects is a primary consideration. The density of the wood as indicated by its specific gravity is a very definite indication of its quality and strength. Its moisture content has also been found to affect its strength probably more than any other one item. Still another important feature is the rate of growth of the tree as shown by the number of annual rings per inch. In some instances the strength of a piece of wood is dependent upon the locality in which it was grown. It is apparent that great care must be taken in selecting a piece of lumber for aircraft use when its strength is all-important.

Specific Gravity vs. Strength. The minimum acceptable specific gravities for aircraft woods are given in Table 13. The strength of a piece of wood varies almost directly in proportion to its specific gravity. It has been found that a 10% increase in the specific gravity will improve the following physical properties in the same proportion: compression parallel to the grain and modulus of elasticity in static bending. At the same time the shock resistance will be increased over 20%.

Because of the great variation in weight caused by different moisture contents, the specific gravity of wood must be determined for an oven-dry condition. The specific gravity of a piece of wood can be readily established by the following method: cut a sample of the wood about 1 inch in length along the grain for any desired cross section. Place the sample in an oven and heat it for two to three days at a temperature of 212° F. until all its moisture is evaporated and its weight has become constant. The oven-dried specimen should be weighed while hot and the weight recorded in grams (1 ounce = 28.4 grams). The volume of the specimen should be calculated from accurate measurements of its dimensions. The accuracy of this calculation can be improved by selecting a smooth, regularly shaped specimen. The volume should be recorded in cubic centimeters (1 cubic inch = 16.4 cubic centimeters). The specific gravity may then be computed by dividing the oven-dry weight in grams by the volume in cubic centimeters. This, of course, is based on the fact that one cubic centimeter of water weighs one gram, and its specific gravity is 1.

Locality of Growth *vs*. Strength. Most woods have equal strength, providing their specific gravities are the same, irrespective of their locality. This is particularly true of Sitka spruce, black walnut, maple, and birch. Douglas fir grown in the Rocky Mountains has considerably less weight and strength than the same species grown on the Pacific Coast. Along with this difference in strength in the two localities it should be noted that there is also a similar difference in weight.

Rate of Growth *vs*. Strength. Hardwoods of very rapid growth are usually above the average in strength properties. An exception to this rule is swamp-grown ash which grows very rapidly but is inferior in weight and strength. Aircraft specifications list this particular type of wood as unacceptable.

The conifers or softwoods, such as spruce, are below the average in strength when rapidly grown. It is customary to specify a minimum number of annual rings per inch for softwoods as a criterion of the rate of growth. For aircraft spruce the requirement is a minimum of six annual rings to each inch when measured in a radial direction on either end section through the zone of maximum growth.

Moisture Content *vs*. Strength. The strength of wood is very dependent upon its moisture content. Under natural service conditions it has been found that the moisture content of wood will stabilize at a maximum of 15% of the dry weight. Since it is not safe to figure on lower moisture contents with their greater strengths, all design calculations are based on figures for wood with 15% moisture content.

Moisture is present in wood as free water in the cell cavities and as hygroscopic moisture in the cell walls. The free water has no effect on the strength of the wood. When the moisture in the cell walls is decreased, the wood shrinks and increases in strength. The amount of moisture present in wood is regulated

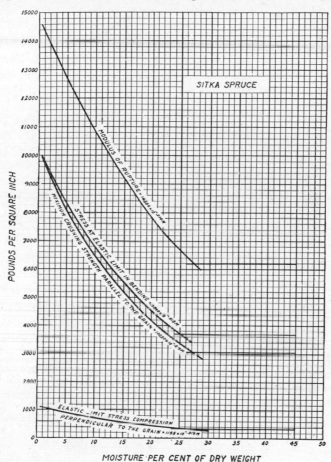

FIGURE 53. RELATIONS BETWEEN STRENGTH AND MOISTURE CONTENT

by a seasoning process. It will be noted in Table 13 that there is considerable shrinkage between green lumber and oven-dry lumber. It is essential that wood be seasoned to approximately the moisture content it will reach in service in order to minimize the shrinkage and swelling of finished parts.

The strength of wood increases very rapidly with a decrease in the moisture content. Figure 53 shows this increase of strength for Sitka spruce that has been carefully dried. It will be noted that a considerable increase of strength is available in wood with less than the standard 15% moisture content. Tests have shown that it is not safe to count on this extra strength, however, since under normal conditions wood will stabilize at 12 to 15% moisture content. This is true even though the wood is thoroughly protected with varnish. The varnish merely delays the absorption of the normal amount of moisture but does not prevent it.

The moisture content of a piece of wood can be determined by the following method: cut a specimen from the wood to be checked that is at least 5 cubic inches in volume but as small in the direction along the grain as possible. It is desirable to have the specimen about one inch long in the direction of the grain in order to shorten the time of drying. After cutting, the specimen should be smoothed up and weighed immediately in order to avoid any change in the moisture content. It should then be placed in a drying oven and dried for 2 to 3 days at 212° F. until the moisture is exhausted and the specimen has reached a constant weight. The dry weight of the specimen should then be determined immediately after removing from the oven. When the dry weight is subtracted from the original weight, the difference represents the weight of moisture in the original specimen. This difference divided by the oven-dry weight and multiplied by 100 is the percentage of moisture content of the specimen tested.

Defects *vs*. Strength. Defects in wood are very common and have a very bad effect on the strength. In purchasing wood for aircraft construction, the type and amount of defects that will be acceptable are always specified.

Sloping grain is the most common defect. This constitutes spiral, diagonal, wavy, curly, interlocked, or other distorted grain. The general rule is to specify that grain cannot have a slope of more than 1 in 20 for important lumber, such as that used for wing spars, and a slope of not more than 1 in 15 for lumber to be used for such items as boat frames, stringers, and interior fitting supports. When a combination of two types of sloping grain is present, such as spiral and diagonal grain, it is necessary to compute the combined slope. These two types of grain occur at right angles to each other, and, therefore, the combined slope can be computed by taking the square root of the sum of the squares of the two slopes. This is best done by converting the slope into decimals before squaring. Thus a spiral grain of 1/25 and a diagonal grain of 1/20 would be 0.04 and 0.05, respectively. Squaring these fractions, adding, and taking the square root will give 0.064 which is 1/15.6. The combined slope then is 1 in 15.6, although the individual slopes were good enough for first-class lumber. Experience has shown that wood with a large sloping grain not only has reduced strength but is very variable in other properties, and is unpredictable.

Knots reduce the strength of wood largely because the grain is distorted in their vicinity. Knots should not be permitted along the edge of a piece of wood or in the flange of a wing spar. An occasional knot is permissible in other locations providing the grain distortion is not greater than 1 in 20 or 1 in 15 because of the presence of the knot. It is usual to restrict the size of knots to 1/4 inch in important members and 1/2 inch in lesser members. The knots should be sound and tight. The weakening effect of knots, due to distorted grain which accompanies them, may be better appreciated when it is realized that the strength of wood along the grain is from 30 to 60 times stronger than across the grain.

Pitch pockets are lens-shaped openings between annual rings which contain resin. They vary from under one inch to several inches in length and are found only in such woods as pine, Douglas fir, and spruce. Pitch pockets are permitted in aircraft wood if they do not exceed 1 1/2 inches in length and 1/8 inch in width, and when not more than one is present in a 12 foot length of wood. Pitch pockets are not permitted in the edge of a member or in a wing spar flange on the same basis on which knots are excluded.

Mineral streaks are dark brown streaks containing mineral matter and are found in such woods as maple, hickory, basswood, and yellow poplar. They extend for several inches to a foot along the grain and are from 1/8 to 1 inch wide. Mineral streaks are frequently accompanied by decay. For this reason close inspection of wood containing them is essential. If decay has set in the toughness of the wood will be greatly reduced.

Compression wood should never be used in aircraft parts. This is the name given to wide annual rings found on the lower side of leaning trees. It has a high specific gravity, very low strength, and abnormally high longitudinal shrinkage. It is subject to excessive warping and twisting. Compression wood is found frequently in conifers but not in hardwoods.

Decay in any form is not permissible in aircraft wood. Decay will reduce the shock resisting qualities of wood in its early stages and seriously reduce all the strength properties as it develops. All stains and discolorations should be carefully inspected, for they may be the start of decay.

Checks, shakes, and splits in wood are causes for rejection. All of these defects weaken the wood, cause internal stress, and are generally unreliable. A *check* is a longitudinal crack in wood running across the annual rings and is usually caused by unequal shrinkage in seasoning; a *shake* is a longitudinal crack running between two annual rings; a *split* is a longitudinal crack in wood caused by rough handling or other artificial means.

Wood containing compression failures must not be used for strength members. These failures which appear as a fine wrinkle across the face of the wood are caused by severe winds bending standing trees, felling trees on irregular ground, or other rough handling inducing high stresses in the wood. Compression failures seriously reduce the bending strength and shock resistance of wood parts. Compression failures are sometimes so small the aid of a microscope is needed to detect them.

STRENGTH PROPERTIES

Table 13 gives the strength values of the various woods used in aircraft construction. Due to the variation in the strength of wood caused by many different factors, it was necessary to standardize a number of these factors in order to establish definite strength figures. The following notes explain the bases on which Table 13 is founded.

An extensive investigation of the moisture content of wood in various locations about the country and aboard battleships at sea showed the average moisture content to be between 12% and 13%. Some wood, however, had a content as high as 15%. Since the strength of wood with 15% moisture content is considerably less than that with only 12%, it was important to establish a standard value of strength that would cover the 15% wood. For this reason the strength values given in Table 13 are based on wood with 15% moisture content.

TABLE 13

STRENGTH VALUES OF WOODS FOR USE IN AIRPLANE DESIGN *

Common and Botanical Names	Specific Gravity (Based on oven-dry vol. and wt.)		Weight at 15% Moisture Content, lb./cu. ft.	Shrinkage from Green to Oven-Dry Condition		Static Bending				Compression Parallel to Grain		Compression Perpendicular to Grain, lb./sq. in.	Shearing Strength Parallel to Grain, lb./sq. in.	Hardness-load in lbs. to imbed 0.444" Ball to 1/2 its Diameter
	Average	Minimum Permitted		Radial %	Tangential %	Stress at Elastic Limit, lb./sq. in.	Modulus of Rupture, lb./sq. in.	Modulus of Elasticity, 1000 lbs./sq. in.	Work to Maximum Load, in.-lb./cu. in.	Stress at Elastic Limit, lb./sq. in.	Max. Crushing Strength, lb./sq. in.			
HARDWOODS														
Ash, commercial white ((Fraxinus...)	.62	.56	41	4.3	6.9	8,900	14,800	1460	14.2	5250	7000	1920	1380	1180
Basswood (Tilia Americana)	.40	.36	26	6.6	9.3	5,600	8,600	1250	6.6	3370	4500	530	720	370
Beech (Fagus atropunicea)	.66	.60	44	6.0	10.6	8,200	14,200	1440	13.5	6500	6500	1430	1300	1060
Birch (Betula...)	.68	.58	44	7.0	8.5	9,500	15,500	1780	18.2	5480	7300	1300	1300	1100
Cherry, black (Prunus serotina)	.53	.48	36	3.7	7.1	8,500	12,500	1330	11.7	5100	6800	1000	1180	900
Elm, cork (Ulmus racemosa)	.66	.60	45	4.8	8.1	7,900	15,000	1340	19.3	5180	6900	790	1360	1230
Gum, red (Liquidambar styraciflua)	.53	.48	34	5.2	9.9	7,500	11,600	1290	10.9	4050	5400	1010	1100	650
Hickory, true (Hicoria...)	.79	.71	51	.....	.....	10,600	19,300	1860	27.5	6520	8700	2650	1440	.....
Mahogany, African (Khaya species)	.47	.42	32	4.8	5.5	7,900	10,800	1280	8.0	4280	5700	1200	980	720
" true (Swietenia species)	.51	.46	34	3.4	4.7	8,800	11,600	1260	7.3	4880	6500	1510	860	790
Maple, sugar (Acer saccharum)	.67	.60	44	4.6	9.2	9,500	15,000	1600	13.7	5620	7500	1850	1520	1270
Oak, white (Quercus alba)	.69	.62	45	4.6	9.0	7,800	13,800	1490	13.6	4950	6600	1600	1300	1240
Poplar, yellow (Liriodendron tulipifera)	.43	.38	28	4.0	7.1	6,000	9,100	1300	6.5	3750	5000	690	800	420
Walnut, black (Juglans nigra)	.56	.52	39	5.2	7.1	10,200	15,100	1490	11.4	5700	7600	1480	1000	990
CONIFERS														
Cedar, Port Orford (Chamaecyparis lawsoniana)	.44	.40	30	4.6	6.9	7,400	11,000	1520	8.7	4880	6100	880	760	520
Cypress, bald (Taxodium distichum)	.48	.43	32	3.9	6.1	7,100	10,500	1270	7.7	4960	6200	1050	720	480
Douglas fir (Pseudotsuga taxifolia)	.51	.45	34	5.0	7.8	8,000	11,500	1700	8.1	5600	7000	1100	810	620
Pine, white (Pinus strobus)	.38	.34	25	2.2	6.0	5,900	8,700	1140	6.3	3840	4800	670	640	380
Spruce (Picea...)	.40	.36	27	4.1	7.4	6,200	9,400	1300	7.8	4000	5000	720	750	440

*Table prepared by Forest Products Laboratory of the United States Department of Agriculture.

In testing wood specimens it was found that the strength values obtained varied considerably. It was at first thought that the arithmetical mean average of the values obtained should be computed and used as the standard value. However, it was discovered that considerably more specimens gave strength values below this average than above it. It was then decided to establish the standard value as the most probable value that would be obtained. From a number of tests on Sitka spruce, Douglas fir, and white ash the most probable strength value was found to be 94% of the average value. This factor was applied to the average strength to obtain the values given in the table for elastic limit and modulus of rupture in static bending, and elastic limit and maximum crushing strength in compression parallel to the grain.

Another factor has also been applied to the test results to arrive at the standard strength values for these stresses as given in the table. This is a factor based on the ability of wood to resist greater stresses for a short period of time than it can carry for an extended period. In view of the fact that aircraft loads are imposed only momentarily, as at the instant of pulling out from a dive or when hitting an air bump, it was decided to base the standard strength values on a 3 second duration of stress. It was found that a piece of wood could sustain a load 1.17 times the normal load sustained over a longer period. The most probable values were thus multiplied by 1.17 to obtain the figures listed in Table 13.

The modulus of elasticity values given in the table are only 92% of the average values of the apparent modulus of elasticity values (E_c) computed from the formula

$$E_c = Pl^3/48dI$$

when applied to a bending test of 2×2 inch beams of 28 inch span, centrally loaded. The use of the modulus of elasticity values given in the table in computing the deflection of ordinary beams of moderate length will give fairly accurate answers. For exactness in the computation of the deflection of I and box beams of short span, a formula that takes shear deformations into account should be used. Such a formula involves E_t (the true modulus of elasticity in bending) and F (the modulus of rigidity in shear). Values of E_t can be obtained by adding 10%

to the modulus of elasticity values given in the table. If the I or box beam has the grain of the web parallel to the axis of the beam, or parallel and perpendicular thereto as in some plywood webs, the value of F is $E_t/16$. If the web is of plywood with the grain at 45° to the axis of the beam, F is $E_t/5$.

The values for work to maximum load in static bending represents the ability of the woods to absorb shock, after the elastic limit is passed, with a slight permanent deformation and some injury to the member. It is a measure of the combined strength and toughness of a material under bending stresses. It is of great importance to aircraft parts subject to shock loads or severe vibration. Material with a low value of work to maximum load is brittle or brash, as it is called in wood, instead of tough as is desirable.

The values in the table for the elastic limit in compression parallel to the grain were obtained by multiplying the values of maximum crushing strength in the next column by 0.80 for conifers and by 0.75 for hardwoods.

The values in the table for compression perpendicular to the grain are partly computed and partly test values. Wood will not exhibit a definite ultimate strength in compression, particularly when the load is applied over only a part of the surface as at fittings. Beyond the elastic limit the wood crushes and deforms while the load increases slowly. The values in the table were obtained by multiplying the average stress at elastic limit by 133⅓%. By this method design values were obtained which are comparable to the values for bending, compression parallel to the grain, and shear as listed in the table.

The values for shearing strength parallel to the grain were obtained by multiplying average values by 0.75. This factor was used because of the variability in strength and to make failure by shear less likely than by other means. The values listed are used for computing the resistance of beams to longitudinal shear. Tests have shown that by the use of a conservative shearing strength value shearing deformations are limited and a better stress distribution occurs. This better stress distribution results in a maximum strength/weight ratio and a minimum variation in strength. These benefits will be realized if the shearing strength values given in the table are used.

AIRCRAFT WOODS AND THEIR USES

The woods described in the following pages are the same as those listed in Table 13. It will be noted that only partial botanical names are given in the table for ash, birch, hickory, and spruce. In each of these cases the generic name is given but not the species. The reason for this is that there are several species of these woods with the same strength values as listed. The complete botanical name for each of these species will be given below.

Ash, White. The following species of ash which are ordinarily marketed under the name of "white ash" are satisfactory for aircraft use:

> White ash (Fraxinus americana)
> Green ash (Fraxinus lanceolata)
> Blue ash (Fraxinus quadrangulata)
> Biltmore ash (Fraxinus biltmoreana)

Ash is fairly heavy but is also hard, strong, and elastic. It resembles oak in many ways but is lighter, easier to work, tougher, and more elastic. A maximum of 16 annual rings per inch is desirable for the best grade of ash. Second growth ash is better than first growth.

Ash is used largely for bent parts. After steaming the wood can be bent to a radius of twelve times the radial width of the member. Ash is sometimes used where toughness and solidity are necessary as in door jams and sills.

Basswood (Tilia americana). Basswood trees are known by many names such as limetrees, linden, teil, beetrees, and bass. The wood is light, soft, easily worked, and tough, but not strong or durable when exposed to the weather. It receives nails without splitting better than most other woods.

Basswood is used extensively for webs and plywood cores.

Beech (Fagus atropunicea). This species of beech is also known as (Fagus grandifolia). Beech wood is heavy, hard, strong, and tough but not durable when exposed. It is liable to check during seasoning.

Beech is frequently used for facing plywood when hardness is desired. It will take a very fine polish.

Birch. The following species of birch are satisfactory for aircraft work:

> Sweet birch (Betula lenta)
> Yellow birch (Betula lutea)

Birch wood is heavy, hard, strong, tough, and fine-grained. It also takes an excellent finish. Due to its hardness and resistance to wear it is often used to protect other woods.

Birch is the best propeller wood among the native species and is also the best wood for facing plywood when a high density wood is desired. Birch plywood is very commonly used in this country.

Cherry, Black (Prunus serotina). Black cherry wood is moderately heavy, hard, strong, easily worked, and fairly straight-grained. It is an excellent base for enamelled paints.

Black cherry is sometimes used in manufacturing aircraft propellers.

Elm, Cork (Ulmus racemosa). Cork elm is also known as rock elm. It is heavy, hard, very strong, tough, elastic, and difficult to split. It will take a beautiful polish. It is low in stiffness but very resistant to shock, because of its tough and elastic qualities. It steam bends well and is used as a substitute for ash. Elm suffers from interlocked grain, and will twist and warp badly if not properly dried.

Gum, Red (Liquidambar styraciflua). Red gum trees are also known as sweet gum. Gum wood is moderately heavy, soft, and suffers from interlocked grain which causes warping if not carefully seasoned. The wood glues and paints well, and also holds nails well.

Gum is used in the manufacture of plywood for semihard faces or cores. The heartwood is used for the faces of plywood.

Hickory. The following hickory trees, which are generally grouped as "true hickories," are satisfactory for use in aircraft:

> Shagbark hickory (Hicoria ovata)
> Bigleaf shagbark hickory (Hicoria laciniosa)
> Mockernut hickory (Hicoria alba)
> Cow oak (Quercus michauxii)

Wood of the true hickories is the heaviest and hardest wood listed in the table. It is also extremely tough.

Hickory is seldom used in aircraft construction because of its weight. Its excellent toughness and hardness are useful for special applications. Commercially it is used largely for axe handles.

Mahogany, African (Khaya senegalensis). African mahogany comprises a number of species. Another also commonly known is called Khaya grandifolia. African mahogany differs somewhat from true mahogany because it does not have well defined annual rings. Mahogany works and glues well and is very durable. It shrinks and distorts very little after it is in place.

African mahogany is used for semihard plywood faces. It is also very decorative and responds well to stain and other finishing processes.

Mahogany, True (Swietenia mahagoni). True mahogany is also known as Honduran mahogany when it comes from that country. Similar mahoganies are obtained from Mexico and Cuba. True mahogany is strong and durable, but brittle. It glues and works well.

True mahogany is used in the manufacture of aircraft propellers and for the semihard faces of plywood.

Maple, Sugar (Acer saccharum). Sugar maple is also called hard maple. It is one of the principal hardwood trees of North America. It is heavy, hard, and stiff, and very difficult to cut across the grain. This wood has a very uniform texture and takes a fine finish. It wears evenly and is used as a protection against abrasion.

Sugar maple is used for hard faces in the manufacture of plywood and occasionally for aircraft propellers. A soft maple is sometimes used for semihard plywood faces.

Oak. The following species of oak are used for propeller construction or for bent parts in aircraft. They are classified as "white oaks."

> White oak (Quercus alba)
> Bur oak (Quercus macrocarpa)
> Post oak (Quercus minor) or (Quercus stellata)
> Cow oak (Quercus michauxii)

A number of red oaks are also used occasionally, but they are more subject to defects and decay, and are inferior to white oaks.

Oak is heavy, hard, strong, and tough. The radial shrinkage in oak is only about one half the tangential shrinkage. This fact makes quarter-sawn oak excellent for propeller construction. Oak propellers are used for seaplanes, particularly because of their resistance to the abrasive action of water spray.

In addition to propeller construction, oak is used for members that must be bent. White oak can be bent to a radius of about 15 inches for finished sections up to 3 inches thick. Steaming before bending is, of course, necessary.

Poplar, Yellow (Liriodendron tulipifera). Yellow poplar is a hardwood whose properties qualify it as a substitute for spruce. It is sometimes called whitewood or tulip poplar. This wood is light, soft, moderately strong, but is brittle and has low shock resistance. It has good working properties, shrinks little, and is hard to split. Another characteristic is that it is free from such defects as checks and shakes. Poplar trees grow very large.

Poplar may be used as a substitute for spruce. It is also used as a core for plywood.

Walnut, Black (Juglans nigra). This wood is heavy, hard, strong, easily worked, and durable. It is difficult to season but holds its shape very well in service.

Black walnut is used in the manufacture of propellers. Next to birch it is rated as the best native propeller wood.

Cedar, Port Orford (Chamaecyparis lawsoniana). Port Orford cedar is one of a group known as white cedars. Its wood is light, strong, durable, and easily worked.

As a substitute for spruce it can be used in aircraft construction. It is also used for semihard faces of plywood.

Cypress, Bald (Taxodium distichum). Bald cypress is also known as southern cypress. Its wood is fairly light, soft, moderately strong, and durable. The living trees are subject to a fungus disease that causes cavities in the wood. When felled the disease stops, and the wood is very durable.

Cypress does not have any special application in aircraft construction.

Douglas Fir (Pseudotsuga taxifolia). This wood, also known as red fir and yellow fir, is not one of the true fir family. Douglas fir trees grow as high as 300 feet with a diameter of over 10 feet. Its wood is moderately heavy and strong, but splits easily and is rather difficult to work. It can be obtained in large pieces and is a good substitute for spruce.

In addition to substituting for spruce, Douglas fir is also used as a core for plywoods.

Pine, White (Pinus strobus). This is used commercially as a general purpose wood. It is light, soft, rather weak, but durable. It works easily; nails without splitting; seasons well; and shrinks and warps less than other pines.

White pine can be used as a substitute for spruce and as a core for plywood.

Spruce. This is the standard structural wood for aircraft. All of the following species are satisfactory for this purpose:

> Sitka spruce (Picea sitchensis)
> White spruce (Picea glauca) or (Picea canadensis)
> Red spruce (Picea rubra)

Spruce is a light, soft wood with a moderate strength. It has an excellent strength/weight ratio and has been obtainable in the past in the sizes required for aircraft construction. These two facts explain its general adoption for aircraft work. It works easily and seasons well.

Due to the extensive use of spruce in aircraft, it has become increasingly difficult to procure lumber of the required quality. For this reason substitutes have been sought and used, as mentioned in the foregoing pages. Specifications for aircraft spruce require the average lengths of a shipment to be 26 feet, with none under 16 feet. Widths vary from 4 to 8 inches and over. It is difficult to obtain material for wing spars when a cross section such as 3 × 3 inches is specified.

SEASONING OF WOOD

As noted previously, wood shrinks considerably as the moisture content is reduced. The percentage reduction in dimensions caused by drying green wood is given in Table 13. When wooden parts are manufactured, it is essential that their moisture content be approximately that which they will attain in service; otherwise they will not hold their shape. Freshly cut "green" lumber is saturated with moisture. It has been found that if this lumber is allowed to stand it will eventually dry to a much lower moisture content. The point at which the moisture content will be in equilibrium is determined by the humidity and temperature of the surrounding air. This point varies for different sections of the country but averages around 12% to 13% moisture content.

The natural drying of lumber by the weather is called air-seasoning. However, air-seasoning is seldom used for aircraft wood, because it takes from one to two years for completion and it cannot be controlled as accurately as artificial seasoning. A method of artificial seasoning known as *kiln-drying* has been developed by which any desired moisture content can be obtained in less than one month.

Air-Seasoning of Wood. The chief use of air-seasoning is on surplus stocks of lumber which, while awaiting selection for manufacture, can be partly air-seasoned. This partial seasoning is an aid in obtaining good kiln-drying of the lumber, since its moisture differential is much less than green stock.

Air-seasoning is performed by carefully piling the green lumber under a shed that will protect it from rain and snow, but will permit air to circulate through it. The foundation for the pile of lumber must be at least 18 inches high and have a slope of one inch per foot from front to rear. In piling the wood, good sized air spaces must be provided to insure ventilation of all wood in the pile. To avoid checking of the ends of the lumber, caused by premature drying, the ends must be painted with a hardened gloss oil, paraffin, or pitch.

Figure 54 has been prepared by the Forest Products Laboratory of the United States Department of Agriculture to show the relationship between the moisture content of wood and the temperature and humidity of the surrounding air. As expected the moisture content is high when the humidity is, but is reduced by an increase in temperature. Lumber stored in the open has a higher moisture content in winter than in summer because of the higher humidities and lower temperatures.

Kiln-Drying of Wood. Kiln-drying of wood is based upon the relationship between external air humidity and temperature and the moisture content of the wood. In the kiln-drying compartment these variables are closely regulated by means of heating coils and sprays. There is also a natural or forced system of ventilation through the carefully piled lumber. The temperature is gradually increased and the humidity lowered in the compartment as the moisture content of the lumber decreases. The exact procedure varies for different species of wood. In the case of spruce drying starts with a temperature of 125° F. and 80% relative humidity when the moisture content is above 25%,

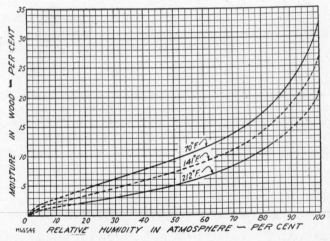

FIGURE 54. ATMOSPHERE HUMIDITY vs. WOOD MOISTURE CONTENT

but these figures are changed with each 5% reduction in moisture content until a temperature of 138° F. and relative humidity of 44% is reached for 15% moisture content. When the moisture content is down to 12%, the temperature is changed to 142° F. and the relative humidity to 38%. Careful adjustment of temperature and humidity is necessary as the drying progresses to insure a steady, even drying and freedom from internal strains.

In order to ascertain the moisture content at any point in the drying process, samples are inserted in the pile of lumber. These samples must represent the thickest, wettest, and slowest drying material in the pile. It is customary to use three samples placing one at average, one at slowest, and one at fastest drying locations. These samples are removed daily and weighed. Since the dry weight of the sample is known from a moisture content determination made on the green sample, the additional weight at any time represents the moisture content.

The kiln-drying of spruce requires from 18 to 24 days. It is desirable to end up with a moisture content just under 12%. When this is done there is no danger of warpage of finished parts due to a large absorption of moisture in service.

BENDING OF WOOD

Wooden parts can be bent either by steam bending or by laminating the member and gluing it in the desired shape. Steam bending can only be applied to hardwoods.

In steam bending the wood is steamed at 212° F. for a period of one hour per inch of thickness. The steamed wood is bent over a form and clamped in place until dry. Wood to be steam bent should be finished approximately to size before steaming. When a piece is wider than it is deep, it is advisable to bend a piece double the required depth and cut it into two parts after it has dried.

Bending by lamination consists in gluing a number of layers of wood together. Each layer is fairly thin along the radius of the curve. Immediately after gluing, the member is clamped to the form and left there until the glue has set and the wood is dry. A variation of this method applicable to hardwoods is to use fairly heavy sections which have been steam bent approximately to shape and thus reduce the number of laminations.

GLUES AND GLUING

In wooden aircraft construction glue plays a very prominent part. Many wood joints depend wholly upon the joining power of glue for their strength. It is necessary for aircraft glue to be absolutely reliable. It must retain its strength under adverse conditions, such as when wet, hot, or attacked by fungus, and must not deteriorate rapidly with age. There are four types of glue commonly used in aircraft which possess the necessary properties to a satisfactory extent. They are *urea resin, casein, blood albumin,* and *animal* glues. Vegetable and liquid glues such as fish glue are not satisfactory for aircraft work. Phenol resin glue

TABLE 14

PROPERTIES OF AIRCRAFT GLUES

CHARACTERISTICS	UREA RESIN	CASEIN	BLOOD ALBUMIN	ANIMAL
Strength (dry)	Very high	Very high to high	High to low	Very high
Strength (wet after soaking in water 48 hours)	75–100% of dry strength	25–50% of dry strength	50 to nearly 100% of dry strength	Very low
Rate of setting	Rapid	Rapid	Very fast with heat	Rapid
Working life	4 hours	Few hours to a day	Few to many hours	4 hours
Temperature requirements	70° F. satisfactory; 140° F. ideal	Unimportant	Heat preferable	Control for glue, wood, and room important
Dulling effect on tools	Negligible	Moderate to pronounced	Slight	Moderate
Tendency to stain wood	None	Pronounced with some woods	Dark glue may show through the veneers	None to very slight

used in the construction of waterproof plywood is described later in this chapter under "Plywood." Table 14 lists the relative properties of the four types of aircraft glues. This table is based upon the use of the best quality of each type. There are many variations in the quality of these glues available on the market; hence care must be exercised in obtaining the proper grade for aircraft work.

Urea Formaldehyde Resin Glues. This glue is an excellent all-purpose glue for aircraft shop work. It is water and fungus resistant. It will cure at room temperature (70° F.) but is superior when cured at 140° F. under pressure for 4 to 8 hours. The pressure required is only that necessary to bring the parts into close contact, or to slightly compress the softer woods such as spruce. This glue has approximately a 4-hour life and can be used within that period after mixing. It will deteriorate if heated in water above 145° F. but is water resistant at normal temperatures.

Urea resin glue is now available as a dried powder under several trade names. When the powder is dissolved in cold water the resulting glue is ready for use.

Casein Glues. Casein glue was the all-purpose glue in aircraft construction prior to the development of urea formaldehyde resin glue. Casein is obtained from curdled milk and is combined with other materials to form a glue. It is usually sold in powdered form, with detailed instructions from the maker on the method of preparing it. Generally, one part of casein glue powder is mixed with two parts of water by weight to form a liquid glue. To obtain the best results it is necessary to follow a definite mixing technique. The powdered glue is sprinkled or sifted into a container of water while a mixing paddle is turning about 100 revolutions per minute. When the powdered glue has all been added, the paddle speed is slowed down to 50 revolutions per minute and kept going for 20 to 30 minutes until a smooth mixture of even consistency is obtained. The speed of stirring is limited to avoid adding an excessive amount of air to the mixture.

Casein glue should only be used within four hours of its preparation. It is customary in most shops to prepare fresh batches each morning and afternoon. All mixing utensils must be thoroughly cleaned before preparing a new batch to prevent inclusion of old glue in the new mixture. The use of Lily cups to hold a small supply for each man is one way of insuring purity. When casein glue is applied to wood, it should be clamped for at least five hours, preferably over night to permit thorough setting.

Blood Albumin Glues. Blood albumin glues are used in gluing standard plywood. They are very water-resistant, exceeding even the best casein glue in this respect. These glues are made from an albuminous base from the blood of slaughtered animals, combined with chemicals, such as lime, caustic soda, or sodium silicate. The blood albumin is obtainable as a powder, and the mixture is added to about twice as much water, more or less, depending upon the consistency desired. Blood albumin glues cannot be bought in the prepared state since they deteriorate rapidly if not used.

In the manufacture of plywood the water-resistant properties of the blood albumin glue is improved by pressing the plywood between two hot plates while the glue is setting. Steam heated plates are used which keep the glue at a temperature of about 160° F. up to 30 minutes, depending on the glue used.

Animal Glues. Animal glues were used extensively in gluing propellers. Urea resin or casein glue has replaced them somewhat because of better all-around qualities. Animal glues are manufactured from the hide, bones, or sinews of animals. These materials are boiled in water, and the extract concentrated and jellied by cooling. When desired for use the dry glue is thoroughly soaked in cold water for several hours and then heated in a closed retort at 140° F. to 150° F. The glue is kept at this temperature while being used. Glue which has been heated for over four hours must be discarded. One pound of dry glue should be mixed with 2¼ pounds of water in order to obtain the normal consistency.

Gluing Wood. Wood to be glued must be seasoned to the proper moisture content. Thin pieces of wood, such as laminations, should have a lower moisture content (5% to 10%) than thicker pieces (8% to 12%) in order to compensate for the relatively greater amount of moisture they absorb from the glue. The moisture content for propeller stock is usually specified as 8% to 10%.

Wood should be machined after seasoning when it is to be glued. The surface must be smooth and square. Surfacing should be done by machine not by hand to avoid irregularities. It is not necessary to scratch or sand the surfaces to be glued.

Glue must be spread uniformly on either or both surfaces of the work. Too thin a glue or not sufficient glue will result in a "starved" joint. An excess of glue is preferable although this may result in a "dried" joint if the glue lacks water. The glued surfaces must be clamped or pressed together with a uniform pressure of from 100 to 200 pounds per square inch. This pressure should be maintained for 5 hours or longer if possible. It is then necessary to allow the glued parts to condition themselves for 2 or more days before machining or finishing. During this conditioning period the glue moisture is absorbed uniformly throughout the wood.

PLYWOOD

Plywood is a material made by gluing a number of plies of thin wood together. Each sheet of thin wood is known as veneer. Veneer over $\frac{1}{10}$ inch thick is seldom used in the manufacture of plywood. The grain of adjacent layers of veneer run at right angles to each other, which makes plywood equally strong in two directions. Except for a special 2-ply plywood, all plywood is manufactured with an odd number of plies to obtain symmetry. The center ply or plies are usually made of a soft wood and are considerably thicker than the two face plies made of a hard wood. A hard wood is used for the face plies to resist abrasion, to furnish a better contact for washers and fittings, and to take a better finish.

Plywood is used in the construction of box spars for wings, webs of ribs, wing and fuselage covering, especially for the leading edge of the wing, as well as for flooring and interior cabin paneling. A plywood with a metal sheet cemented to one face to take excessive wear is often used for flooring.

The following woods are generally used in the manufacture of plywood:

HARD FACES	SEMIHARD FACES	CORES
Birch	Mahogany	Basswood
Beech	Sycamore	Douglas fir
Maple (hard)	White elm	Fir
	Maple (soft)	Gum
	Red gum (heart)	Pine
	Port Orford cedar	Poplar
	Spruce	Redwood
		Spruce
		Port Orford cedar
		Western hemlock

Birch and mahogany plywood are most commonly used in aircraft construction. Basswood is the most common core material. The special 2-ply material mentioned above is made of spruce and is used almost exclusively for the webs of box spars. In this application the grain of the two plies are at right angles to each other and at 45° to the axis of the spar. Other plywoods vary from 3 to 15 plies with 3 being most commonly used. When 9 plies or more are used the 2 outside plies on each side must be hardwood of the same species. Several different veneers are sometimes used in one plywood but any one layer must be all of the same material.

The veneers used in making plywood are either rotary cut, sliced, or sawed. Rotary cut veneers are thin circumferential slices of wood cut from logs revolving in a lathe. Due to the slight taper of a tree trunk it is impractical to cut the veneers in an exact tangential plane, and consequently the grain is not absolutely parallel. Excessive cross grain is not permitted in aircraft plywood. Sliced or sawed veneers are cut tangential to the annual rings and are not so strong as rotary cut veneer. The veneer for aircraft plywood must be sound, clear, smooth, of uniform thickness, and without defects.

Army-Navy Aeronautical Specification AN-NN-P-511 covers aircraft plywood. This specification provides for the use of the woods listed above and for thickness and plies as tabulated on page 281.

Aeronautical Specification AN-NN-P-511 provides for two types of plywood:

Type 1—Standard plywood.
Type 2—Waterproof plywood.

Standard plywood is the older type of plywood assembled
with blood albumin, soya bean, or starch glue. It is not resistant
to boiling water or prolonged soaking in water and is subject to

Total Thickness of Plywood (In.)		Number of Plies	Thickness of Face Plies	Weight/Sq. Ft.	
Nominal	Limits			Birch Poplar	Mahogany Poplar
$\frac{3}{64}$	.058–.040	3	$\frac{1}{64}$	.21	.18
$\frac{1}{16}$	.075–.055	3	$\frac{1}{48}$	.25	.22
$\frac{3}{32}$	.105–.085	3	$\frac{1}{32}$	.35	.29
$\frac{1}{8}$	.135–.115	3	$\frac{1}{32}$	.43	.37
$\frac{5}{32}$	.170–.145	3	$\frac{1}{20}$–$\frac{1}{28}$	.50	.43
$\frac{3}{16}$	.200–.170	3, 5	$\frac{1}{20}$–$\frac{1}{28}$	.58	.50
$\frac{7}{32}$	.235–.205	5	$\frac{1}{20}$–$\frac{1}{28}$	.74	.65
$\frac{1}{4}$	.265–.235	5	$\frac{1}{20}$	.80	.71
$\frac{5}{16}$	.325–.300	5	$\frac{1}{16}$	.95	.84
$\frac{3}{8}$	.390–.360	5	$\frac{1}{16}$–$\frac{1}{20}$	1.05	.97
$\frac{7}{16}$	.460–.420	7	$\frac{1}{16}$	1.30	1.19
$\frac{1}{2}$	.520–.480	7	$\frac{1}{16}$	1.47	1.36
$\frac{9}{16}$	.580–.545	7	$\frac{1}{12}$–$\frac{1}{16}$	1.62	1.47
$\frac{5}{8}$	.650–.600	9	$\frac{1}{12}$–$\frac{1}{16}$	1.96	1.70
$\frac{3}{4}$	.775–.725	9, 11	$\frac{1}{12}$–$\frac{1}{16}$	2.35	2.01
$\frac{7}{8}$	.910–.845	11, 13	$\frac{1}{12}$–$\frac{1}{16}$		
1	1.035–.965	11, 13, 15	$\frac{1}{12}$–$\frac{1}{16}$		

fungus attack. A comparison of the shear strength of standard
and waterproof plywood after water soaking, and fungus attack
is as follows:

Type	Shear Strength—Minimum—Pounds/Sq. In.		
	Dry	Soaked in Water 48 Hours	After 10-day Fungus Exposure
Standard.......	300	160	...
Waterproof.....	300	250	250

Waterproof Plywood. Waterproof plywood is resistant to
water and fungus. It can be steamed or soaked in boiling water
as an aid in bending without affecting the glue.

Waterproof plywood is a hot-pressed resin plywood assembled with a synthetic resin adhesive. At the present time a
thermo setting phenol formaldehyde resin glue is universally used

TABLE 15

TENSILE STRENGTH OF AIRCRAFT PLYWOOD (Estimated)*

NOMINAL THICK-NESS (INCHES)	NUMBER OF PLIES	FACE PLIES → INNER PLIES →	BIRCH BIRCH		BIRCH POPLAR		MAHOGANY POPLAR		POPLAR POPLAR	
			Long.	Tran.	Long.	Tran.	Long.	Tran.	Long.	Tran.
3/64	3		600	440	600	260	300	240	340	250
1/16	3		820	730	810	430	430	390	470	420
3/32	3		1210	880	1200	530	620	470	680	520
1/8	3		1270	1420	1260	820	680	760	740	810
5/32	3		1670	1670	1660	970	880	890	970	970
3/16	3		2000	2000	1990	1170	1050	1075	1160	1160
3/16	5				1660	1170	1085	1100	1140	1160
7/32	5				2740	1060	1800	970	1910	1050
1/4	5				2790	1340	1860	1230	1960	1320
5/16	5				3400	1420	2240	1300	2370	1410
3/8	5				3150	2340	2220	2230	2320	2320
7/16	7				3900	2720	2730	2600	2870	2700
1/2	7				4370	3160	3210	3040	3340	3140
9/16	7				5120	3250	3510	3090	3740	3230
5/8	9				5230	3570	4070	3440	4190	3550
3/4	9				6290	4410	4740	4250	4900	4390

* Strength is given in lb./inch width. Estimated by Haskelite from data given in ANC–5 of tests on 3-ply veneer in which all 3 plies were same thickness and species.

TABLE 16

BEARING STRENGTH OF AIRCRAFT PLYWOOD (Estimated)*

Nominal Thickness (Inches)	Number of Plies	Face Plies → Inner Plies →	Birch Birch		Birch Poplar		Mahogany Poplar		Poplar Poplar	
			Long.	Tran.	Long.	Tran.	Long.	Tran.	Long.	Tran.
3/64	3		230	154	221	110	202	115	154	106
1/16	3		307	269	298	182	269	192	202	182
3/32	3		451	317	442	221	394	221	307	211
1/8	3		464	528	451	365	403	374	317	355
5/32	3		614	514	595	432	538	432	413	413
3/16	3		739	739	720	518	643	518	499	499
3/16	5		720	739	624	509	576	509	490	499
7/32	5		1306	566	1114	394	1037	403	863	374
1/4	5		1325	768	1123	538	1046	538	902	518
5/16	5		1613	787	1373	547	1277	547	1054	518
3/8	5		1478	1478	1219	1018	1142	1018	958	998
7/16	7				1517	1171	1421	1171	1258	1142
1/2	7				1728	1363	1632	1363	1450	1334
9/16	7				2016	1373	1891	1382	1651	1344
5/8	9				2131	1498	2035	1498	1853	1469
3/4	9				2515	1872	2390	1882	2150	1843

* Strength is given in lbs./inch width. Estimated by Haskelite for their product based on following values in lbs./sq. in.:

	Birch	Mahogany	Poplar	Spruce
Bearing strength along grain of veneer.......	7300	6500	5000	5000
" " " across " "	400	440	200	220

for this purpose. This glue is inserted between the veneer panels as a thin solid film, or as a liquid glue. Heat and pressure are then applied to cure the glue. A temperature of 300° F. is required but the pressure varies depending upon the wood. A 125 lb./sq. in. pressure is required for spruce, and a 250 lb./sq. in. pressure for birch. The temperature and pressure must be maintained for about 5 minutes for $\frac{1}{16}$-inch plywood, and about 12 minutes for $\frac{5}{16}$-inch plywood. With thick plywoods it is difficult to cure the inner layers of glue without damaging the outer veneer layers with the excessive heat. A high frequency electrostatic method of curing resins in thick plywoods has been devised to overcome this difficulty. In this method the desired heat is generated in the resin layers and to a lesser extent in the wood veneer. This method of curing is applicable to the shank of aircraft propeller blades constructed of resin impregnated wood or plywood.

All plywood, whether standard or waterproof, must be protected by paint to avoid moisture absorption by the wood. The normal moisture content of plywood is 7 to 12% but this will vary with the humidity if the plywood is not properly protected. The edges are particularly important.

Superpressed Resin Plywood. This plywood is the same as the waterproof resin plywood described above but is assembled under pressures from 500 to 1500 pounds per square inch. Under these pressures the density of the plywood is greatly increased and plywood manufactured in this manner is sometimes referred to as "High Density" plywood. This development is only in the experimental stage but tests already conducted indicate that shear strength can be increased about 7 times when the density of the plywood is slightly more than doubled.

Molded Airplane Parts. With proper dies it is a simple matter to cure resin bonded plywood in the desired shape. Wing leading edges are frequently supplied by the plywood manufacturer with the required curve. This eliminates the necessity for steaming or soaking in boiling water to permit bending.

This technique of curing to shape has been applied successfully to entire half fuselages. By the use of properly designed jigs it is possible to glue rings, longitudinals, or stiffeners to the plywood fuselage shell in the same operation. One solid form is used and an even pressure is exerted on the opposite side of the plywood by means of air pressure in a restrained rubber bag.

The main limitation on the molding of plywood parts to finished shape is the cost of the jig or dies. If a sufficient number of parts are involved the cost can probably be justified. This technique has definite possibilities for large scale production.

CHAPTER XVII

FABRICS AND DOPE

Some modern airplanes are of all metal construction, including the wing and fuselage covering.. A good many, however, still use fabric for covering wings, fuselages, and control surfaces. In this country cotton fabric is used exclusively for this purpose; in England, home-grown linen is used for covering in place of the rarer cotton. The strengths of cotton and linen fabric are equivalent, so that the selection of one or the other depends wholly upon the source of supply.

To facilitate the discussion of fabrics and tapes the following definitions are given:

Warp is the direction along the length of the fabric.

Warp ends are the woven threads that run the length of the fabric.

Filling or *weft* is the direction across the width of the fabric.

Filling picks are the woven threads that run across the fabric.

Count is the number of threads per inch in warp or filling.

Ply is the number of yarns making up a thread. Thus a thread designated as 16/4 means four yarns of size sixteen twisted together to form one thread.

Twist refers to the direction of twist of the yarn making up a thread. Twist is said to be right-handed when a thread is held vertically and the spirals or twists incline downward in a right-hand direction.

Mercerization is the process of dipping cotton yarn or fabric, preferably under tension, in a hot solution of dilute caustic soda momentarily. The material acquires greater strength and luster due to this treatment. Its stretch is also somewhat reduced.

Sizing is a material, such as starch, which is used to condition the yarns to facilitate the weaving of the cloth.

AIRPLANE FABRIC

A mercerized cotton cloth is universally used in this country for fabric covering of wings, fuselages, and tail surfaces. This cloth can be obtained commercially in the following widths: 36, 42, 60, 69 and 90 inches. The 36-inch width is standard, but the others are used when for some special reason it is desired to have less seams in the covering.

Grade A fabric contains from 80 to 84 threads per inch in both the warp and filling. A 2-ply yarn is used. A minimum tensile strength of 80 pounds per inch in both warp and filling is required. The normal weight of this fabric is 4 ounces per square yard, and it must be under 4.5 ounces to meet government specifications. This fabric must have a smooth, napless surface to obtain the best results. The cloth is rolled or calendered to obtain this surface. The sizing content is limited to a maximum of 2½%. Another requirement is the mercerization of the yarn prior to weaving while under tension. This method of mercerization is preferable to mercerizing the woven cloth. A 60/2 yarn will give the strength properties required for this grade of fabric.

Light airplane fabric and glider fabric have the following approximate characteristics:

	LIGHT AIRPLANE	GLIDER
Weight (oz./sq. yd.),	2.6	2.7
Threads per inch—Warp	115	95
— Fill	115	100
Strength per inch— Warp	50	45
—Fill	40	36
Width (standard)	37	38

Linen fabric made from the best grade of Irish flax is used universally in England but not at all in this country. This fabric is practically identical with Grade A cotton fabric insofar as weight, strength, and threads per inch are concerned. While linen fabric will take on acetate dope finish excellently, cotton fabric will not.

Surface Tape. Surface tape is the finishing tape that is doped over each rib or seam to cover the stitching. It provides a neat, smooth, finished appearance. It can be obtained with serrated or pinked edges, or with a straight edge impregnated with a sealing compound. This compound or the pinked edges provide better adherence to the fabric covering. Surface tape is made from Grade A fabric in various widths from 1¼ to 3¾ inches, from glider fabric in 1½ and 2 inch widths, and from a balloon cloth in 2¼, 3, and 4 inch widths. This latter cloth is usually required for military airplanes.

The balloon cloth used for surface tape is a cotton cloth that has been singed, desized, and calendered to give it a smooth finish without fuzz or nap. This cloth weighs 2.0 ounces per square yard and has a tensile strength of 40 pounds per inch in the warp or fill. It is made with a single-ply thread of which there are at least 120 per inch. Tape made from this cloth is pre-doped on both sides with a nitrate dope to obtain best results. Sufficient dope must be used to increase the weight at least ½ ounce per square yard when dry.

Reinforcing Tape. Reinforcing tape is used over fabric and under the rib stitching to prevent the stitching cord from cutting through the fabric. It is also used for cross-bracing ribs and for binding. This tape has an extremely strong warp. The warp ends are made from cotton yarn No. 20/3/4 or its equivalent, and the filling picks are cotton yarn No. 24/2. Tape made from these yarns has the following characteristics:

WIDTH IN.	WARP ENDS TOTAL	FILLING PICKS PER IN.	STRENGTH POUNDS	WEIGHT PER 144 YDS., OUNCES
1/4	7	20	80	16
3/8	10	20	120	22
1/2	14	20	150	31
5/8	18	20	170	40
3/4	22	20	200	48
1	30	20	250	67

A herringbone tape largely used for commercial airplanes can also be obtained in widths from ¼ inch to 1¼ inches. This tape is less bulky than that described above and is amply strong.

Sewing Thread. To machine sew a Grade A fabric, an unbleached, silk-finish, left-twist, cotton thread is used. It is a No. 16/4 thread and has a tensile strength of 6.80 pounds minimum. Silk (or glace) finished thread is polished and has a smooth dressed surface.

A No. 24/4 thread is used for machine sewing of light airplane or glider fabric. It is the same as No. 16/4 thread but is lighter and has a tensile strength of 4.70 pounds minimum.

For hand sewing a No. 30, 3-cord, right-hand twist, linen thread is mostly used. This thread is made from long-line flax fibre and has a tensile strength of 10 pounds minimum. A slightly heavier thread, No. 25/3, with a 12-pound breaking strength is sometimes preferred. A cotton hand sewing thread is also used. This thread is a No. 10/3, right-hand twist, cotton thread with a 10-pound breaking strength.

Rib Lacing Cord. Rib lacing cord is used to sew the fabric to the ribs. It must be strong to transmit the suction on the upper surface of the wing from the fabric to the ribs which, in turn, carry the load into the main wing structure. The cord must also resist fraying due to the weaving action of the fabric and wing ribs. Both linen and cotton cords are used for rib lacing cord.

A 5-ply, silk-finished, cotton cord is frequently used on small commercial planes. It makes a tight knot, resists fraying, and is quite durable.

Another cotton cord, No. 20/3/3/3, which is unusually strong and fray resistant is also used. This type is used on military airplanes.

A third type of cord, No. 8/11, with a soft or natural cotton finish is also used. It has a breaking strength of 42 pounds.

A linen thread is preferred for naval airplanes and for large transport planes. A 9-ply, lock-stitch-twist cord with a breaking strength of 55 pounds is used. This cord is made from the best Irish flax.

APPLICATION OF CLOTH SURFACES

The proper application of cloth on the surfaces is essential if a good appearance, the best results, and strength are to be obtained from the material selected. A good covering job is not only important from a strength and appearance standpoint, but it affects the performance of the airplane in no small degree. It is essential that all covering be taut and smooth for best performance. To obtain smoothness it is common practice to sand the surface after each coat of dope is applied. This sanding can be overdone to the injury of the fabric and should, therefore, be practiced with caution.

All fabric materials to be used in covering should be stored in a dry place and protected from direct sunlight until needed. The room in which the sewing and application of the covering is done should be clean and well ventilated. Its relative humidity should be slightly lower than the relative humidity of the dope room.

All machine sewing should have two rows of stitches with 8 to 10 stitches per inch. A lock stitch is preferred. All seams should be made with the aim of securing the smoothest job possible combined with adequate strength. Stitches should be approximately $\frac{1}{16}$ inch from the edge of the seam, and $\frac{1}{4}$ to $\frac{3}{8}$ inch from the adjacent row of stitches. Longitudinal seams should be as nearly parallel to the line of flight as possible. Seams should never be located over a rib in order to avoid penetrating a seam with the rib lacing cord.

Hand sewing is necessary to close up the final openings in the covering. This is sometimes done by tacking on wooden wings, but sewing is preferable. In hand sewing a baseball stitch of 6 to 8 stitches per inch is used. It is finished with a lock-stitch and knot. A $\frac{1}{2}$-inch hem should be turned under on all seams to be hand sewn. Holding the fabric under tension preparatory to hand sewing can be done by tacks on wooden wings, or by pinning the fabric to a piece of adhesive tape pasted to the trailing edge of metal wings.

Thread for hand sewing and lacing cord should be waxed lightly before using. The wax should not exceed 20% of the weight of the finished cord. A beeswax free from paraffin should be used for waxing.

Reinforcing tape is used under all lacing to protect the fabric from cutting through. This tape should be under a slight tension and secured at both ends. It should be slightly wider than the member it covers. A double width is sometimes necessary for very wide members.

Surface tape or finishing tape should be placed over all lacing, seams (both machine and hand-sewn), corners, edges, and places where wear is likely to occur. It is placed around the entire leading and trailing edges of wings. Tape is applied after the first coat of dope has dried, and is set on a second wet coat, after which another coat of dope is applied over the tape immediately. By this means both surfaces of the tape are impregnated with dope, and it adheres firmly to the covering.

Reinforcing patches are always placed over holes in fabric-covered surfaces through which wires, controls, or other items project. These patches may be either another layer of fabric doped on, or a leather patch sewed to the fabric covering. Patches

should fit the protruding part as closely as possible to prevent
the entrance of moisture and dirt.

Celluloid drainage grommets should be doped to the underside of fabric surfaces wherever moisture can be trapped. It is
customary to place one of these grommets adjacent to the trailing edge of each wing rib. They also serve to ventilate fabric-
covered surfaces. Ventilation is necessary to reduce corrosion
and also to relieve the pressure inside the surface when the plane
is at altitude.

Inspection doors and access holes are required in all surfaces
whether fabric or metal covered. On fabric-covered surfaces
the simplest method to provide these holes is to dope a zipper
equipped patch in the desired place. When the dope dries the
fabric is cut along the line of the zipper. Each patch is equipped
with two zippers that meet at an angle and thus provide a trian-
gular opening for access or inspection. Another method applicable to cloth or metal surfaces is the provision of a boundary
framework inside the wing to which a cover plate can be attached
by screws. These frameworks are built-in wherever access or
inspection holes are necessary—for example, where wing wires
are attached.

Wing Covering. Wings may be covered with fabric by the
envelope, blanket, or combination method. The envelope method
is preferable and should be used whenever possible. In all methods the warp of the cloth should run parallel to the line of flight.

The envelope method of covering wings consists of sewing up
several widths of fabric of definite dimensions, and then running
a transverse seam to make an envelope or sleeve. This sleeve
is then pulled over the wing through its one open end. The open
end is then hand-sewed or tacked. If the envelope is of the
proper dimensions it will fit the wing snugly. When possible
the transverse seam should be placed along the trailing edge.
The advantage of this method lies in the fact that practically all
sewing is by machine, and there is an enormous saving in labor
in fitting the covering. It is particularly applicable to production airplanes.

The blanket method consists of machine sewing a number of
widths of fabric together, placing it over the wing, and hand sewing the transverse seam along the trailing edge. Care must be

taken to apply equal tension over the whole surface. This method of covering wings is almost invariably used on experimental airplanes.

The combination method consists of using the envelope method as much as possible, and the blanket method on the remainder of the covering. This method is applicable to wings with obstructions or recesses that prevent full application of an envelope.

After the cover is sewed in place, reinforcing tape is placed over each rib and the fabric is laced to each rib. Except on very thick wings the rib lacing passes completely around the rib. On thick wings the lacing passes around one chord member only, but both top and bottom surfaces must be laced in this manner. Lacing should be as near as possible to the capstrip. The rib should not have any rough or sharp edges in contact with the lacing or it will fray and break. Each time the lacing cord goes around the rib it is tied over the upper center or edge of the rib, and then the next stitch is made at the specified distance away. The first and last stitches are made with slip knots to provide for tightening these stitches. All other stitches are tied with a non-slip or seine knot. Rib lacing should extend from the leading to the trailing edge, except when the leading edge of the wing is covered with plywood or metal. In these cases the lacing should start immediately after these coverings.

In order not to overstress the lacing, it is necessary to space the stitches a definite distance apart depending upon the speed of the airplane. Due to the additional buffeting caused by the propeller slipstream, a closer spacing of the stitching must be used on all ribs included within the propeller circle. It is customary to use this closer spacing on the rib just outboard of the propeller diameter as well. A satisfactory spacing for rib lacing is as follows:

AIRPLANE SPEED (MAX.)	OUTSIDE SLIPSTREAM	INSIDE SLIPSTREAM
Up to 175 m.p.h.	4 in.	2 in.
176 to 250 m.p.h.	2 in.	1 in.
Over 250 m.p.h.	1 in.	1 in.

In very high speed airplanes difficulty is often experienced with rib lacing breaking or fabric tearing. These troubles are usually experienced in the slipstream. To overcome this trouble a double rib lacing job is sometimes done in this region. This is accomplished by simply rib lacing the wing twice in the af-

fected region. Each lacing job is wholly independent of the other
except that the same holes are picked up in the fabric to avoid
making too many holes. A tape of Grade A fabric cut on a bias
is often sewed and doped to the fabric covering under the reinforcing tape to strengthen the fabric against tearing at the stitching holes. After the wing surface has been covered, rib laced, and
given several coats of dope, a blanket is sometimes doped over
entire areas to reinforce the whole assembly. This blanket consists of Grade A fabric extending over the affected area of the
wing (the slipstream usually) and runs from the trailing edge up
over the leading edge and back on the under surface to the trailing edge again. In placing this blanket the under area is thoroughly soaked with dope, the blanket laid and rubbed smooth
to eliminate all trapped air, and then the outer surface of the
blanket is doped immediately. Only small areas are doped and
laid at a time. High speed airplanes with all three reinforcing
measures described in this paragraph, including double stitching,
bias tape, and blanket, have stood up perfectly in service.

Fuselage Covering. Fuselages are covered by either a sleeve
or blanket method which are similar to the methods described
for covering wings. In the sleeve method several widths of
fabric are joined by machine-sewed seams to form a sleeve which
when drawn over the end of the fuselage will fit snugly. When
the sleeve is in place, all seams should be as nearly parallel as
possible to longitudinal members of the fuselage.

In the blanket method all seams are machine sewed, except
one final longitudinal seam along the bottom center of the fuselage. In some cases the blanket is put on in two or three sections and hand-sewed on the fuselage. All seams should run
fore and aft.

Fuselage fabric is seldom laced in place. When the fuselage
has convex sides, the tension of the fabric holds it taut. The
front and rear ends of the cover are tacked or sewed in place.
In high speed planes or flat sided fuselages the fabric can be laced
to a longitudinal fairing strip parallel to the line of flight.

DOPES AND DOPING

In order to tauten fabric covering, and to make it air and
watertight, the cloth is brushed or sprayed with dope. This
dope also protects the fabric from deterioration by weather or

sunlight, and when polished imparts a smooth surface to the fabric which reduces skin friction. Dopes must be applied under ideal conditions to obtain satisfactory and consistent results. A clean, fresh, dry atmosphere with a temperature above 70° F. and a relative humidity below 60%, combined with good ventilation is necessary in the dope room. The dope must be of the proper consistency and be applied uniformly over the entire surface.

Dopes will deteriorate seriously if stored in too warm a place for a long period. The temperature should not exceed 60° F. for long time storage, and must not exceed 80° F. for periods up to four months. Precautions against fire should be taken wherever dope is stored or used because of its inflammable nature. Dope and paint rooms are always isolated from the rest of the factory by metal partitions and fireproof doors when they are not located in a separate building.

As stated above, the most desirable condition in a dope room is a temperature above 70° F. and a relative humidity below 60%. At lower temperatures the dope will not flow freely without the addition of excessive thinners. The relative humidity can be lowered by raising the temperature if the dope shop is not equipped with humidity control. In order to condition fabric surfaces to the desired temperature and moisture conditions, they should be allowed to stand about 4 hours in the dope room after covering and prior to doping. By this means an ideal dry condition of the fabric will be obtained.

The number of coats of dope applied to a fabric surface depends upon the finish desired. It is customary to put 2 to 4 coats of clear dope on, followed by two coats of pigmented dope. Sufficient clear dope should be put on to increase the weight of the fabric by 2.25 to 2.50 ounces per square yard. The clear dope film should weigh this amount after drying for 72 hours. The pigmented dope film should weigh at least 2.00 ounces per square yard. With fabric weighing 4 ounces the total weight of fabric and dope is approximately 9.5 ounces per square yard.

Panels should be doped in a horizontal position whenever possible to prevent dope running to the bottom of the panel. The first coat of dope should be brush applied and worked uniformly into the fabric. A minimum of 30 minutes under good atmospheric conditions should be allowed for drying between coats. Surface tape and patches should be applied just prior to the second coat of dope. This second coat should also be brushed on as smoothly as possible. A third and fourth coat of clear dope can be applied by either brushing or spraying. These coats of clear dope provide a taut and rigid surface to the fabric covering. If desired this surface may be smoothed by lightly rubbing with #0000000 sandpaper or a similar abrasive. When it is being rubbed, all surfaces should be electrically grounded to dissipate static electricity. The doping is completed by spraying the proper colored pigmented dope on the surface in two or more coats.

Under certain unfavorable atmospheric conditions a freshly doped surface will blush. Blushing is caused by the precipitation of cellulose ester which is due largely to a high rate of evaporation and/or high humidity. High temperatures or currents of air blowing over the work increase the evaporation rate and increase blushing tendencies. Blushing seriously reduces the strength of the dope film and should be guarded against. When a doped surface blushes, it becomes dull in spots or white in extreme cases.

In order to prevent the dope from "lifting" the paint on the surface under the fabric, it must be protected by some means. The commonest method is the application of dope-proof paint or zinc chromate primer over all parts of the surface that come in contact with doped fabric. Another excellent method is to cover this surface with aluminum foil 0.0005 inch thick. This foil is glued to the surface and prevents the penetration of dope. It is applied over the regular finish. Other materials, such as a cellophane tape, have also been successfully used in place of aluminum foil.

Nitrocellulose Dope. Nitrocellulose dope is a solution of nitrocellulose and a plasticizer, such as glycol sebacate, ethyl acetate, butyl acetate, butyl alcohol, and toluene. The nitrocellulose base is made by dissolving cotton in nitric acid. The plasticizer aids in producing a flexible film. Both the plasticizer and the solvents are responsible for the tautening action of dope. Thinners such as benzol or ethyl alcohol are sometimes added to the dope to obtain the proper consistency. These thinners evaporate off with the volatile solvents.

Pigmented dopes must be applied over the clear dopes in order to protect the fabric from the sunlight. Sufficient pigment must be added to the dope to form an opaque surface. Pigmented dopes consist of the proper colored pigment added to the clear dope. When an aluminum finish is desired one gallon of the clear nitrocellulose dope is mixed with twelve ounces of aluminum powder and an equal additional amount of glycol sebacate plasticizer. Sufficient thinner is then added, so that two coats of this dope will give a film weight of about 2 ounces per square yard.

Nitrocellulose dopes are very generally used in this country. They are cheap, have good tautening qualities, and are not particularly susceptible to changes in the atmosphere.

Cellulose Acetate Dope. Cellulose acetate dope consists of a solution of cellulose acetate and plasticizers, such as dibutyl tartrate and diethyl phthalate, in such solvents as ethyl acetate, acetone, and others. Thinners are added to obtain the desired consistency. To make aluminum pigmented dope of this type, 12 ounces of aluminum powder and 3 ounces of additional plasticizers are added to one gallon of the clear dope. It is then thinned as necessary to obtain the proper weight film.

This type of dope is more expensive than nitrocellulose dope; then, too, it does not give quite as satisfactory a finish on cotton fabric. It is used almost exclusively in England in conjunction with linen fabric.

Cellulose acetate dope is more fire resistant than nitrocellulose dope and is sometimes used on cotton fabric surfaces behind exhaust outlets. Its application is accomplished by applying it in pigmented form on top of several coats of clear nitrocellulose dope. All surface tape and patches must be fully applied during the clear nitrate doping operation or they will not adhere properly.

Chapter XVIII

PLASTICS

Plastics is the group name given to synthetic materials such as bakelite, micarta, formica, and similar compounds. These materials are very commonly used in aircraft construction for such purposes as electric insulators, instrument panels, handles, control pulleys, and cabin paneling. Micarta propellers have also been successfully built and used. There is a possibility that future development of these materials will lead to their use as structural members of aircraft. They are now being considered for control surface tabs, tail surfaces, and ailerons. Laminated plastics are being used successfully for turtle deck fairings, bomb doors, and similar applications. They are now available as sheet, strip, rods, tubes, angles, and channels. These materials are homogeneous, impervious to moisture, free from shrinkage, do not decay, and are not readily inflammable. They also have an exceptionally smooth surface which fits them for external wing or fuselage covering. Unfortunately, their modulus of elasticity is very low and any structure composed of them would have excessive deflections. Future development may overcome this handicap, since these materials are relatively new and there are still many untried combinations of ingredients.

The first plastic ever developed was made by treating cotton cellulose with nitric acid. The resultant nitrocellulose plastic was given the name celluloid. Subsequently a second plastic was developed when sour milk was mixed with formaldehyde. The resultant casein plastic has found a commercial adaptation in buttons and buckles. The real development of plastics, however, began with the discovery of bakelite. Bakelite is made by mixing phenol (carbolic acid) with formaldehyde. A large number of other compounds including micarta and formica are made by this same method. This group of plastics is known as the phenolic-resin family.

297

Plastics are synthetic materials built up chemically and are not found in nature. The ingredients of plastics do not undergo a simple chemical change when united. They retain their chemical identity but polymerize. Polymerization is the process wherein substances combine by enlargement of the molecular structure without a change in chemical composition. A catalyst is necessary to assist this reaction.

Classification

Plastics used in aircraft may be classified in two general groups according to their basic ingredients. These groups are as follows:

1. *Vegetable matter* (such as cellulose). In this group belong plastecele and celluloid. Plastecele is a cellulose acetate compound, and celluloid is a nitrocellulose compound. These materials are described more in detail in the chapter on Transparent Materials where they are grouped with glass. They are frequently used for windows, windshields, and transparent cabin hoods.

2. *Synthetic resins* (such as phenol, which is carbolic acid). Mixing phenol with formaldehyde is the method of manufacturing many plastics including bakelite, durez, catalin, marblette, joanite, formica, and micarta. The exact proportions of the ingredients used and the treatment they are subjected to determine the product. Other types of synthetic resins are vinyl, acrylic, styrene, alkyd, urea, and thio-urea resins.

Plastics may be divided into two specific groups:

Thermoplastics

Thermoplastic materials are rigid at normal temperatures but soften upon the application of heat and deform under pressure. They are frequently heated and formed to the desired contour in the aircraft factory.

This group includes cellulose nitrates (pyralin), cellulose acetates (plastecele, lumarith), polyacrylates (plexiglas, lucite), and polyvinyls (vinylite). These materials are used largely for windshields as described in Chapter XIX, Transparent Materials.

Injection Molding. Injection molding of thermoplastics is a recent development. In this process heated thermoplastic material is forced under pressure into a cool mold chamber where it is cooled quickly and uniformly to the finished shape. Molded parts of the type are used for control handles and similar parts where the quantity justifies the mold cost.

Compression Molding. Thermoplastics can be compression molded to the desired shape by heating, compressing, and cooling in the mold. The cycle is quick and uniform results are readily obtainable.

Extrusions. Rods, tubes and special shapes can be extruded.

Available Shapes. Pyralin, plastecele, lumarith, vinylite, plexiglas, and lucite may be purchased as sheet, rod, or tubing.

THERMOSETTING PLASTICS

Thermosetting plastics will undergo internal changes under the influence of heat and pressure to become an infusible and insoluble material. Subsequent heating will not alter the state of these materials.

The thermosetting group of plastics includes phenol-aldehydes, and amino-aldehydes (urea and thio-urea resins). Commercial plastics such as bakelite, micarta, formica, catalin, textolite, and numerous others are made from these synthetic resins.

The thermosetting plastics are available as molded, cast, and laminated products.

Molding. Molded plastic parts can be obtained with a variety of properties, depending upon the material and filler used. These parts are compression molded and accurate control of timing, pressure, and temperature is essential. Automatic compression molding machines are now used to insure uniformity of product.

Molded phenol formaldehydes, such as bakelite and durez, are made by mixing definite proportions of phenol, formaldehyde, and a catalyst together and heating them to a high temperature. At this temperature the compound is a clear, resinous liquid. It is then solidified by cooling, and pulverized into a powder. A filler, such as wood flour or asbestos, is added to the pulverized compound. Under heat and pressure this mixture first softens and then molds into a hard, infusible substance. Articles can be molded by this method to practically any desired finished shape.

Casting. Cast phenol formaldehydes, such as catalin, marblette, and joanite, are made by pouring the liquid phenol formaldehyde solution while hot into forms. No filler is added. This cast material is usually purchased in bar or rod form and machined to the desired shape.

Laminated Plastics. Laminated phenol formaldehyde products, such as formica and micarta, are made with the aid of paper or fabric. The paper used is strong, fibrous, uniform, and absorbent. The fabric is also a special grade. The material used, whether fabric or paper, is impregnated by passing it through the phenol formaldehyde mixture. It is then dried thoroughly in a long, heated drier. The impregnating and drying operations are continuous with the dried material being rolled at the end. The rolls of impregnated material are then taken to a cutting machine and cut into sheets of the desired size.

To manufacture laminated sheet a number of impregnated sheets are piled together and placed in a hydraulic press. Heat and pressure are applied to the mass of sheets, and the resultant product is a hard, compact sheet of laminated formica, micarta, bakelite or similar product. The temperature and pressure required in this operation vary with different materials and grades but are of the order of 360° F. and from 2000 to 4000 lbs./sq. in. When removed from the press the edges of the material are trimmed with a saw, and it is then ready for shipment. If a highly polished metal plate is used in the press, a polished surface will be obtained on the sheet.

Laminated tubing is made either by rolling or molding. Rolled tubing is formed by rolling impregnated paper or fabric on a mandrel under high tension and pressure, after which it is cured by baking without further pressure. Molded tubing is made by rolling the impregnated material on a mandrel and then curing it in a mold under heat and pressure. Rod is made in the same manner as molded tubing. But angles and channels are made in a mold and cured in the same manner as sheet material.

Physical Properties

At the present time the mechanical properties of laminated plastics are not high enough to warrant their use in the primary structure. Airplanes have been built of resin-impregnated plywood which is sometimes referred to as a "plastic." A description of this material is given in Chapter XVI.

Commercially available laminated plastics are made with various grades of paper, fabric, or asbestos. They were developed primarily for electrical purposes and are best known by their N.E.M.A. (National Electrical Manufacturers Association) designation. The average mechanical values of these laminated plastics are given in Table 17. (See p. 302.)

Considerable research work is under way to improve the properties of plastics by changing the material of the filler. Wire mesh and metal plates among other things are being tried. Improvement of the tensile strength, modulus of elasticity, and creep stress are necessary to make plastics a primary structural material.

WORKING PROPERTIES

Joining. Plastic materials are usually connected by rivets, screws, or bolts. There are several cements that have been developed for them but they have no particular application in aircraft at the present time. An effective cement will be very essential when plastics are used for structural purposes. It will be possible but not very practical to mold long lengths in one piece. Until the quantity required justifies the expense, the cost of dies and equipment would be out of proportion. The joining of relatively small sections will be important and necessary until one piece molds are practical.

Working. When using thermosetting plastics, it is only possible to get a double curvature by molding. A single curve of generous radius can be made with sheet material. The formaldehyde plastics are brittle and will not flow under a rapid application of load as in bumping or forming. Practically any shape is obtainable by molding if a die is made.

Plastics can be machined without difficulty. In turning, a stellite tool should be used in conjunction with high speed and light cuts. Overheating, caused by excessively high speed or a dull tool, will result in a poor finish and inaccurate dimensions. In milling, large diameter cutters with many teeth should be used at high speeds. Drilling should be done with high speed steel drills which are frequently ground and kept sharp. Reaming and tapping can be done with the same tools used for metal. Threads

TABLE 17

PHYSICAL PROPERTIES—LAMINATED PLASTICS

NEMA DESIGNATION	TYPE	AVERAGE TENSILE STRENGTH Lbs./Sq. In.	AVERAGE FLEXURAL STRENGTH Lbs./Sq. In.	AVERAGE COMPRESSIVE STRENGTH Lbs./Sq. In.	USE
			SHEET		
X	Paper	12,500	21,000	* 35,000	Mechanical applications. Poor under humid conditions.
XX	Paper	8,000	16,000	34,000	Good machineability. Moisture resistant.
C	Fabric	9,500	20,000	38,000	Used for gears. Good impact strength.
L	Fabric	9,000	20,000	35,000	Used for small gears and fine machining under $\frac{1}{2}''$.
AA	Asbestos Fabric	10,000	20,000	38,000	Moisture and heat resistant.
			TUBING		
X rolled	Paper	10,500	....	** 15,000	Good punching and fair machining.
XX rolled	Paper	10,000	....	17,000	Good punching and threading qualities. Moisture resistant.
LE rolled	Fabric	7,500	....	18,000	Good machining. Bearing retainers.
L molded	Fabric	8,500	....	21,000	Smooth machining.
			ROD		
C	Fabric	9,500	....	25,500	Good machining.
L	Fabric	11,400	....	30,000	Smooth machining.

* Compressive values for sheet are given for flatwise compression. Edge compression values are approximately 50% of flatwise compression.
** Axial compression strength is given for tubing and rod,
Modulus of elasticity—1,200,000–2,500,000 lbs./sq. in.
Specific gravity—Phenol products 1.3 to 1.4
—Urea products 1.5

are cut best with a milling cutter. Dies are only satisfactory on small diameter work. Band or circular type metal-cutting saws can be used for sawing but should operate at 6000 and 8000 feet per minute, respectively. In punching, the clearance between die and punch must be much less than used for metal and both punch and die must be sharp.

USES

Probably the most important use for plastics is as insulation in electrical work. Some grades have higher dielectric qualities than others. When combined with good machining qualities, the material is excellent for general insulation purposes. It is used frequently in aircraft construction to break up a continuous metal circuit around radio loops.

The timing gears of automobiles are usually manufactured with plastics. These gears are quiet and elastic. A heavy fabric base phenol formaldehyde material is used most frequently for gearing. This type material has good impact and shock resistance.

Bakelite resins are frequently used in the paint and varnish industry. An excellent phenolic resin glue is also used in the manufacture of plywood. This glue and plywood are highly water resistant.

Sheet material is used for cabin paneling, turtle-decking, doors and instrument boards. Highly polished, decorative finishes can be obtained.

Control pulleys are made exclusively of this material.

Handles for landing gear cranks, tab controls, and similar purposes are machined from a laminated paper plastic with excellent results, or they may be molded to the finished shape.

Wooden propellers are impregnated with plastic resins under pressure which serve the double purpose of increasing the strength and waterproofing the wood.

It is generally anticipated that future developments in plastics will evolve a material suitable for structural purposes. When this day comes, it should be possible to mold an entire wing in one operation. The low modulus of elasticity and creep stress of plastics are the chief obstacles to greater structural use of these materials.

CHAPTER XIX

TRANSPARENT MATERIALS

Transparent materials are used in aircraft for windshields and for general cabin glazing. Two types of material are used: glass and a variety of transparent plastics. A shatterproof glass is used in the interest of safety. A high grade laminated plate glass is used for windshields and bomber's windows where perfect vision is essential. For the relatively unimportant side windows and skylights a cheaper grade of laminated sheet glass or one of the transparent plastics is used. In some planes, where weight and/or expense are important considerations, transparent plastics are used throughout. In general, transparent plastics will scratch, discolor, and distort much more than glass and must be frequently replaced.

GLASS

Shatterproof or nonscatterable glass consists of two pieces of glass held together by a single-ply filler of a transparent plastic. A cellulose acetate or vinyl plastic is most often used for this purpose. An adhesive is used on both sides of the filler to bind the two pieces of glass together. The filler is cut back a short distance from the edge to allow space for a sealing compound. This sealing compound is waterproof and protects the adhesive. It extends from $\frac{1}{16}$ to $\frac{5}{32}$ inch in from the edge of the glass.

There are two types of nonscatterable glass available.

1. *Laminated plate glass.* This glass is made of two pieces of class A polished plate glass. It is obtainable in thicknesses from $\frac{3}{16}$ inch up. Generally $\frac{3}{16}$ and $\frac{1}{4}$ inch glass are used for aircraft windshields. The dimensions of the windshield determines the thickness necessary. It is easier to obtain $\frac{1}{4}$ inch glass because of the difficulty in procuring clear plate glass thin enough so that two layers will be only $\frac{3}{16}$ inch thick.

2. *Laminated sheet glass.* This glass is made from class B, clear window glass of the best quality. It is obtainable in thick-

nesses from ⅛ inch up. For side windows, skylights, and similar secondary applications ⅛ inch glass is generally used. This type glass has considerably more distortion than plate glass and should not be used for windshields.

Physical Properties. In the design of planes to fly in the substratosphere it will be necessary to consider the strength of glass. A pressure differential of 10 to 12 pounds per square inch may exist between the inside of the cabin and the outside atmosphere. Glass manufacturers recommend that a factor of 10 be applied to these loads to insure against glass breakage. The mechanical properties of glass are as follows:

Tensile strength (lbs./sq. in.)............... 6,500
Compressive strength " 36,000
Modulus of elasticity " 10,000,000
Weight (¼ in. glass)..................... 3.29 lb./sq. ft.

Plate glass expansion coefficient ($-70°$ F. to $-100°$ F.) is .00000451 per °F. This expansion is two-thirds that of steel and one-third that of aluminum.

Testing Nonscatterable Glass. An impact test is made on this type glass to determine its effectiveness in preventing flying glass in a crash. The impact test consists of dropping a ½ pound spherical steel weight from a height of 16 feet on the center of a one square foot surface of the glass. The glass is supported along all edges by a wooden frame extending ⅜ inch in from each edge. The glass must be at a temperature between 70° F. and 80° F. To pass this test the glass must not separate from the adhesive and there must be no puncture of the filler. Small chips of glass may leave the underside of the sheet due to fracture within the bottom plate.

The glass must also stand a heat resistance test without signs of cracking. In this test the glass is maintained at 32° F. for 30 minutes and then raised uniformly within 2 minutes to 104° F. It is maintained at this temperature for 40 minutes and then cooled down to 32° F. again within 5 minutes. This test apparently simulates an airplane climbing to altitude, where the temperature is colder, and then descending to a warmer temperature somewhat more quickly.

Bubbles, scratches, and other defects are checked by the unaided eye under good illumination.

A test for definition and distortion is made by means of a 6-power telescope focused on a distant target. When the glass is interposed in the line of vision the target must still appear clearly defined and undistorted. The glass specimen should be shifted in order to check different portions.

TEMPERED GLASS

This is an exceptionally strong glass that may be very useful in planes designed for high altitude flight. It is produced by heating glass uniformly over the entire surface to 1250° F. and then suddenly quenching it to room temperature. By this process the outermost surface of the glass is placed under high compression and the inside under tension. The strength of tempered glass is due to the surface compression which must first be overcome before the ordinary strength of the glass comes into play. Tempered glass has a compressive and tensile strength of approximately 36,000 lbs./sq. in. Its coefficient of expansion is only .000003 per °F. It can only be manufactured in ¼-inch thickness or greater.

TRANSPARENT PLASTICS

The ideal transparent plastic for aircraft use should be strong, scratch-resistant, noninflammable, colorless, transparent, and unaffected by sunlight or temperature changes. In addition it should be possible to mold it to the desired shape in the aircraft manufacturers' plant and should be obtainable in reasonably large sizes. In common with all aircraft materials it should also be homogeneous, light, and readily available at a reasonable price. Unfortunately, no transparent material yet devised can meet all these specifications. New materials derived from acrylic acid have been recently announced. These acrylate plastics appear to be better than the cellulose plastics now used. At the present time it is customary to replace windshields and cabin enclosures at frequent intervals when the old material becomes distorted, discolored, or excessively scratched.

The chief problem in the use of plastics for windshields and cabin hoods is to allow for the expansion and contraction of these materials with change in temperature. In almost any flight to altitude an airplane goes through a temperature differential of well over 50° F. When installing transparent plastics in a framework, it is necessary to allow for a ¼-inch movement in 12 inches to permit free expansion and contraction. This is usually done by drilling oversize holes in the plastic material and using shoulder rivets in the frame to avoid clamping down on the plastic material. If tight riveting is employed, the plastic material will contract sufficiently to cause it to crack under the slightest outside pressure. If touched lightly with the finger under these conditions it will shatter. At temperatures reached around 25,000 feet it will crack of its own accord due to the magnitude of internal contraction strains. Installation in channels is the ideal method for eliminating contraction strains. The expansion that occurs when exposed to a hot sun and warm weather will permanently distort the material unless oversize holes are drilled or other means provided to permit the take-up.

A brief description of several transparent plastic materials commonly used for aircraft windshields and cabin enclosures, as well as inspection hole covers, follows.

Pyralin. This material is a pyroxylin nitrocellulose plastic. It is a solid solution of nitrocellulose in camphor. The nitrocellulose used is nonexplosive and less inflammable than gun cotton nitrocellulose. The nitrocellulose used is known as pyroxylin. The pyroxylin is mixed with camphor and alcohol, heated, and pressed into solid blocks. The desired thickness of sheet is sliced from these blocks.

Sheets of this material may be purchased for aircraft work from 0.030 to 0.150 inch thick. A full sheet is usually limited in size to 21 by 50 inches. The weight of a sheet of this size in the thicknesses available are listed below:

THICKNESS—INCHES	WEIGHT—POUNDS
.030	1⅔
.040	2¼
.050	2⅔
.060	3⅛
.070	3¾
.080	4¼
.090	4¾
.100	5¼
.125	6½
.150	8–0

This is a thermo-plastic material and can be softened by heating, and molded under pressure into forms with double curvature such as is used on the tops of sliding cabin hoods. It can be readily sawed and drilled. Pyralin is inflammable. In the past it has been very commonly used on commercial airplanes.

Plastecele. This material is a cellulose acetate plastic. It is manufactured in the same manner as nitrocellulose plastics. The sizes obtainable and their weights are the same as listed above for pyralin.

This material is flame-resisting and is frequently used on military airplanes. It will burn only slowly when a lighted match is held to it. The test for transparency requires that standard typewritten copy on blueprint paper, which is white on a blue background, shall be wholly legible to the normal eye when held 6 inches behind the material and viewed through it in daylight.

This material is also thermo-plastic and can be readily shaped by means of heat and pressure. Hot water at 150° F. can be used to soften the material, and air applied at 50 lbs./sq. in. pressure will press the softened material into the mold. This air also cools and sets the material.

Like other transparent plastics this material suffers from too great contraction and expansion. It is fairly satisfactory in other respects. Proper mounting to permit give and take with temperature changes will greatly increase its service life.

Plexiglas. This is a relatively new thermo-plastic made with acrylic acid. It is colorless and transparent, and does not discolor with age. It is inflammable only to the extent that it will burn slowly when warmed and ignited by a flame. Plexiglas will not scratch quite so easily as the cellulose plastics. It also has a relatively high coefficient of expansion and should be installed in channels or with oversize holes to permit free movement.

Plexiglas can be softened by heating to 90-125° C. with hot water or steam. It can then be bent or formed by pressing. Plexiglas is available in thicknesses from 0.080 to 0.375 inch. Its specific gravity is 1.18.

Lucite. This material is a new thermo-plastic derived from methacrylic acid. It has essentially the same properties as plexiglas.

Lumarith. This material is a cellulose acetate plastic which is reputed to be more resistant to discoloration by sunlight than the usual cellulose acetate plastic. It has a specific gravity of 1.29. Lumarith may be softened for forming by heating to 250° F. for 6-15 minutes.

Vinylite. This material is a copolymer resin of vinyl chloride and vinyl acetate. It is non-inflammable and has the general properties required for aircraft cabin enclosures. It is available in the usual range of commercial sizes.

Chapter XX

SELECTION OF MATERIALS

The weight, strength, and reliability of materials used in aircraft construction are extremely important. All materials used must have a good strength/weight ratio in the form used, and must be thoroughly reliable to eliminate any possibility of dangerous, unexpected failures. In addition to these general properties the material selected for a definite application must have specific properties that make it suitable for the purpose. No one material is adaptable for all purposes. A particular part, member, or assembly must be studied from many angles before the best material that can be used in its construction is determinable. In order to make the best choice the designer must have a thorough knowledge of the materials available. In the foregoing pages the author has attempted to describe all the materials and processes used in aircraft work in sufficient detail to enable the reader to choose the proper material for any application. In this chapter the author will enumerate the points to be considered in selecting a material. The materials used in the construction of each part of an airplane at the present time will also be given.

CONSIDERATIONS

The author has arbitrarily divided the points to be considered in selecting a material into economic considerations and engineering considerations. The engineer is apt to neglect the economic considerations with the result that construction will be very costly due to the cost of the material itself, and delays incident to obtaining the required material and the reworking of jigs and tools.

Economic. The economic points that should be considered before selecting a material may be itemized as follows:

1. *Availability.* It is extremely important that any material selected for use in the construction of aircraft should be available

in sufficient quantities to satisfy normal and emergency requirements. The material should also be purchasable from a reputable manufacturer who can guarantee a reasonable delivery date. This latter point is particularly important in the construction of an experimental plane when material requirements cannot be anticipated.

2. *Cost.* The cost per pound should be compared with the cost of other available materials. In making this comparison the savings resulting from a higher strength/weight ratio or better working properties must be considered.

3. *Shop Equipment Required.* The initial and maintenance cost of shop equipment required for the working of the material selected must be considered. In an established factory the possibility of using jigs and dies on hand is a factor in the choice of a material.

4. *Standardization of Materials.* It is advantageous to stock as few materials as possible. In selecting a material for a particular application the possibility of using one already on hand for other purposes should be considered.

5. *Reliability.* It is essential that the material selected be of consistent high quality. The author has known many instances where a batch of material was received that cracked when bent, or would not take the required heat treatment. The selection of a standard material manufactured by a reputable manufacturer will minimize the likelihood of obtaining a sour lot of material.

6. *Supplementary Operations Required.* In selecting a material the cost and time necessary for such operations as heat treatment, cleaning, plating, and so on, should be considered. A material that can be used in its natural state has a great advantage from a manufacturing standpoint over one that requires one or more supplementary operations.

Engineering. The engineering considerations that determine the choice of a particular material may be itemized as follows:

1. *Strength.* The material must be capable of developing the required strength within the limitations imposed by dimensions and weight. Dimensional limitations are particularly important for external members and for wing beams in shallow wings.

2. *Weight.* Weight is usually considered in conjunction with strength. The strength/weight ratio of a material is a fairly

reliable indication of its adaptability for structural purposes. In some applications, such as the skin of monocoque structures, bulk is more important than strength. In this instance the material with the lightest weight for a given thickness of sheet is best. Thickness or bulk is necessary to prevent local buckling or damage because of careless handling.

3. *Corrosion.* Due to the thin sections and small safety factors used in the design of aircraft, it would be dangerous to select a material that is subject to severe corrosion under the conditions in which it is to be used. For specialized applications, such as seaplane hull construction, the most corrosion-resistant material available should be used. For other general uses an efficient protective coating should be specified if materials subject to corrosion are used.

4. *Working Properties.* The ability to form, bend, or machine the material selected to the required shape is important. After the type of material is determined, the proper temper must be chosen to facilitate the mechanical operations that are necessary for the fabrication of the fitting or part.

5. *Joining Properties.* The ability to make a structural joint by means of welding or soldering, as well as by mechanical means, such as riveting or bolting, is a big help in design and fabrication. When other properties are equal, the material that can be welded has a definite advantage.

6. *Shock and Fatigue Strength.* Aircraft are subject to both shock loads and vibrational stresses. It is essential that materials used for critical parts should be resistant to these loads.

Specific Material Applications

In the following pages the author will enumerate the various parts of an airplane and list the materials that are used at the present time in their construction. Insofar as possible the major reasons for the choice of a particular material will also be presented. In many instances two or more materials are used for identical parts. This difference of opinion between designers may be due to local operating conditions, the price range of the airplane, or the previous experience of the designer. Many designers are progressive and adopt new materials rapidly, while others are content to lag behind and let the first type break new ground for them. It must be remembered that new developments in the near future may result in many changes in the present type of construction.

In the listing of aircraft parts, the author has taken a standard single-engine tractor airplane and named the parts beginning with the propeller and working aft to the tail. It is hoped by this means to make the reader's task easier in spotting a particular part despite any differences in terminology between him and the author. General parts such as bolts, bushings, and so forth, are enumerated at the end.

Propeller Blades. Propeller blades are made from aluminum alloy, wood, steel, magnesium, and pressed wood.

25ST aluminum alloy forgings are most commonly used in this country for propeller blades of high quality. This material is light, strong, uniform, and unaffected by variations in weather. This type blade is adaptable to adjustable, controllable, and constant speed propellers.

In this country wooden propellers are used mostly on small commercial planes. They are commonly made from birch, walnut, oak, or mahogany. They are lighter than metal propellers but must be made thicker for strength, and they do not have as high an efficiency.

Hollow chrome-vanadium steel propeller blades welded along the trailing edge have been successfully used in one type of controllable propeller. They have about the same advantages as aluminum alloy propeller blades.

Magnesium alloy propeller blades are still in an experimental stage but because of their light weight may some day supersede aluminum and steel for this purpose. The corrosion of this type blade is somewhat of a problem, particularly when used on seaplanes.

Pressed wood impregnated with resins is being used in the manufacture of large propellers. This type of propeller is relatively light in weight.

Propeller Hubs. Propeller hubs are usually manufactured from forgings of chrome-vanadium steel or chrome-nickel-molybdenum steel. Both these steels machine readily and can be heat treated to 150,000 lbs./sq. in., which is the usual strength required for a hub. In addition, they both have excellent fatigue strength so essential in a part subjected to vibrational stresses.

Cowl Ring. The engine cowl ring is made from aluminum alloy. It has been customary to use 3S½H, or 2S aluminum. 52S, in either the annealed, ¼H, or ½H temper, is now being used because of its greater tensile and fatigue strength. A sheet thickness of 0.040 to 0.050 inch is normally used for ring cowls. 24SO aluminum alloy has been satisfactorily used for spinnings but must be heat-treated before installation. 24ST and Alclad 24ST are used frequently for side panels.

3S½H material has been generally used as a compromise material with good forming and welding characteristics and moderate strength.

2S aluminum has been used when exceptional ease of forming was desired. It is not as strong as 3S material.

52S material is difficult to form in the harder tempers but can be welded satisfactorily. Its high fatigue strength is ideal for cowling to resist cracking induced by the vibrational stresses imposed by the engine and propeller.

24ST has good fatigue and tensile strength.

Exhaust Collector. Exhaust stacks, manifolds, or collectors are made from 18-8 corrosion-resisting steel, Inconel, and carbon steel. The thickness of the material used for exhaust collectors varies from 0.035 to 0.049 inch. The latter thickness is preferable for high powered engines using high octane fuel.

An 18-8 corrosion-resisting steel containing a small amount of columbium or titanium is used. The columbium or titanium reduces the corrosion embrittlement at operating temperatures. This material is available in sheet form, and as welded or seamless tubing. After fabrication and welding the finished stacks must be heat treated, or stabilized, to reduce carbide precipitation and corrosion embrittlement. They must then be pickled or polished, followed by passivating to restore their corrosion resistance.

Inconel is obtainable in sheet form and as welded or seamless tubing. It can be readily fabricated and welded the same as 18-8 steel. Both materials are generally used in the sheet or welded tubing form for the fabrication of exhaust collectors. Inconel does not require heat treatment after fabrication or polishing to restore its corrosion resistance. It can be heat treated to eliminate internal stresses due to fabrication or welding if desired.

Mild carbon or chrome-molybdenum steel stacks are sometimes used in small commercial airplanes that do not use high octane gasoline. This type stack is likely to scale internally and rust externally due to the temperature variations to which it is subjected.

Other types of material have been tried for exhaust stacks but none have served the purpose so well as 18-8 corrosion-resistant steel or Inconel.

Cowling. In general, the material used for engine cowling is the same as that previously described for the ring cowl. The thickness of sheet is somewhat lighter, however, varying from 0.032 to 0.040 inch. In some airplanes 17ST, 24ST or Alclad aluminum alloy is used for engine cowling when excessive forming is not necessary. In many cases this material is used for the cowling supports in which strength and rigidity are necessary.

Engine Mount. Chrome-molybdenum and mild carbon steel tubing are used for engine mounts. It is customary to weld the entire assembly together, but some mounts are assembled by bolting or riveting.

Firewall. The firewall is usually constructed of a sheet of aluminum alloy either 0.032 or 0.040 inch thick. Some firewalls consist of two sheets of aluminum alloy 0.020 inch thick, with 1/8 inch asbestos sandwiched between them. Corrosion-resisting steel sheet and terneplate are also used for firewalls.

Oil Tank. Oil tanks are almost invariably constructed of aluminum or aluminum alloy sheet, although some work is now being done on the construction of magnesium alloy tanks. If the tank is welded, either 2S, 3S, or 52S aluminum alloy is used depending upon the material selected for cowling. Riveted tanks are made from these materials or 17ST, 24ST or Alclad aluminum alloy. In the construction of oil tanks the thickness of the sheet used varies from 0.040 to 0.065 inch according to the size of the tank, its shape, and the size of unsupported areas.

Oil Lines. Oil lines are made from any of the following materials: 52SO aluminum alloy, copper, copper-silicon, various types of flexible tubing. A wall thickness of 0.035 to 0.049 inch is used with the solid tubing. This type tubing requires a flexible connection which is made by means of a rubber hose nipple held with hose clamps. Duprene hose, a synthetic rubber compound, is commonly used because it is not affected by the hot oil.

Engine Controls. Engine controls, such as push-pull rods, jack-shafts, and bell-cranks are fabricated from chrome-molybdenum or mild carbon steel. Push-pull rods that pass close to compasses are made from 17ST or 24ST aluminum alloy tubing. Push-pull rods are usually ⅜ inch in diameter and have a wall thickness of 0.035 for steel and 0.058 for aluminum alloy. These sizes may vary somewhat depending upon the length of the rod and the force transmitted.

Fuel Tanks. The same materials described above for oil tanks are used for fuel tanks, but the thickness of sheet is somewhat greater because of their larger size.

Fuel Lines. The same materials described above for oil lines are used for fuel lines. The sizes of solid lines vary from ½ inch diameter with an 0.035 inch wall for engines under 600 horsepower to 1¼ inch diameter with an 0.049 inch wall for larger engines.

Landing Gear. Most landing gears are still made of welded chrome-molybdenum tubing. Chrome-molybdenum steel forgings are frequently used for fittings on this type gear. Sub-assemblies of welded steel landing gears are usually heat treated to 150,000 or 180,000 pounds per square inch. Some landing gears have been constructed from aluminum alloy forgings.

Fuselage. Fuselages are either welded steel tubing or aluminum alloy monocoque construction. In rare instances monocoque fuselages using corrosion-resisting steel or plywood have been manufactured in this country.

Welded steel fuselages are made from either chrome-molybdenum or mild carbon steel tubing. The diameter of the tubing used varies from ½ inch up to 1½ inches depending upon the loads carried.

Monocoque fuselages differ in detail construction but usually consist of extruded or rolled sections for frames and bulkheads, covered by sheet between 0.025 and 0.040 inch thick. 24ST aluminum alloy, Alclad 24ST, or Alclad 17ST are commonly used for this purpose.

Hulls and Floats. Hulls and floats are very similar to monocoque fuselages in construction and are made with the same materials. Alclad material is preferable because of the severe corrosion conditions that are met.

Several spot welded corrosion-resisting steel hulls have been manufactured in this country. Their corrosion resistance is excellent, but it is necessary to use much thinner material than is used in aluminum alloy construction to obtain a comparable weight.

Wings. There are any number of different materials used in the construction of wings. The most common types of wing construction are as follows:

1. Wood with plywood wing covering
2. Wood with fabric covering
3. Wooden beams with metal ribs, covered with fabric
4. Metal, including the covering
5. Metal with fabric covering

The choice of a particular type of wing construction depends upon the type of airplane, the manufacturing skill available, and the preference of the designer.

The specific materials used in wing construction are described below under the title of the sub-assembly.

Wing Leading Edge. The leading edge of a wing forward of the front beam is usually covered with plywood or sheet metal to maintain a perfect contour in this important region. ⅟₃₂ to ⅟₁₆ inch plywood is normally used for this purpose on wooden wings. In metal wing construction the leading edge covering is usually 17ST or 24ST aluminum alloy sheet from 0.014 to 0.020 inch thick. Alclad is also used for this purpose.

Wing Ribs. Wing ribs are made from wood, aluminum alloys, steel, and corrosion-resisting steel.

Wooden ribs are usually made from spruce. The capstrips and diagonals are ¼ or 5⁄16 inch square in the smaller commercial planes. Plywood gussets glued and tacked in place are used at the joints. The webs of some ribs are made entirely of plywood.

Aluminum alloy ribs are made from 17ST or 24ST material. They are either stamped in one piece from sheet stock, or built up from drawn or rolled sections and riveted at the joints. Material from 0.014 to 0.032 inch thick is commonly used in the manufacture of this type rib.

Steel and corrosion-resisting steel ribs are made from very light gage material in a "U" or tubular section. Joints are made by spot welding.

Wing Covering. Wings are covered with fabric, plywood, or aluminum alloy. This latter covering is either 17ST or 24ST aluminum alloy, or the Alclad version of these materials. When Alclad is used for this purpose there is no need to paint the surface for protection against corrosion.

Wing-Tip Bow. The wing-tip bow is made from ash bent to shape, from a chrome-molybdenum or mild steel tube, or from an aluminum alloy tube or formed section. Aluminum alloy sections formed to the desired shape are commonly used on metal wings.

Wing Beams. Wing beams are made from spruce, poplar, Douglas fir, steel, corrosion-resisting steel, and aluminum alloys.

Wooden beams are generally made of spruce although in regions where spruce is scarce or expensive, substitute woods such as fir, poplar, and even white pine have been successfully used. At the present time it is difficult to obtain spruce of aircraft grade in sufficiently long lengths or required cross-sectional dimensions for any but the smaller commercial airplanes.

Aluminum alloy wing beams are very generally used in this country at the present time. They are made of any one or combination of the following alloys: 24ST, 17ST, 14ST (flanges only), Alclad 24ST. Of these alloys 14ST is the strongest but it can be obtained only as a forging. For this reason it can be used only for flanges on a few types of beams without excessive machining. 24ST aluminum alloy is the most practical for wing beams. This material has a fairly high yield point and is available as sheet, tubing, and extrusions.

Steel spars have been constructed of chrome-molybdenum steel tubing, either round or oval in cross section, welded at the joints. These spars are usually heat treated to develop greater strength. They are difficult to manufacture due to the likelihood of welding cracks and of distortion during the heat treatment operation.

Corrosion-resisting steel beams are fabricated from high tensile strip or sheet, rolled or drawn to shape and spot welded together. This type spar is fairly easy to manufacture if spot welding equipment is available and has good strength properties. It works out well for a heavily loaded wing, which permits the use of moderately heavy sheet without penalizing the strength/weight ratio.

Wing Fittings. Wing fittings are made from the high strength aluminum alloys such as 24ST, 17ST, 14ST, and A51ST, and from various types of steel. Chrome-molybdenum steel (X4130) and chrome-nickel steel (3140) heat treated to 150,000 pounds per square inch are very commonly used. Chrome-nickel-molybdenum steel (X4340) is used in heat treatments up to 200,000 pounds per square inch.

Wing Supporting Struts. Wing struts are streamline tubing made of 17ST, 24ST, 53ST or 61ST aluminum alloy, or chrome-molybdenum steel. Corrosion-resisting steel streamline struts have recently been developed and may find some applications particularly for bracing seaplane floats.

Wing Wires. Wing wires or tie-rods are made from 1050 carbon steel, and from corrosion-resisting steel. Tie-rods made from corrosion-resisting steel are rapidly displacing carbon steel tie-rods both for external and internal bracing. Their strengths are the same.

Ailerons. Ailerons are usually made from the same materials used in the construction of the wings. Due to the fact that it is necessary to design for static balance of the ailerons, they are usually covered with fabric in order to reduce the weight behind the hinge line.

Wing Flaps. Wing flaps, especially the split type, are constructed with aluminum alloy sheet backed by stiffeners. The shallow depth of split flaps makes metal construction almost mandatory.

Windshield. Windshields and cabin enclosures are frequently constructed of one of the transparent plastics such as pyralin, plexiglas, lucite, plastecele, Lumarith or Vinylite. A thickness of $1/16$ to $1/8$ inch of this material is used.

Nonscatterable glass is used for windshields on most airplanes. A minimum thickness of $3/16$ inch, with preferably $1/4$ inch, is used in the interest of clear vision.

Windshield frames are made from light steel or aluminum sheet. Inconel strip has also been used successfully.

Instrument Board. Instrument boards are made from 17ST or 24ST aluminum alloy sheet from $1/16$ to $1/8$ inch thick. In some planes the instrument board is made from a plastic such as formica or bakelite. These materials are from $1/8$ to $1/4$ inch thick when used for this purpose.

Instrument Tubing. Small diameter tubing with a light wall is used in conjunction with airspeed meters, oil and fuel pressure gages, primers, and other instruments. This tubing is made from one of the following materials: 52SO aluminum alloys, 2S aluminum, or copper.

Seats. Seats are made from aluminum alloy or magnesium alloy sheet and tubing or from light steel tubing. They are usually purchased complete, particularly for commercial planes where padding and tilting devices are desired.

Flooring. Flooring is fabricated from plywood or aluminum alloy sheet. A composite material made up from plywood and aluminum alloy glued together is also used. Formica or bakelite might work out satisfactorily for flooring in some instances.

Controls. Control parts, such as control sticks, rudder pedals, torsion tubes, push-pull tubes, bell-cranks, and horns are manufactured from aluminum alloys or steel. 17ST or 24ST aluminum alloy tubing is frequently used for control parts. Because of their nonmagnetic qualities they are particularly good for control sticks and other parts that operate near a compass. When control parts must be wear-resistant and strong as well as non-magnetic, the use of K Monel will solve the problem.

Chrome-molybdenum steel sheet and tubing are frequently used in the fabrication of control parts. When parts are welded, it is advisable to normalize them or to give them a moderate heat treatment as a precaution against cracks due to vibration.

Aluminum alloy casting material No. 195-T4 is frequently used for rudder pedals, sockets, horns and other parts. It is advisable to design these parts 100% overstrength to allow for any irregularities in the castings.

Flexible and extra-flexible control cable are both used for the operation of control surfaces. Extra-flexible cable should be used if a marked change in direction is necessary in running the cable.

Tail Surfaces. Tail surface construction is very similar to wing construction. Fixed surfaces constructed of aluminum alloys are often covered with sheet of the same material from 0.014 to 0.032 inch thick. Movable surfaces, such as the elevators and rudder, are fabric covered to help obtain static balance. Tail surfaces are also built with steel tubing welded at the joints and covered with fabric. In this type construction about ¼ inch diameter tubing is used for the rib members and large diameter tubing for the spar members.

Tail Wheel Structure. Tail wheel structures are built chiefly from steel tubing and sheet the same as the main landing gear. In some cases aluminum alloy forgings are used.

Bushings. Bushings are used in all fittings subjected to reversals of stress. They are held in place by a drive fit and can be replaced when worn. They are made from chrome-molybdenum steel tubing or bar stock heat treated to 125,000 or 150,000 pounds per square inch.

Bearings. Bearings are used in joints that rotate. Ball or roller bearings packed with grease are generally the most satisfactory. Controls and control surface hinges are ideal places to use ball bearings. In some places where loads are heavy and rotation is slight, such as the joints of a retractable landing gear, bronze bushings are used. These bronze bushings are grooved and the surrounding fitting tapped for a grease fitting to permit thorough lubrication. Chrome-plated hardened steel bushings are also used in landing gear joints and similar applications.

Bolts. AN standard bolts made from nickel steel (2330) are used for all structural connections. Occasionally it is necessary to position a bolt in place by tack welding the head. For this purpose the bolt is manufactured from chrome-molybdenum steel since nickel steel cannot be welded satisfactorily. Unless the entire assembly to which the head of the bolt is tack welded is subsequently heat treated, the chrome-molybdenum bolt will not have quite as high strength as the standard nickel steel bolt. AN standard bolts are all heat treated to 125,000 pounds per square inch. Special high strength bolts heat-treated to 200,000 pounds per square inch are made of chrome-nickel-molybdenum steel (X4340).

Rivets. 17ST and 24ST aluminum alloy rivets are used for joining structural assemblies. 24ST rivets are seldom used because of their tendency to crack if not used almost immediately after heat treatment. A17S rivets which do not require heat treatment just before driving are being used very generally in all but heavily loaded structural assemblies.

Steel rivets are not generally available and are seldom used. An excellent steel rivet can be made from nickel steel rod when needed.

Springs. Flat springs are made from high carbon steel (1090) sheet stock. Small unimportant coil springs are also made from this material in wire form. Larger coil springs, like those used for engine valve springs, and landing gear oleos, are made from chrome-vanadium steel (6140).

CONCLUSION

The selection of the proper material for a particular part is the first step in good design. It must be remembered, however, that good detail design of the part is equally important if the properties of the material are to be fully realized. Whenever possible the troubles experienced by airplanes in service should be studied in relation to the material and design of defective parts. In this way a background can be obtained that will be invaluable in the design of later airplanes.

APPENDIX

WEIGHTS OF COMMON AIRCRAFT MATERIALS

Material	Specific Gravity	Weight (lbs./cu. in.)
Aluminum Alloys		
2S	2.71	.098
3S	2.73	.099
4S	2.72	.098
14S	2.80	.101
17S	2.79	.101
24S	2.77	.100
25S	2.79	.101
43	2.67	.096
A51S	2.69	.097
52S	2.67	.096
53S	2.69	.097
195	2.77	.100
Asbestos	2.46	.089
Bakelite	1.35	.049
Brass	8.45	.305
Bronze, aluminum	7.70	.278
Bronze, phosphor	8.88	.322
Copper	8.90	.323
Cork, compressed	.23	.008
Felt	.08	.003
Formica	1.35	.049
Glass, nonscatterable	2.53	.091
Inconel	8.55	.309
K Monel	8.58	.310
Lead	11.40	.411
Magnesium alloys	1.80	.065
Micarta	1.35	.049
Monel	8.90	.323
Plastecele	1.35	.049
Plexiglas	1.18	.043
Pyralin	1.35	.049
Steel	7.84	.283
Steel, corrosion-resisting	7.86	.284
Wood	(See Table 13)	

APPENDIX 2
STANDARD GAGES

GAGE NUMBER	GAGE NAMES—THICKNESS IN DECIMALS OF AN INCH		
	Birmingham (B.W.G.) or Stubs	American or Browne & Sharpe	American Steel or Washburn & Moen
0	.340	.325	.306
1	.300	.289	.283
2	.284	.258	.262
3	.259	.229	.244
4	.238	.204	.225
5	.220	.182	.207
6	.203	.162	.192
7	.180	.144	.177
8	.165	.128	.162
9	.148	.114	.148
10	.134	.102	.135
11	.120	.091	.120
12	.109	.081	.105
13	.095	.072	.091
14	.083	.064	.080
15	.072	.057	.072
16	.065	.051	.062
17	.058	.045	.054
18	.049	.040	.047
19	.042	.036	.041
20	.035	.032	.035
21	.032	.028	.032
22	.028	.025	.027
23	.025	.023	.026
24	.022	.020	.023
25	.020	.018	.020
26	.018	.016	.018
27	.016	.014	.017
28	.014	.0126	.016
29	.013	.011	.015
30	.012	.010	.014

Birmingham Wire Gage (B.W.G.) is used to specify thicknesses of steel sheet, and all tubing including steel and aluminum alloy.

Browne & Sharpe Gage (B. & S.) is used for nonferrous sheet. particularly aluminum alloy and magnesium alloy sheet. Also wire,

American Steel and Wire Gage (formerly Washburn & Moen) is used for steel and iron wire.

Appendix 3

STEEL TUBING—ROUND

Standard Sizes and Tolerances

WEIGHTS IN POUNDS PER FOOT LISTED FOR STANDARD SIZES

Outside Diameter	Wall Thickness									Tolerance Outside Diameter	Tolerance Wall Thickness
	.022	.028	.035	.049	.058	.065	.083	.095	.120		
3/16	.039	.048	.057							+0.005 −0.000	±15% Wall Thickness
1/4	.054	.066	.081	.105							
5/16	.068	.085	.104	.138	.158						
3/8	.083	.104	.127	.171	.197						
1/2			.174		.274						
5/8			.221	.302	.352						
3/4			.27	.37	.43						
7/8			.31	.43	.51						
1			.36	.50	.58						
1 1/8			.41	.56	.66						
1 1/4			.45	.63	.74	.82					
1 3/8			.50	.60	.82	.91					
1 1/2			.55	.76	.89	1.00	1.25	1.42	1.77	+0.010 −0.000	±10% Wall Thickness
1 5/8				.82	.97	1.08					
1 3/4				.89	1.05	1.17	1.48	1.68	2.09		
1 7/8					1.13	1.26					
2					1.20	1.34	1.70	1.93	2.41		
2 1/4						1.52	1.92	2.19	2.73		
2 1/2						1.69	2.14	2.44	3.05		
2 3/4							2.36	2.69	3.37		

Appendix 4
ALUMINUM ALLOY TUBING—ROUND
Standard Sizes and Tolerances
WEIGHTS IN POUNDS PER FOOT LISTED FOR STANDARD SIZES

Outside Diameter	Wall Thickness											Tolerance Outside Diameter
	.022	.028	.032	.035	.042	.049	.058	.065	.072	.083	.095	
¼	.018	.023				.036		.044				±0.003
5⁄16	.023	.029		.035		.047		.059				
3⁄8	.028	.036		.043		.058		.074				
7⁄16	.033	.042		.051			.080					
½	.038	.049		.059		.080	.094	.104				
5⁄8		.061		.075		.103	.120	.133				±0.004
¾		.074		.091		.125	.147	.163				
7⁄8				.107		.147	.173	.193				
1				.123		.170	.200	.222				
1⅛				.139		.193	.23					±0.005
1¼				.155		.21	.26	.27				
1⅜				.17		.24						
1½				.18		.26	.31	.33				
1⅝				.19								
1¾				.21			.36	.39				
1⅞				.23								
2				.25		.35		.45				
2⅛						.37						±0.006
2¼						.39	.47	.51				
2⅜						.42						
2½						.44	.52	.57				
2⅝							.545					
2¾							.57	.63				
2⅞								.66				
3								.69	.77			
3¼									.83			±0.008
3½									.90	1.04		
3¾										1.11		
4										1.19	1.34	
4¼											1.43	
Tolerance Wall Thickness	±0.002				±0.003		±0.004					

STREAMLINE TUBING

ALUMINUM ALLOY, CORROSION-RESISTING STEEL, CHROME-MOLYBDENUM STEEL—STANDARD SIZES AND DIMENSIONS

BASIC ROUND TUBE DIAMETER	WALL THICKNESS	MAJOR AXIS LENGTH	MINOR AXIS WIDTH
1	0.035	1.349	0.571
1⅛	0.035	1.517	0.643
1¼	0.035	1.685	0.714
	0.049		
1⅜	0.035	1.855	0.786
	0.049		
1½	0.049	2.023	0.857
	0.058		
1⅝	0.049	2.192	0.929
	0.058		
1¾	0.049	2.360	1.000
	0.058		
	0.065		
1⅞	0.049	2.528	1.071
	0.058		
	0.005		
2	0.058	2.697	1.143
	0.065		
2¼	0.058	3.035	1.286
	0.065		
2½	0.065	3.372	1.429
	0.083		
2¾	0.065	3.708	1.571
	0.083		
3	0.065	4.045	1.714
	0.083		
3¼	0.083	4.383	1.857
3½	0.095	4.720	2.000
3¾	0.095	5.057	2.143
4	0.120	5.394	2.285
4¼	0.134	5.732	2.428
4½	0.156	6.069	2.571
4¾	0.188	6.406	2.714

Appendix 6

STRENGTH OF STEEL CABLE

Construction	Diameter	Tinned Carbon Steel Spec.-AN-RR-C-43		Corrosion-Resisting Steel Spec.-AN-RR-C-48	
	Inch	Breaking Str., lbs.	Weight lbs./100 ft.	Breaking Str., lbs.	Weight lbs./100 ft.
7 × 7	1/16	480	0.75	480	0.75
	3/32	920	1.53	920	1.53
7 × 19	1/8	2,000	2.90	1,900	2.90
	5/32	2,800	4.44	2,600	4.44
	3/16	4,200	6.47	3,900	6.47
	7/32	5,600	9.50	5,200	9.50
	1/4	7,000	12.00	6,600	12.00
	9/32	8,000	14.56	8,000	14.56
	5/16	9,800	17.71	9,600	17.71
	3/8	14,400	26.45	13,000	26.45
6 × 19 (IWRC)	7/16	17,600	35.60	16,000	35.60
	1/2	22,800	45.80	22,800	45.80
	9/16	28,500	59.00	28,500	59.00
	5/8	35,000	71.50	35,000	71.50
	3/4	49,600	105.20	49,600	105.20
	7/8	66,500	143.00	66,500	143.00
	1	85,400	187.00	85,400	187.00
	1 1/8	106,400	240.00	106,400	240.00
	1 1/4	129,400	290.00	129,400	290.00
	1 3/8	153,600	330.00	153,600	330.00
	1 1/2	180,500	420.00	180,500	420.00

TIE-RODS
STREAMLINE, ROUND, SQUARE
STRENGTH

SIZE	STRENGTH lbs.	BEND TEST REQUIREMENTS	
		Round or Square	Streamline
(Carbon Steel Tie-Rods—S. A. E. 1050)			
6–40	1,000	11	13
10–32	2,100	11	13
1/4–28	3,400	9	11
5/16–24	6,100	7	9
3/8–24	8,000	7	9
7/16–20	11,500	7	9
1/2–20	15,500	7	9
9/16–18	20,200	..	7
5/8–18	24,700	..	7
(Corrosion-Resisting Steel Tie-Rods)			
6–40	1,000	10	12
10–32	2,100	10	12
1/4–28	3,400	9	10
5/16–24	6,100	6	8
3/8–24	8,000	6	8
7/16–20	11,500	6	8
1/2–20	15,500	6	8
9/16–18	20,200	..	6
5/8–18	24,700	..	6

The number listed under Bend Test Requirements refers to the number of 90-degree bends the tie-rod must withstand when bent over a radius equal to three times its minor axis.

INDEX

Acid-resistant paint, 249
Ailerons, material of, 319
Alclad aluminum alloys, 158
Alkali-chromate treatment, 244
Allotropic substances, definition, 44
Alrok, 243
Alumilite, 242
Aluminum alloys, 152
  alclad, 158
  Alrok process, 243
  Alumilite, 242
  annealing, 170
  anodic oxidation process, 239
  castings, 188
    chemical composition, 189
    die, 193
    heat-treated, 189
    permanent, mold, 192
    sand, 190
    specifications, 187, 195
  classification of, 155
  corrosion, 158, 176, 183
  extrusions, 160
  forgings, 161
  heat treatable, 155, 178
    chemical composition, 178
    corrosion, 183
    heat treatment, 164, 179
    mechanical properties, 179
    physical properties, 178
    shapes available, 184
    uses, 185
    welding, 182
    working properties, 181
  heat treatment, 164, 172, 179
  heat treatment of rivets, 169
  heat treatment soaking time, 167
  nomenclature, 154
  pickling, 231
  rivets, heat treatment of, 169
  specifications, 187, 195
  spot welding, 163, 218
  strain-hardened, 155, 171
    bend radii, 174
    chemical composition, 172
    corrosion, 176
    heat treatment, 172
    mechanical properties, 173
    physical properties, 172

Aluminum alloys, strain-hardened,
  shapes available, 177
  uses, 177
  welding, 175, 215
  working properties, 173
  tubing, round—standard sizes, 328
  tubing, streamlined—standard
    sizes, 329
  welding, 163, 175, 215
Aluminum bronze, 149
AN aeronautical specifications, 34
Animal glue, 278
Annealing, 3
  aluminum alloys, 170, 172
  corrosion-resisting steel, 101
  inconel, 130
  monel, 135
  steel, 54
Anodic oxidation process, 239
Anodizing, 239
Application, specific material, 312
Arc welding, 216
Ash, white, 268
Austenite, 52

Bakelite, 298
Basswood, 268
Beams, wing—material of, 318
Bearings, material of, 321
Beech, 268
Beeswax and grease, 250
Bending tests, 18
  flattening test, 20
  reverse bend test, 19
Bending wood, 275
Beryllium copper, 144
Birch, 269
Bituminous paint, 250
Blood albumin glue, 278
Bolts, material of, 322
Bonderizing, 235
Brass, 145
  season cracking, 151
Brazing, 220
  flux, 221
  inconel, 132
  K monel, 141
Brinell hardness test, 15
Brittleness, definition, 2

333